NCERT
SOLUTIONS
◇◇
Science

with *Selected* **NCERT Exemplar Problems**

CLASS
9

by
Richa Agarwal Physics
Geeta Rastogi Chemistry
Dr. Kanchan Upreti Biology

✳arihant
Arihant Prakashan (School Division Series)

✳arihant

Arihant Prakashan (School Division Series)

All Rights Reserved

ꖹ Administrative & Production Offices

Regd. Office

'Ramchhaya' 4577/15, Agarwal Road, Darya Ganj, New Delhi -110002
Tele: 011- 47630600, 43518550

ꖹ Head Office

Kalindi, TP Nagar, Meerut (UP) - 250002
Tel: 0121-7156203, 7156204

ꖹ Sales & Support Offices

Agra, Ahmedabad, Bengaluru, Bareilly, Chennai, Delhi, Guwahati, Hyderabad, Jaipur, Jhansi, Kolkata, Lucknow, Nagpur & Pune.

ꖹ ISBN   978-93-27197-13-6

PO No : TXT-XX-XXXXXXX-X-XX

Published by Arihant Publications (India) Ltd.

For further information about the books published by Arihant, log on to
www.arihantbooks.com or e-mail at info@arihantbooks.com

Follow us on

Preface

Feeling the immense importance and value of NCERT books, we are presenting this book, having the **NCERT Exercises Solutions.** For the overall benefit of the students we have made this book unique in such a way that it presents not only solutions but also detailed explanations. Through these detailed and through explanations, students can learn the concepts which will enhance their thinking and learning abilities.

We have introduced some Additional Features with the solutions which are given below :

- **Explanatory Solutions** Along with the solutions to questions we have given all the points that tell how to approach to solve a problem. Here we have tried to cover all those loopholes which may lead to confusion. All formulae and hints are discussed in full detail.

- **Note** We have provided notes also to solutions in which special points are mentioned which are of great value for the students.

- This book also covers solutions to selected problems of **NCERT Exemplar Problems.**

Apart from all those who helped in the compilation of this book a special note of thanks to Ms. Akansha Tomar. With the hope that this book will be of great help to the students, we wish great success to our readers.

Richa Agarwal
Geeta Rastogi
Dr. Kanchan Upreti

Contents

1

Matter in Our Surroundings

Important Concepts

1. Anything that has mass and occupies space is known as matter.
2. Early Indian Philosophers classified matter into five basic elements, the 'Panch Tatva'–air, earth, fire, sky and water.
3. Matter is made up of tiny particles, known as molecules.
4. Molecules are too small to be seen with naked eyes or even with the help of a microscope.
5. Molecules are bound together in a matter with a force of attraction, known as intermolecular force of attraction.
6. There is some distance between the particles (molecules) of matter, called the intermolecular space.
7. The states of matter, i.e., solid, liquid and gas vary among themselves due to the difference in the attraction force and space between their molecules.
8. Solids have the maximum attraction force between their molecules and gases have the least.
9. Gases have the maximum intermolecular space and solids have the least.
10. The smell of perfume reaches our nose quickly due to the process of diffusion.
11. Diffusion is the process of movement of molecules from a higher concentration place to a lower concentration place.

12. A gas in a container exerts pressure due to the force exerted by the (random movement of) gas particles per unit area on the walls of the container.

13. A definite temperature at which a solid starts melting is called its melting point.

14. When a liquid boils, its temperature (boiling point) remains constant because during this period the heat energy is utilised in breaking the attraction force between water molecules. This heat is called latent heat of vaporisation.

15. $t\,°C + 273 = T\,K$
    where, C = Celcius and K = Kelvin

16. Camphor, ammonium chloride, naphthalene and iodine are some solids that change directly from solid to gas on heating (sublimation).

17. Dry ice is solid carbon dioxide.

18. Rate of evaporation increases on
    (i) increasing surface area
    (ii) decreasing humidity
    (iii) increasing temperature
    (iv) increasing wind speed

19. Light coloured cotton clothes are preferred during summers because
    (i) cotton absorbs the sweat which evaporates easily (as evaporation causes cooling).
    (ii) light colours absorb less heat.

20. Earthern pots like pitcher (matka) keep the water cool because water evaporates through the tiny pores of pitcher (matka) and the remaining water becomes cool.

Intext Questions

On Page 3

Question 1. Which of the following are matter?
Chair, air, love, smell, hate, almonds, thought, cold, lemon water smell of perfume.

Answer   Chair, air, smell, almonds, cold-drink and smell of perfume are matter because they have some weight and occupy space.

Question 2. Give reasons for the following observation
The smell of hot sizzling food reaches you several metres away, but to get the smell from cold food you have to go close.

Answer Hot food evaporates easily. Its vapours diffuse between the air molecules and reach within a short time to a distant place. But the case is different with the cold food because it remains in solid form and does not mix with air molecules, so we have to go close to smell it.

Question 3. A diver is able to cut through water in a swimming pool. Which property of matter does this observation show?

Answer The phenomena of cutting the water by the diver show that matter has space between its particles.

Question 4. What are the characteristics of the particles of matter?

Answer Characteristics of particles of matter :
1. Particles of matter have space between them.
2. Particles of matter are continuously moving.
3. Particles of matter have an attraction force between them.
4. Particles of matter are very small in size.

On Page 6

Question 1. The mass per unit volume of a substance is called density. (Density = mass/volume). Arrange the following in order of increasing density – air, exhaust from chimneys, honey, water, chalk, cotton and iron.

Answer The order of density is gas< liquid< solid. Thus,

Air, exhaust from chimneys, water, honey, cotton, chalk, iron

| Gas | Liquid | Solid |

Increasing order of density

Question 2.
(a) Tabulate the differences in the characteristics of states of matter.
(b) Comment upon the following:
rigidity, compressibility, fluidity, filling a gas container, shape, kinetic energy and density.

Answer

S.No.	Solids	Liquids	Gases
1.	Generally solids have a definite shape (exceptions are sponge, rubber band etc).	Liquids do not have a definite shape. They take the shape of the container.	Gases do not have a definite shape.
2.	Solids have a definite volume.	Liquids have a definite volume too.	Gases do not have a definite volume. (Their volume also varies with the container in which they are stored.)
3.	Solids have high densities hence they are hard too.	Liquids have low densities.	Gases also have low densities.

S.No.	Solids	Liquids	Gases
4.	Solids are rigid.	Liquids are not rigid.	Gases are not rigid.
5.	Solids are generally incompressible (except sponge, rubber etc.)	Liquids are almost incompressible.	Gases are compressible.
6.	Solids do not tend to flow.	Liquids tend to flow.	Gases also tend to flow.
7.	Solids can be heaped.	Liquids cannot be heaped.	Gases cannot be heaped.
8.	In solids, molecules are packed in a closed arrangement.	In liquids, molecules are loosely packed as compared to solids.	In gases, molecules are very far from each other.
9.	There is a strong attraction force between the molecules of a solid.	There is less attraction force between the liquid molecules as compared to that of solid molecules.	Attraction force between the gaseous molecules is the least, *i.e.*, negligible.
10.	There is negligible (least) intermolecular space between the molecules of a solid.	Intermolecular space between the molecules of a liquid is less than that in solid molecules.	

(b) (i) **Rigidity** The property due to which an object retains its shape and size is known as rigidity. Solids are rigid whereas liquids and gases are not.

(ii) **Compressibility** Compressibility is the property due to which a substance can be compressed, *i.e.*, its volume can be decreased. Gases are compressible whereas solids and liquids are not.

(iii) **Fluidity** The property due to which a substance tends to flow is called fluidity. Gases and liquids are fluids, solids are not.

(iv) **Filling a gas container** A gas can be filled in a gas container by compressing it under high pressure. The property of compressibility (of gases) helps them in this regard.

(v) **Shape** The property of having a definite geometry is called shape of a particular substance. Solids have a definite shape whereas gases and liquids do not have.

(vi) **Kinetic energy** The energy possessed by an object or by the molecules of an object due to its state of motion is called kinetic energy. Molecules of gases posses highest kinetic energy. Increasing the temperature also increases the kinetic energy of a substance (or its molecules).

(vii) **Density** The mass per unit volume of a substance is called density.
$$\text{Density} = \frac{\text{Mass}}{\text{Volume}} = \frac{m}{V}$$
Unit of density is $kg\,m^{-3}$ or $g\,cm^{-3}$.

Question 3. Give reasons

(a) A gas fills completely the vessel in which it is kept.

(b) A gas exerts pressure on the walls of the container.

(c) A wooden table should be called a solid.

(d) We can easily move our hand in air but to do the same through a solid block of wood we need a karate expert.

Answer
  (a) There is negligible force of attraction between the molecules of gases. Therefore, molecules of gases occupy the maximum space available to them. High kinetic energy possessed by their molecules also helps for the same.

  (b) In the gaseous state, the particles move randomly at high speed. Due to this random movement, the particles hit each other and also the walls of the container. The pressure exerted by the gas is due to this force exerted by these particles per unit area on the walls of the container.

  (c) There is a strong force of attraction between the molecules of wood and the intermolecular space is the least. So, a wooden table has a definite shape and volume and it should be called a solid.

  (d) Air molecules are very-very far from each other due to negligible force of attraction working between them. So, our hand gets sufficient space to move in air and we also displace some air molecules by applying force. But a solid block of wood has closely packed molecules so there is no question of the movement of hand through it, in absence of suitable force in proper direction.

Question 4. Liquids generally have lower density as compared to solids. But you must have observed that ice floats on water. Find out why?

Answer Generally liquids have lower density than that of solids. Water is also expected to have less density than that of ice. But the case is not so. The reason is that ice has a cage-like structure, *i.e.*, the vacant spaces are left when water (H_2O) molecules are linked in ice. The number of these spaces are comparatively less in water. Being more porous than water, ice is lighter than water and floats over the surface of water.

On Page 9

Question 1. Convert the following temperature to celsius scale
  (a) 300 K   (b) 573 K

Answer For converting the temperature scale from kelvin to celcius, we have to subtract 273 from the given value
$$T\,K - 273 = t\,°C$$
  (a) $300\,K - 273 = 27\,°C$ (b) $573\,K - 273 = 300\,°C$

Question 2. What is the physical state of water at
  (a) 250°C   (b) 100°C ?

Answer As the boiling point of water is 100°C so
  (a) at 250°C, the state of water will be steam or water vapour, *i.e.*, gaseous state.

  (b) at 100°C, there is a transition of liquid state into the gaseous state. So, at this temperature, the state is/may be liquid as well as gaseous.

Question 3. For any substance, why does the temperature remain constant during the change of state?

Answer The temperature remains constant during the change of state of a substance. This can be understood with the help of an example. When a solid is heated to its melting point, the temperature first rises and becomes constant when reaches its melting point. Now, on further heating, the heat energy provided to the substance helps to break the attraction force between the solid molecules. This heat is called latent heat. That is why, the temperature does not rise.

Question 4. Suggest a method to liquefy atmospheric gases.

Answer Applying high pressure and cooling a gas to low temperature helps in the liquifaction of atmospheric gases. The reason is that under such conditions of temperature and pressure, the molecules of gases come closer, their kinetic energy becomes less and the gas is liquefied.

On Page 10

Question 1. Why does a desert cooler cool better on a hot dry day?

Answer The rate of evaporation increases with increase in temperature and decrease in humidity. A desert cooler functions on the basis of evaporation. As evaporation increases when the day is hot and dry, so the desert cooler functions to a better extent.

Question 2. How does the water kept in an earthen pot (matka) become cool during summer?

Answer The surface of the earthen pot (matka) has tiny pores. The water stored in the earthen pot (matka) evaporates faster through these pores due to the increased exposed surface area. As the process of evaporation causes cooling, the stored water inside the earthen pot (matka) becomes cool.

Question 3. Why does our palm feel cold when we put some acetone or petrol or perfume on it?

Answer Acetone, petrol, perfume etc., being volatile, evaporate very fast when exposed to larger surfaces. During the process they absorb the required latent heat of vaporisation from the palm (if kept on palm). So, the process causes cooling and the palm feels cool.

Question 4. Why are we able to sip hot tea or milk faster from a saucer rather than a cup?

Answer In a saucer, the exposed surface area of tea or milk is greater as compared to the cup. Therefore, the evaporation is faster and it is easier to sip colder tea or milk.

Question 5. What type of clothes should we wear in summer?

Answer   We should wear light coloured cotton clothes in summer because
1. Cotton is a good absorber of water/sweat. It provides more surface area for the sweat to evaporate.
2. Light colours absorb less heat.

So, wearing light coloured cotton clothes helps us feeling cool and comfortable.

Exercises

Question 1. Convert the following temperatures to the celcius scale.

(a) 293 K   (b) 470 K

Answer   In order to covert temperature from kelvin to celcius scale, we have to subtract 273 from the given value because $K - 273 = °C$

(a) 293 K $- 273 = 20°C$
(b) 470 K $- 273 = 197°C$

Question 2. Convert the following temperatures to the kelvin scale.

(a) 25°C   (b) 373°C

Answer   To convert temperature from celcius to kelvin scale, add 273 to the given values because $°C + 273 = K$

(a) $25°C + 273 = 298$ K
(b) $373°C + 273 = 646$ K

Question 3. Give reason for the following observations.

(a) Naphthalene balls disappear with time without leaving any solid.

(b) We can get the smell of perfume sitting several metres away.

Answer
(a) Naphthalene is a substance which directly changes from solid to gas on heating by the process of sublimation. So, the naphthalene balls disappear with time as they sublime due to heat of surroundings.
(b) The smell (aroma) of perfume reaches several metres away due to the fast diffusion of the gaseous perfume particles through the air.

Question 4. Arrange the following substances in increasing order of forces of attraction between the particles-water, sugar, oxygen.

Answer   The interparticle forces of attraction are strongest in solids and weakest (or negligible) in case of gases. Sugar is a solid, water is in liquid form and oxygen is a gas so, the order of forces of attraction is

oxygen < water < sugar.

Question 5. What is the physical state of water at

(a) 25°C   (b) 0°C   (c) 100°C ?

Answer 0° is the temperature at which water (liquid) starts to convert into its solid form (ice) and 100°C is the temperature at which water (liquid) starts to change into water vapours. Between 0° to 100°C it remains in liquid state. Thus,

(a) Liquid state

(b) Solid or/and liquid state (Transition state)

(c) Liquid or/and gaseous state (Transition state)

Question 6. Give two reasons to justify

(a) water at room temperature is a liquid.

(b) an iron almirah is a solid at room temperature.

Answer

(a) Water is a liquid at room temperature because

(i) It has a tendency to flow.

(ii) It takes the shape of the container in which it is filled, but its volume remains the same.

(b) An iron almirah is a solid at room temperature because

(i) Its shape and volume are definite.   (ii) It is hard and rigid.

(iii) Its density is high.

Question 7. Why is ice at 273 K more effective in cooling than water at the same temperature?

Answer When ice melts, it absorbs the energy equal to the latent heat of fusion too from the surroundings so it causes cooling more effectively than the water at same temperature (because water does not absorb energy from the surroundings).

Question 8. What produces more severe burns, boiling water or steam?

Answer Steam causes more severe burns than boiling water. The reason is that it releases the extra amount of heat (latent heat) which it has already taken during vaporisation (when the steam was formed from water).

Question 9. Name *A, B, C, D, E* and *F* in the following diagram showing change in its state.

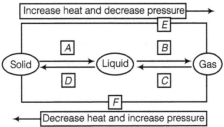

Answer A = Melting or fusion, here the solid changes into liquid.

B = Evaporation or vaporisation, here the liquid changes into gas.

C = Condensation or liquification, here the gas changes into liquid.

D = Freezing or solidification, here the liquid changes into solid.

E = Sublimation, here solid directly changes into gas without coming in liquid state.

F = Sublimation, here gas changes into solid without coming to liquid state.

Selected NCERT Exemplar Problems

Multiple Choice Questions

Question 1. Which one of the following sets of phenomena would increase on raising the temperature?

(a) Diffusion, evaporation, compression of gases

(b) Evaporation, compression of gases, solubility

(c) Evaporation, diffusion, expansion of gases

(d) Evaporation, solubility, diffusion, compression of gases

Answer (c) Evaporation rate increases because kinetic energy increases on increasing the temperature so the molecules present at the surface of the liquid leave the surface quickly. Diffusion and expansion of gases also increase as the molecules move faster and also try to occupy more space.

Question 2. Seema visited a Natural Gas Compressing Unit and found that the gas can be liquefied under specific conditions of temperature and pressure. While sharing her experience with friends she got confused. Help her to identify the correct set of conditions.

(a) Low temperature, low pressure

(b) High temperature, low pressure

(c) Low temperature, high pressure

(d) High temperature, high pressure

Answer (c) On applying low temperature, the kinetic energy of the particles decreases and the particles come closer. Increased pressure also brings the particles closer, so the gases liquefy.

Question 3. The property to flow is unique to fluids. Which one of the following statements is correct?

(a) Only gases behave like fluids

(b) Gases and solids behave like fluids

(c) Gases and liquids behave like fluids

(d) Only liquids are fluids

Answer   (c) Both gases and liquids tend to flow due to the distance between particles and less attraction force as compared to solids.

Question 4.   During summer, water kept in an earthen pot becomes cool because of the phenomenon of
(a) diffusion   (b) transpiration
(c) osmosis   (d) evaporation

Answer   (d) Tiny pores present in the earthen pot (matka) help to provide a large surface area for the evaporation of water which causes cooling effect.

Question 5.   A few substances are arranged in the increasing order of 'forces of attraction' between their particles. Which one of the following represents a correct arrangement?
(a) Water, air, wind
(b) Air, sugar, oil
(c) Oxygen, water, sugar
(d) Salt, juice, air

Answer   (c) Because force of attraction increases in the order
Gas < liquid < solid.

Question 6.   On converting 25°C , 38°C and 66°C to kelvin scale, the correct sequence of temperature will be
(a) 298 K, 311 K and 339 K
(b) 298 K, 300 K and 338 K
(c) 273 K, 278 K and 543 K
(d) 298 K, 310 K and 338 K

Answer   (a) $26\,°C + 273 = 298\,K$
$38\,°C + 273 = 311\,K$
$66\,°C + 273 = 339\,K$
$(\because\ °C + 273 = K)$

Question 7.   Choose the correct statement of the following.
(a) Conversion of solid into vapours without passing through the liquid state is called vaporisation
(b) Conversion of vapours into solid without passing through the liquid state is called sublimation
(c) Conversion of vapours into solid without passing through the liquid state is called freezing
(d) Conversion of solid into liquid is called sublimation

Answer   (b) Conversion of solid into vapours on heating or vapours into solid on cooling without undergoing liquid state is called sublimation.

Question 8. The boiling points of diethyl ether, acetone and n-butyl alcohol are 35°C, 56°C and 118°C respectively. Which one of the following correctly represents their boiling points in kelvin scale?

(a) 306 K, 329 K, 391 K
(b) 308 K, 329 K, 392 K
(c) 308 K, 329 K, 391 K
(d) 329 K, 392 K, 308 K

Answer (c)   35 °C + 273 = 308 K
            56 °C + 273 = 329 K
            118 °C + 273 = 391 K   (∵ °C + 273 = K)

Question 9. Which condition out of the following will increase the evaporation of water?

(a) Increase in temperature of water
(b) Decrease in temperature of water
(c) Less exposed surface area of water
(d) Adding common salt to water

Answer (a) Because it increases the kinetic energy of water molecules so water molecules present at the surface leave the surface faster.

Question 10. In which of the following conditions, the distance between the molecules of hydrogen gas would increase?

 (i) Increasing pressure on hydrogen contained in a closed container
 (ii) Some hydrogen gas leaking out of the container
(iii) Increasing the volume of the container of hydrogen gas
(iv) Adding more hydrogen gas to the container without increasing the volume of the container

(a) (i) and (iii)
(b) (i) and (iv)
(c) (ii) and (iii)
(d) (ii) and (iv)

Answer (c)
 (ii) Hydrogen leaking from the container leave some vacant space inside the container.
(iii) If volume of the container is increasing, then also gases molecules will get some more space as gaseous molecules occupy all the space available to them.

Short Answer Type Questions

Question 11. A sample of water under study was found to boil at 102°C, at normal temperature and pressure. Is the water pure? Will this water freeze at 0°C? Comment.

Answer   The boiling point of pure water is 100°C. The given sample, boiling at 102°C, indicates that it contains dissolved impurities.

No, the water will not freeze at 0°C. Instead it will freeze below 0°C.

Note *The presence of impurities increase the boiling point and decrease the freezing point/melting point of a substance.*

Question 12. A student heats a beaker containing ice and water. He measures the temperature of the content of the beaker as a function of time. Which of the following (see figure) would correctly represent the result? Justify your choice.

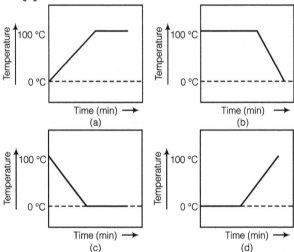

Answer   Fig. (d) would correctly represent the result. Because when heat is provided to the mixture of water and ice at 0°C, the ice absorbs this and converts into the water at 0°C. During this period, there is no rise in temperature. On further heating, the temperature starts rising.

Question 13. 'Osmosis is a special kind of diffusion'. Comment.

Answer   Diffusion is the process in which molecules of a substance move from the place of (their) higher concentration to the place of lower concentration. (No membrane required).

But during osmosis, the water molecules move from (their) higher concentration to the place of their lower concentration through a semipermeable membrane. Thus, osmosis is termed as a special kind of diffusion.

Question 14. Classify the following into osmosis/diffusion.
(a) Swelling up of a raisin on keeping in water.
(b) Spreading of virus on sneezing.
(c) Earthworm dying on coming in contact with common salt.
(d) Shrinking of grapes kept in thick sugar syrup.
(e) Preserving pickles in salt.
(f) Spreading of smell of cake being baked through out the house.
(g) Aquatic animals using oxygen dissolved in water during respiration.

Answer

Osmosis	Diffusion
(a) Swelling up of a raisin on keeping in water.	(b) Spreading of virus on sneezing.
(c) Earthworm dying on coming in contact with common salt.	(f) Spreading of smell of cake being baked through out the house.
(d) Shrinking of grapes kept in thick sugar syrup.	(g) Aquatic animals using oxygen dissolved in water during respiration.
(e) Preserving pickles in salt.	

Note *In osmosis a semipermeable membrane is required and only water (solvent) molecules can move whereas in diffusion no such membrane is required and any substance can move from its higher to lower concentration.*

Question 15. Water as ice has a cooling effect, whereas water as steam may cause severe burns. Explain these observations.

Answer When ice melts, it absorbs the energy equal to the latent heat of fusion from the surroundings therefore causes cooling effect. But steam releases the extra heat (equal to the latent heat of vaporisation) which it has absorbed when water was converted into steam. So, steam produces severe burns.

Question 16. A glass tumbler containing hot water is kept in the freezer compartment of a refrigerator (temperature $< 0°C$). If you could measure the temperature of the content of the tumbler, which of the following graphs (see figure) would correctly represent the change in its temperature as a function of time.

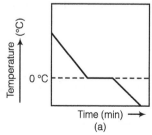

(a)

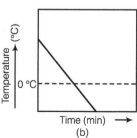

(b)

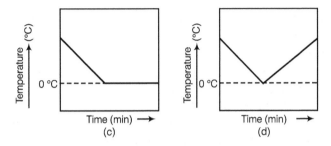

Time (min) ⟶
(c)

Time (min) ⟶
(d)

Answer   Fig. (a) represents the change of temperature with time correctly. The temperature of water first decreases up to zero degree celcius then remains constant for some time (till the ice is formed), then again starts decreasing.

Question 17. Look at figure and suggest in which of the vessels *A, B, C* or *D* the rate of evaporation will be the highest? Explain.

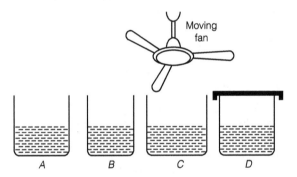

Answer   The rate of evaporation will be the highest in vessel *C* as the surface area exposed for evaporation is larger than *A* (equal size). The moving fan increases the wind speed which also increases the rate of evaporation

Question 18.
   (a) Conversion of solid to vapour is called sublimation. Name the term used to denote the conversion of vapour to solid.
   (b) Conversion of solid state to liquid state is called fusion; what is meant by latent heat of fusion?

Answer
   (a) It is also called sublimation.
   (b) The amount of heat energy required to change 1 kg of a solid into liquid at atmospheric pressure at its melting point is known as the latent heat of fusion.

Long Answer Type Questions

Question 19. It is a hot summer day. Priyanshi and Ali are wearing cotton and nylon clothes respectively. Who do you think would be more comfortable and why?

Answer Priyanshi would be more comfortable. The reason is that cotton absorbs sweat from the body and provides it a larger surface area for evaporation. Increased evaporation causes more, cooling effect.

Nylon does not absorb sweat so the sweat does not evaporate and Ali would feel uncomfortable.

Question 20. You want to wear your favourite shirt to a party, but the problem is that it is still wet after a wash. What steps would you take to dry it faster?

Answer We can take (any one or more) following steps
  (a) Dry it under the fan
  (b) Use hanger for exposing its larger surface to air
  (c) Dry in sun
  (d) Use iron

2

Is Matter Around us Pure?

Important Concepts

1. Pure substance is made up of single type of particles (atoms or/ and molecules).

2. Elements and compounds are considered to be pure as they have characteristic melting point and boiling point.

3. A mixture may be homogeneous or heterogeneous in nature.

4. A solution is a homogeneous mixture of two or more substances.

5. Alloys are solutions of solid in solid.

6. Mass by mass percentage of a solution $= \dfrac{\text{Mass of solute}}{\text{Mass of solution}} \times 100$

7. Particles of a suspension are visible while those of a true solution are not.

8. When a beam of light is passed through a colloidal solution, its particles scatter light and in the path of light, the particles become visible (Tyndall effect).

9. A mixture of common salt and ammonium chloride can be separated by sublimation.

10. Crystallisation is the method of preparing pure crystals of a solid by slowly cooling its hot saturated solution placed in undisturbed condition.

11. During distillation, the impure liquid is heated and the obtained vapours of the liquid are cooled and condensed to get the pure liquid.

12. Physical changes may involve the change in physical properties (size, shape, physical state etc.) only while chemical changes involve the change in chemical composition of a substance.

13. Mixture can be separated into its constituents by simple physical methods while compound cannot be divided into its constituents by these methods.

14. Elements are the building blocks of matter as the alphabets are the building blocks of a language or bricks are the building blocks of a building.

15. A compound does not exhibit the properties of its constituent elements while a mixture does so.

Intext Questions

On Page 15

Question 1. What is meant by a substance?

Answer A substance is that which is made up of single type of particles.

For example, hydrogen, water etc., are pure.

Note *All elements and compounds are considered to be pure.*

Question 2. List the points of differences between homogeneous and heterogeneous mixtures.

Answer

S.No.	Homogeneous mixture	Heterogeneous mixture
1.	Its constituents particles cannot be seen easily.	Its constituent particles can be seen easily.
2.	There are no visible boundaries of separation in a homogeneous mixture.	There are clear and visible boundaries of separation between the constituents.
3.	Its constituents cannot be easily separated.	Its constituents can be separated by simple methods.
4.	**Examples** Alloys, solution of salt in water etc.	**Examples** Mixture of sand and common salt, mixture of sand and water etc.

On Page 18

Question 1. Differentiate between homogeneous and heterogeneous mixtures with examples.

Answer Same as the previous one.

Question 2. How are sol, solution and suspension different from each other?

Answer

S.No.	Solution	Sol (colloidal solution)	Suspension
1.	Solution or true solution is homogeneous.	Sol or colloidal solution is heterogeneous (may appear homogeneous).	Suspension is also heterogeneous.
2.	The particle size of solute is less than 1 nm.	The particle size ranges from 1 to 100 nm.	The particle size is greater than 100 nm.
3.	It does not show Tyndall effect.	It shows Tyndall effect.	It also shows Tyndall effect.
4.	The particles pass through the filter paper *i.e.*, solute particles cannot be filtered by using a filter paper.	The particles pass through the filter paper so the constituents cannot be separated by ordinary filter paper.	The particles are quite large so they do not pass through the filter paper and separated easily by filtration.
5.	True solution is transparent.	It may be transparent or translucent.	It may be translucent or opaque.
6.	The particles do not settle at all.	The particles settle on centrifugation or some other specific conditions *e.g.*, curdling of milk.	The particles settle down when the suspension is left undisturbed.
7.	**Examples** Sea water, alloys, solution of lemon juice in water etc.	**Examples** Milk of magnesia, cough syrup, mist, fog, clouds, smoke, mud etc.	**Examples** Mixture of sand in water, mixture of chalk in water etc.

Question 3. To make a saturated solution, 36 g of sodium chloride is dissolved in 100 g of water at 293 K. Find its concentration at this temperature.

Answer Mass of sodium chloride (solute) = 36 g

Mass of water (solvent) = 100 g

We know that, mass of solution = mass of solute + mass of solvent

$$= 36\,g + 100\,g = 136\,g$$

Concentration (mass percentage) of the solution

$$= \frac{\text{Mass of solute}}{\text{Mass of solution}} \times 100 = \frac{36\,g}{136\,g} \times 100 = 26.47\%$$

On Page 24

Question 1. How will you separate a mixture containing kerosene and petrol (difference in their boiling points is more than 25°C), which are miscible with each other?

Answer A mixture of kerosene and petrol (b.p. differ by more than 25°C) can be separated by the process of **simple distillation.**

Method In a distillation flask, a mixture of kerosene and petrol is taken as shown in figure. The mixture is heated slowly and the temperature is noted with the help of thermometer. Petrol (b.p. = 70°C to 120°C) vaporises first and the temperature becomes constant for some time (till all petrol evaporates from the mixture). Vapours of petrol are condensed and collected in another container while the kerosene remains in the distillation flask. As soon as the temperature starts rising again, the heating is stopped and both the components are collected separately.

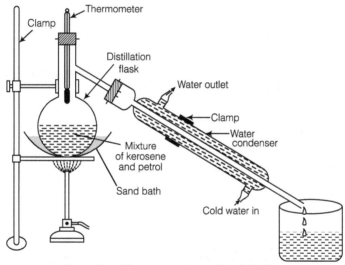

Separation of kerosene and petrol by distillation.

Question 2. Name the technique to separate
   (i) butter from curd
  (ii) salt from sea water
 (iii) camphor from salt

Answer
   (i) Butter can be separated from curd by centrifugation.
  (ii) Salt from sea water can be separated by the method of evaporation. Water vaporises on evaporation leaving behind the salt.

(iii) Camphor from salt can be separated by sublimation method. On subliming camphor will be converted into vapour leaving behind the salt.

Question 3. What type of mixtures are separated by the technique of crystallisation?

Answer   Crystallisation method can be used to purify those mixtures which
     (a) contain insoluble and/or soluble impurities.
     (b) have crystalline nature.
     (c) either decompose or get charred (*e.g.* sugar) on heating to dryness, *i.e.*, which cannot be separated by evaporation.
     (d) cannot be separated by filtration as some impurities are soluble.

Question 4. Classify the following as chemical or physical changes

   (a) Cutting of trees,

   (b) Melting of butter in a pan,

   (c) Rusting of almirah,

   (d) Boiling of water to form steam,

   (e) Passing of electric current, through water and the water breaking down into hydrogen and oxygen gases,

   (f) Dissolving common salt in water,

   (g) Making a fruit salad with raw fruits, and

   (h) Burning of paper and wood

Answer

(a) Physical change	(b) Physical change
(c) Chemical change	(d) Physical change
(e) Chemical change	(f) Physical change
(g) Physical change	(h) Chemical change

Criteria for classification   A change in which no new substance is formed *i.e.*, only the form or physical state changes is said to be physical. A change in which the chemical composition changes is called a chemical change.

Question 5. Try segregating the things around you as pure substances or mixtures.

Answer   Few things around us are as follows

(a) Wood – Mixture	(b) Coal – Mixture
(c) Milk – Mixture	(d) Sugar – Pure substance
(e) Common salt – Pure substance	(f) Soap – Compound/mixture
(g) Soil – Mixture	(h) Rubber – Pure substance

Exercises

Question 1. Which separation techniques will you apply for the separation of the following?

(a) Sodium chloride from its solution in water.

(b) Ammonium chloride from a mixture containing sodium chloride and ammonium chloride.

(c) Small pieces of metal in the engine oil of a car.

(d) Different pigments from an extract of flower petals.

(e) Butter from curd.

(f) Oil from water.

(g) Tea leaves from tea.

(h) Iron pins from sand.

(i) Wheat grains from husk.

(j) Fine mud particles suspended in water.

Answer

(a) **Evaporation** Water will evaporate on heating the mixture. Sodium chloride will remain behind.

(b) **Sublimation** On heating the mixture,ammonium chloride will go into vapour phase. On collecting and cooling these vapours, solid ammonium chloride is recovered. Sodium chloride remains in the previous pan.

(c) **Filtration** Small metal pieces can be filtered by using a suitable filter.

(d) **Chromatography** Pigments (different colours) of flower petal extract are separated by chromatography.

(e) **Centrifugation** By using centrifugal machine or churning the curd by hand.

(f) **Decantation by using separating funnel** Oil and water form separate layers which are separated by using separating funnel.

(g) **Filtration** Tea leaves are filtered with the help of a tea-strainer by the process of filtration.

(h) **Magnetic separation** Iron pins are separated from sand by the process of magnetic separation.

(i) **Winnowing** Husk from wheat grains is separated by the process of winnowing.

(j) **Coagulation and decantation** Alum is added to the muddy water which makes the soil particles heavier so they settle down. The clear water is then separated by decantation.

Question 2. Write the steps you would use for making tea. Use the words solution, solvent, solute, dissolve, soluble, insoluble, filtrate and residue.

Answer   Method of preparation of tea

  (i) Take some water (solvent) in a pan and heat it.

 (ii) Add some sugar (solute) and boil to dissolve the sugar completely the obtained homogeneous mixture is called solution.

(iii) Add tea leaves (or tea) in the solution and boil the mixture.

(iv) Now add milk and boil again.

 (v) Filter the mixture through the tea stainer and collect the filtrate or soluble substances, *i.e.*, tea in a cup. The insoluble tea leaves left behind as residue in the 8 trainer.

Question 3. Pragya tested the solubility of three different substances at different temperatures and collected the data as given below (results are given in the following table, as grams of substance dissolved in 100 grams of water to form a saturated solution).

Substance dissolved	Temperature in K				
	283	293	313	333	353
	Solubility				
Potassium nitrate	21	32	62	106	167
Sodium chloride	36	36	36	37	37
Potassium chloride	35	35	40	46	54
Ammonium chloride	24	37	41	55	66

  (a) What mass of potassium nitrate would be needed to produce a saturated solution of potassium nitrate in 50 grams of water at 313 K?

  (b) Pragya makes a saturated solution of potassium chloride in water at 353 K and leaves the solution to cool at room temperature. What would she observe as the solution cools? Explain.

  (c) Find the solubility of each salt at 293 K. Which salt has the highest solubility at this temperature?

  (d) What is the effect of change of temperature on the solubility of a salt?

Answer

  (a) Mass of potassium nitrate needed to produce its saturated solution in 100 g of water at 313 K = 62 g

     Mass of potassium nitrate needed to produce its saturated solution in 50 g of water at 313 K = $\dfrac{62}{100} \times 50\ g = 31\ g$

  (b) Crystals of potassium chloride are formed. This happens as solubility of a solid decreases with decreasing the temperature.

(c) **Solubility of each salt at 293 K**

Potassium nitrate	32 g per 100 g water
Sodium chloride	36 g per 100 g water
Potassium chloride	35 g per 100 g water
Ammonium chloride	37 g per 100 g water

Note *Solubility of a solid is that amount in gram which can be dissolved in 100 g of water (solvent) to make saturated solution at a particular temperature.*

Ammonium chloride has the maximum solubility (37 g per 100 g of water) at 293 K.

(d) Solubility of a (solid) salt decreases with decrease in temperature while it increases with rise in temperature.

Question 4. Explain the following giving examples.

(a) Saturated solution (b) Pure substance (c) Colloid (d) Suspension

Answer

(a) **Saturated solution** A solution in which no more amount of solute can be dissolved at a particular temperature is called saturated solution *e.g.*, when sugar is dissolved repeatedly in a given amount of water, a condition is reached at which further dissolution of sugar is not possible in that amount of water at room temperature. Such solution in which no more solute can be dissolved is called the saturated solution.

(b) **Pure substance** A substance made up of single type of particles (atoms and/or molecules) is called pure substance. All elements and compounds are said to be pure, *e.g.*, water, sugar etc.

(c) **Colloid** Colloid is a heterogeneous mixture in which the solute particle size is too small to be seen with the naked eye, but is big enough to scatter light. The solute particles are called the dispersed phase and the medium in which they are spread is called the dispersion medium. Milk, clouds etc., are the example of colloid.

(d) **Suspension** A suspension is a heterogeneous mixture in which the solute particles do not dissolve but remain suspended throughout the bulk of the medium. Particles of a suspension are visible to the naked eye. *e.g.*, mixture of sand, water and muddy water etc.

Question 5. Classify each of the following as a homogeneous or heterogeneous mixture.

Soda water, wood, air, soil, vinegar, filtered tea

Answer **Homogeneous mixtures** Air, soda water, vinegar, filtered tea.
Heterogeneous mixtures Wood, soil,

Note *Homogeneous mixtures have same composition throughout but the composition of heterogeneous mixture is not uniform.*

Question 6. How would you confirm that a colourless liquid given to you is pure water?

Answer Boiling point is a characteristic feature of a pure substance. Boiling point of pure water is 100°C. If the given colourless liquid boils at 100°C sharp, it is pure water, otherwise not.

Question 7. Which of the following materials fall in the category of a "pure substance"?

   (a) Ice   (b) Milk   (c) Iron   (d) Hydrochloric acid
   (e) Calcium oxide   (f) Mercury   (g) Brick   (h) Wood   (i) Air

Answer Ice, iron, calcium oxide, mercury are pure substance as they have definite composition.

Note *Milk is a colloid, so is a heterogeneous mixture. Hydrochloric acid is also a mixture of hydrogenchloride gas and water.*

Question 8. Identify the solutions among the following mixtures.

   (a) Soil (b) Sea water (c) Air (d) Coal (e) Soda water

Answer Sea water, air and soda water, as these are the homogeneous mixtures of two or more substances

Note *Sea water is also considered as heterogeneous solution.*

Question 9. Which of the following will show "Tyndall effect"?

   (a) Salt solution   (b) Milk
   (c) Copper sulphate solution   (d) Starch solution

Answer Milk and starch solution will show "Tyndall effect" as both of these are colloids.

Question 10. Classify the following into elements, compounds and mixtures.

   (a) Sodium   (b) Soil   (c) Sugar solution (d)   Silver
   (e) Calcium carbonate   (f) Tin (g) Silicon   (h) Coal (i) Air
   (j) Soap   (k) Methane (l) Carbon dioxide   (m) Blood

Answer Elements have only one kind of atoms, compounds have atoms of more than one kind but in definite proportion whereas mixtures have two or more substance in any proportion (*i.e.,* composition of mixture is not definite). Thus,

   Elements Sodium, silver, tin, silicon,

   Compounds Calcium carbonate, methane, carbon dioxide.

   Mixtures Soil, sugar solution, coal, air, soap, blood.

Question 11. Which of the following are chemical changes?

   (a) Growth of a plant   (b) Rusting of iron
   (c) Mixing of iron filings and sand
   (d) Cooking of food   (e) Digestion of food
   (f) Freezing of water   (g) Burning of a candle

Answer Growth of a plant, rusting of iron, cooking of food, digestion of food, burning of a candle are chemical changes, because here the chemical composition of substance changes.

Selected NCERT Exemplar Problems
Multiple Choice Questions

Question 1. Which of the following statements are true for pure substances?

(i) Pure substances contain only one kind of particles.

(ii) Pure substances may be compounds or mixtures.

(iii) Pure substances have the same composition throughout.

(iv) Pure substances can be exemplified by all elements other than nickel.

    (a) (i) and (ii)   (b) (i) and (iii)

    (c) (iii) and (iv)   (d) (ii) and (iii)

Answer (b) These are the properties of pure substance. All elements and compounds are included in pure substances.

Question 2. Rusting of an article made up of iron is called

    (a) corrosion and it is a physical as well as chemical change

    (b) dissolution and it is a physical change

    (c) corrosion and it is a chemical change

    (d) dissolution and it is a chemical change

Answer (c) The process is called corrosion and it is a chemical change because rust is a chemical compound (hydrated iron oxide $Fe_2O_3 \cdot xH_2O$) totally different from element iron. The reaction is

$$4Fe + 3O_2 + xH_2O \longrightarrow \underbrace{2Fe_2O_3 \cdot xH_2O}_{Rust}$$

Question 3. A mixture of sulphur and carbon disulphide is

    (a) heterogeneous and shows Tyndall effect

    (b) homogeneous and shows Tyndall effect

    (c) heterogeneous and does not show Tyndall effect

    (d) homogeneous and does not show Tyndall effect

Answer (a) Because sulphur is a solid and carbondisulphide is a gas.

Question 4. Tincture of iodine has antiseptic properties. This solution is made by dissolving

    (a) iodine in potassium iodide   (b) iodine in vaseline

    (c) iodine in water   (d) iodine in alcohol

Answer (d) Tincture of iodine is made by dissolving iodine in alcohol.

Question 5. Which of the following are homogeneous in nature?

(i) Ice   (ii) Wood   (iii) Soil   (iv) Air
(a) (i) and (iii)   (b) (ii) and (iv)   (c) (i) and (iv)   (d) (iii) and (iv)

Answer (c) As particles are not distinctly visible.

Question 6. Which of the following are physical changes?

(i) Melting of iron metal   (ii) Rusting of iron
(iii) Bending of an iron rod   (iv) Drawing a wire of iron metal
  (a) (i), (ii) and (iii)   (b) (i), (ii) and (iv)
  (c) (i), (iii) and (iv)   (d) (ii), (iii) and (iv)

Answer (c) In these processes only the form changes but not the chemical composition.

Question 7. Which of the following are chemical changes?

(i) Decaying of wood
(ii) Burning of wood
(iii) Sawing of wood
(iv) Hammering of a nail in to a piece of wood
  (a) (i) and (ii)   (b) (ii) and (iii)   (c) (iii) and (iv)   (d) (i) and (iv)

Answer (a) Because in these processes, the chemical composition changes and a new substance is obtained.

Question 8. Two substances, A and B were made to react to form a third substance A_2B according to the following reaction

$$2A + B \longrightarrow A_2B$$

Which of the following statements concerning this reaction are incorrect?

(i) The product A_2B shows the properties of substances A and B.
(ii) The product will always have a fixed composition.
(iii) The product so formed cannot be classified as a compound.
(iv) The product so formed is an element.
  (a) (i), (ii) and (iii)   (b) (ii), (iii) and (iv)
  (c) (i), (iii), and (iv)   (d) (ii), (iii) and (iv)

Answer (c) Above mentioned 'points' do not show the properties of a compound (here A_2B).

Question 9. Two chemical species X and Y combine together to form a product P which contains both X and Y.

$$X + Y \rightarrow P$$

X and Y cannot be broken down into simpler substances by simple chemical reactions. Which of the following concerning the species X, Y and P are correct?

(i) P is a compound.
(ii) X and Y are compounds.
(iii) X and Y are elements.
(iv) P has a fixed composition.

    (a) (i), (ii) and (iii)   (b) (i), (ii) and (iv)
    (c) (ii), (iii) and (iv)   (d) (i), (iii) and (iv)

Answer (d) An element cannot be broken down into simpler substances by simple chemical reactions. So X and Y are elements. Elements combine together to form compound or molecule, so P is a compound.

A compound has a fixed composition of the constituent elements.

Short Answer Type Questions

Question 10. Suggest the separation technique(s) one would need to employ to separate the following mixtures.

    (a) Mercury and water
    (b) Potassium chloride and ammonium chloride
    (c) Common salt, water and sand
    (d) Kerosene oil, water and salt

Answer

    (a) Decantation by using separating funnel as they form separate layers.
    (b) Sublimation because ammonium chloride being a sublimate, sublimes leaving behind the potassium chloride.
    (c) Decantation to separate sand and evaporation to separate common salt.
    (d) (i) Decantation by using separating funnel as oil and salt solution for separate layers.
       (ii) Evaporation because water evaporates and salt remains as residue.

Question 11. Salt can be recovered from its solution by evaporation. Suggest some other technique for the same.

Answer Simple distillation can be used. Pure water is collected in the receiver and salt remains in the distillation flask.

Question 12. The 'sea water' can be classified as a homogeneous as well as heterogeneous mixture. Comment.

Answer 'Sea water' is called homogeneous as it contains dissolved salts in it. It may be called heterogeneous as it contains various insoluble components too as sand, microbes, shells made of calcium carbonate and so many other things.

Question 13. While diluting a solution of salt in water, a student by mistake added acetone (boiling point 56°C). What technique can be employed to get back the acetone? Justify you choice.

Answer Acetone can be get back by simple distillation because the difference in the boiling points of acetone and water is more than 25°C.

B.P. of acetone	—	56°C
B.P. of water	—	100°C

Question 14. What would you observe when
- (a) a saturated solution of potassium chloride prepared at 60°C is allowed to cool at room temperature?
- (b) an aqueous sugar solution is heated to dryness?
- (c) a mixture of iron filings and sulphur powder is heated strongly?

Answer (a) Crystals of potassium chloride are formed because solubility decreases with decrease in temperature.

(b) As water evaporates completely, sugar gets charred and turns black.

(c) The compound iron sulphide is formed.

$$Fe + S \xrightarrow{\Delta} FeS$$

Question 15. Explain why particles of a colloidal solution do not settle down when left undisturbed?

Answer Colloidal particles always ramain in a state of zig-zag motion, called the Brownian movement, which counters the force of gravity acting on colloidal particles and hence, helps in providing stability to colloidal sols by not allowing them to settle down.

Question 16. Smoke and fog both are aerosols. In what way are they different?

Answer Aerosol means in both smoke and fog, dispersion medium is the same, *i.e.* gas but they differ in dispersed phase. In smoke the dispersed phase is solid while in fog the dispersed phase is liquid.

Question 17. Classify the following as physical or chemical properties.
- (a) The composition of a sample of steel is 98% iron, 1.5% carbon and 0.5% other elements.
- (b) Zinc dissolves in hydrochloric acid with the evolution of hydrogen gas.
- (c) Metallic sodium is soft enough to be cut with a knife.
- (d) Most metal oxides form alkalis on interacting with water.

Answer (a) Chemical property (b) Chemical property
(c) Physical property (d) Chemical property

Question 18. Name the process associated with the following

(a) Dry ice is kept at room temperature and at one atmospheric pressure.

(b) A drop of ink placed on the surface of water contained in a glass spreads throughout the water.

(c) A potassium permanganate crystal is in a beaker and water is poured into the beaker with stirring.

(d) A acetone bottle is left open and the bottle becomes empty.

(e) Milk is churned to separate cream from it.

(f) Settling of sand when a mixture of sand and water is left undisturbed for some time.

(g) Fine beam of light entering through a small hole in a dark room, illuminates the particles in its paths.

Answer

(a) Sublimation   (b) Diffusion

(c) Dissolution   (d) Evaporation/Vaporisation

(e) Centrifugation   (f) Sedimentation

(g) Tyndall effect

Question 19. You are given two samples of water labelled as '*A*' and '*B*'. Sample '*A*' boils at 100°C and sample '*B*' boils at 102°C. Which sample of water will not freeze at 0°C? Comment.

Answer Sample '*B*' boils at 102°C while the boiling point of pure water is 100°C. It means this sample contains impurities. So, it will not freeze at 0°C. Instead it will freeze below 0°C.

Question 20. What are the favourable qualities given to gold when it is alloyed with copper or silver for the purpose of making ornaments?

Answer When alloyed with copper or silver, the gold becomes harder and stronger and its brittleness decreases.

Question 21. An element is sonorous and highly ductile. Under which category would you classify this element? What other characteristics do you expect the element to possess?

Answer This element is categorised as a **metal**. (Because metals are sonorous and highly ductile.)

Characteristics of metals

1. They possess metallic lustre.
2. They are good conductors of heat and electricity.
3. They are ductile.
4. They are malleable.
5. They have silver-grey or golden yellow colour.
6. They have high tensile strength.
7. They have high densities and melting point/boiling point too.

Question 22. Give an example each for the mixture having the following characteristic. Suggest a suitable method to separate the components of these mixtures.

(a) A volatile and non-volatile component.

(b) Two volatile components with appreciable difference in boiling points.

(c) Two immiscible liquids.

(d) One of the components changes directly from solid to gaseous state.

(e) Two or more coloured constituents soluble in some solvent.

Answer

(a) **Example**   Mixture of acetone and water.

   Method   Simple distillation can be used to separate a mixture of volatile and non-volatile liquid.

(b) **Example**   Mixture of kerosene and petrol.

   Method   Simple distillation can be used to separate two volatile components with appreciable difference in boiling points.

(c) **Example**   Mixture of mustard oil and water.

   Method   Separating funnel is used to separate a mixture of immiscible liquids.

(d) **Example**   Mixture of ammonium chloride and common salt.

   Method   Sublimation can be used to separate the mixture in which one component changes directly from solid to gas.

(e) **Example**   A mixture of different pigments from an extract of flower petals.

   Method   Chromatography

Question 23. Can we separate alcohol dissolved in water by using a separating funnel? If yes, then describe the procedure. If not, explain.

Answer   No, alcohol cannot be separated from water by using a separating funnel because alcohol is completely miscible in water.

Question 24. On heating calcium carbonate gets converted into calcium oxide and carbon dioxide.

(a) Is this a physical or a chemical change?

(b) Can you prepare one acidic or one basic solution by using the products formed in the above process? If so, write the chemical equation involved.

Answer

(a) The phenomena given in question is a chemical change because the composition of product formed is different from the substance taken. The reaction involved is

$$[CaCO_3 \xrightarrow{\Delta} CaO + CO_2]$$

(b) Yes, (i) $CaO + H_2O \longrightarrow Ca(OH)_2$
(Basic solution)

(ii) $CO_2 + H_2O \longrightarrow H_2CO_3$
(Acidic solution)

Question 25. Non-metals are usually poor conductors of heat and electricity. They are non-lustrous, non-sonorous, non-malleable and are coloured.

(a) Name a lustrous non-metal.
(b) Name a non-metal which exists as a liquid at room temperature.
(c) The allotropic form of a non-metal is a good conductor of electricity. Name the allotrope.
(d) Name a non-metal which is known to form the largest number of compounds.
(e) Name a non-metal other than carbon which shows allotropy.
(f) Name a non-metal which is required for combustion.

Answer

(a) Iodine	(b) Bromine	(c) Graphite (Carbon)
(d) Carbon	(e) Phosphorus	(f) Oxygen

Question 26. Classify the substances given below into elements and compounds.

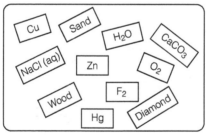

Answer

Elements	Compounds
Cu	Sand
O_2	H_2O
Zn	$CaCO_3$
F_2	NaCl(aq)
Hg	
Diamond (Carbon)	

Note *Wood is neither an element nor compound. It is a mixture. An element is made of the same type of atoms but compound is a mixture of different elements.*

Question 27. Which of the following are not compounds?
- (a) Chlorine gas
- (b) Potassium chloride
- (c) Iron
- (d) Iron sulphide
- (e) Aluminium
- (f) Iodine
- (g) Carbon
- (h) Carbon monoxide
- (i) Sulphur powder

Answer

(a) Chlorine gas	(c) Iron	(e) Aluminium
(f) Iodine	(g) Carbon	(i) Sulphur powder

Substances mentioned above are the elements, not compounds.

Long Answer Type Questions

Question 28. Fractional distillation is suitable for separation of miscible liquids with a boiling point difference of about 25 K or less. What part of fractional distillation apparatus makes it efficient and possess an advantage over a simple distillation process? Explain using a diagram.

Answer

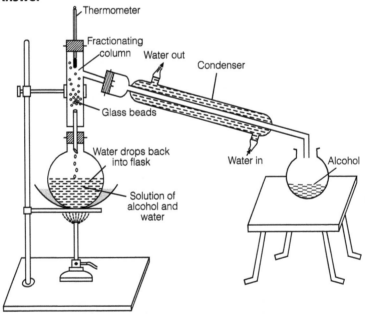

Separation of miscible liquids by fractional distillation

Fractionating column is the most important part of the fractional distillation apparatus. This column is provided with some glass beads in it. It helps to obstruct the upward movement of the vapours of the two liquids. The vapours of high boiling liquid gets condensed earlier (at lower level). The energy (latent heat) released helps to take the vapours of low boiling liquid to a height in the fractionating column.

Advantages

1. This method can separate the liquids with a boiling point difference about or less than 25 K.

2. During the process, both evaporation and condensation take place simultaneously.

3. A mixture (like petroleum) can also be separated by fractional distillation process which contains several components.

Question 29.

(a) Under which category of mixtures will you classify alloys and why?

(b) A solution is always a liquid. Comment.

(c) Can a solution be heterogeneous?

Answer

(a) Alloys, although solids are classified as solutions because of their uniform composition throughout. Actually these are solid solutions, *i.e.*, homogeneous mixtures of metals and/or non-metal.

(b) A solution is generally a liquid, not always. **For example** Alloys are known to be solid solutions.

(c) The term solution is generally used for **'true solution'**. In this case, the solution is always homogeneous.

   In case of 'colloidal solution', that is not a true solution, the solution is heterogeneous.

Question 30. Iron filings and sulphur were mixed together and divided into two parts, A and B. Part A was heated strongly while part B was not heated. Dilute hydrochloric acid was added to both the parts and evolution of gas was seen in both the cases. How will you identify the gases evolved?

Answer   **Part A** $\underbrace{Fe + S \xrightarrow{\Delta} FeS}_{Part\ A}$

$$\underset{[A]\quad\ \ dil.}{FeS + 2HCl} \longrightarrow FeCl_2 + H_2S \uparrow$$

Part B is not heated so the reaction will be as such
$$\underset{(in\ Part\ B)\quad dil.}{Fe\quad + 2HCl} \longrightarrow FeCl_2 + H_2 \uparrow$$

In part A, **H₂S gas** is produced, which is identified by its characteristic smell of rotten egg.

In part *B*, **H₂ gas** is produced. Hydrogen gas is tested by bringing a burning match stick near the mouth of the test tube. It burns with a pop sound and water is formed.

Question 31. A child wanted to separate the mixture of dyes constituting a sample of ink. He marked a line by the ink on the filter paper and placed the filter paper in a glass containing water as shown in the figure. The filter paper was removed when the water moved near the top of the filter paper.

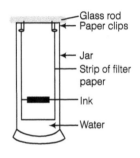

  (i) What would you expect to see, if the ink contains three different coloured components?

 (ii) Name the technique used by the child.

(iii) Suggest one more application of this technique.

Answer
  (i) Three different coloured spots are obtained on the strip at different heights.

 (ii) Chromatography (paper chromatography).

(iii) The chromatography method is also employed to separate drugs from the blood.

Question 32. A group of students took an old shoe box and covered it with a black paper from all sides. They fixed a source of light (a torch) at one end of the box by making a hole in it

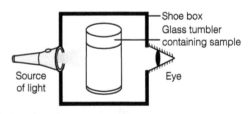

and made another hole on the other side to view the light. They placed a milk sample contained in a beaker/tumbler in the box as shown in the figure. They were amazed to see that milk taken in the tumbler was illuminated. They tried the same activity by taking a salt solution but found that light simply passed through it?

  (a) Explain why the milk sample was illuminated. Name the phenomenon involved.

  (b) Same results were not observed with a salt solution. Explain.

  (c) Can you suggest two more solutions which would show the same effect as shown by the milk solution?

Answer

  (a) The milk sample was illuminated because milk is a colloidal solution and hence, scatter the light passing through it. The phenomenon observed is called "Tyndall effect".

  (b) As salt solution is a true solution *i.e.*, solute particle size is too small to scatter the light, it does not show "Tyndall effect".

  (c) **Examples of colloid** Gold sol, arsenius sulphide (As_2S_3) sol.

Question 33. Classify each of the following as a physical or a chemical change. Give reasons.

  (a) Drying of a shirt in the sun.

  (b) Rising of hot air over a radiator.

  (c) Burning of kerosene in a lantern.

  (d) Change in the colour of black tea on adding lemon juice to it.

  (e) Churning of milk cream to get butter.

Answer

  (a) **Physical change** Because evaporation of water takes place but no change occurs in the composition of the substance.

  (b) **Physical change** It is also involving only movement of air, no change in composition of air

  (c) **First physical change** When kerosene vaporises. After that, burning of kerosene is a chemical change as new products are formed.

  (d) **Physical change** As there occurs only the dissolution.

  (e) **Physical change** As there is no change in composition. Only the separation of components takes place by the physical phenomenon centrifugation.

Question 34. During an experiment the students were asked to prepare a 10% (mass/mass) solution of sugar in water. Ramesh dissolved 10 g of sugar in 100 g of water while Sarika prepared it by dissolving 10 g of sugar in water to make 100 g of the solution.

  (a) Are the two solutions of the same concentration?

  (b) Compare the mass % of the two solutions.

Answer   (a) No

  (b) **Ramesh's solution's concentration**

$$\text{Mass \%} = \frac{\text{Mass of solute}}{\text{Mass of solution}} \times 100$$

$$= \frac{10\,g}{(10+100)g} \times 100 = \frac{10}{110} \times 100 = \frac{100}{11} = 9.09\% \approx 9.1\%$$

Sarika's solutions's concentration

$$\text{Mass \%} = \frac{10}{100} \times 100 = 10\%$$

Question 35. Arun has prepared 0.01% (by mass) solution of sodium chloride in water. Which of the following correctly represents the composition of the solutions?

(a) 1.00 g of NaCl + 100 g of water
(b) 0.11 g of NaCl + 100 g of water
(c) 0.01 g of NaCl + 99.99 g of water
(d) 0.10 g of NaCl + 99.90 g of water

Answer   (c) is the correct answer.

$$\text{Mass \%} = 0.01\% = \frac{\text{Mass of solute}}{\text{Mass of solution}} \times 100$$

$$0.01 = \frac{0.01g}{(0.01 + 99.99)g} \times 100 = \frac{0.01}{100.00} \times 100 = 0.01$$

$$\text{LHS} = \text{RHS}$$

Hence, it is the right answer.

Note *Students can check the other options by using the formula for mass percentage.*

Question 36. Calculate the mass of sodium sulphate required to prepare its 20% (mass percent) solution in 100 g of water?

Answer Mass % of sodium sulphate solution = 20%

Mass of the solvent = 100 g

Let the mass of solute (sodium sulphate) = x g

Applying the formula, $\text{Mass \%} = \dfrac{\text{Mass of solute}}{\text{Mass of solution}} \times 100$

$$20 = \frac{x\,g}{(x + 100)\,g} \times 100$$

$$20\,(x + 100) = 100x$$
$$20x + 2000 = 100\,x$$
$$100\,x - 20\,x = 2000$$
$$80\,x = 2000$$
$$x = \frac{2000}{80} = 25\,g$$

Mass of sodium sulphate = 25 g

3

Atoms and Molecules

Important Concepts

1. Previously atom (parmanu) was thought to be indivisible or the smallest known particle. Maharishi Kanad, Democritus, Dalton and Leucippus supported this idea.

2. According to **'Law of conservation of mass'**, matter can neither be created nor destroyed during a chemical reaction.

3. **'Law of constant** (or definite) **proportions'** states, 'In a chemical substance, the elements are always present in definite proportions by mass'.

4. The chemical formula of a compound is the symbolic representation of its composition.

5. While writing the formula of a compound, atoms (or groups) are written with their own valencies. Then the valencies are exchanged with each other.

6. A mole is a group of 6.022×10^{23} particles (atoms, molecules or ions).

7. 6.022×10^{23} is also known as **'Avogadro's number'**.

8. Symbols of elements are just like abbreviations, based on their Latin names.

9. IUPAC, *i.e.*, International Union of Pure and Applied Chemistry governs all the rules and regulations related to chemistry.

10. Atomicity is the number of atoms present per molecule of an element or compound.

11. Atomic radius is measured in nanometres. $(1 \text{ nm} = 10^{-9} \text{ m})$

12. Anion is the negatively charged ion and cation is the positively charged ion.

13. Mass of one mole atom of an element is equal to its atomic mass.

14. Mass of one mole molecule of a substance (element or compound) is equal to the molar mass (formula mass) of the element or compound.

15. Valency of an element is the combining capacity of the element with other elements.

16. Atoms are very reactive and cannot exist independently.

Intext Questions

On Page 32

Question 1. In a reaction, 5.3 g of sodium carbonate reacted with 6 g of acetic acid. The products were 2.2 g of carbon dioxide, 0.9 g water and 8.2 g of sodium acetate. Show that these observations are in agreement with the law of conservation of mass.

Sodium carbonate + acetic acid $\longrightarrow$ sodium acetate + carbon dioxide + water

Answer $\underset{5.3\,g}{Na_2CO_3} + \underset{6\,g}{2CH_3COOH} \longrightarrow \underset{8.2\,g}{2CH_3COONa} + \underset{2.2\,g}{CO_2} + \underset{0.9\,g}{H_2O}$

Law of conservation of mass states that mass is neither created nor destroyed during a chemical reaction.

It means the mass remains the same. So, we add the mass of the reactants on LHS and add the mass of all products on RHS

$$LHS = 5.3\,g + 6\,g = 11.3\,g$$
$$RHS = 8.2\,g + 2.2\,g + 0.9\,g = 11.3\,g$$
$$\therefore \qquad LHS = RHS$$

So, the observations are in agreement with the law of conservation of mass.

Question 2. Hydrogen and oxygen combine in the ratio of 1 : 8 by mass to form water. What mass of oxygen gas would be required to react completely with 3 g of hydrogen gas?

Answer 'Law of constant proportions' states that composition of a compound is always fixed. Applying this

$\because$ 1 g of hydrogen gas combines with oxygen $= 8\,g$

$\therefore$ 3 g of hydrogen gas will combine with oxygen $= 8 \times 3 = 24\,g$

Question 3. Which postulate of Dalton's atomic theory is the result of the law of conservation of mass?

Answer Following postulate of Dalton's atomic theory is the result of the law of conservation of mass. 'Atoms are indivisible particles, which cannot be created or destroyed in a chemical reaction.'

Question 4. Which postulate of Dalton's atomic theory can explain the law of definite proportions?

Answer Following postulate of Dalton's atomic theory can explain the 'law of definite proportions'.

'The relative number and kinds of atoms are constant in a given compound.'

On Page 35

Question 1. Define the atomic mass unit.

Answer One atomic mass unit (amu) is a mass unit equal to exactly one-twelfth $(1/12^{th})$ the mass of one atom of carbon-12.' The relative atomic masses of all the elements have been found with respect to an atom of carbon-12.

Question 2. Why is it not possible to see an atom with naked eyes?

Answer As an atom is extremely small in size, it is not possible to see it with naked eyes. Generally radius of an atom is of the order of nanometres. For example, atomic radius of hydrogen atom is 10^{-10} m (or 10^{-1} nm).

On Page 39

Question 1. Write down the formulae of
  (i) sodium oxide
  (ii) aluminium chloride
  (iii) sodium sulphide
  (iv) magnesium hydroxide

Note *While writing the formula of a compound, the valencies of the atoms/groups are written along with their formulae and then exchanged.*

Answer (i) Sodium oxide   (ii) Aluminium chloride

$$\underset{Na}{\overset{1+}{}}\times\underset{O}{\overset{2-}{}} \qquad \underset{Al}{\overset{3+}{}}\times\underset{Cl}{\overset{1-}{}}$$

Formula = Na_2O Formula = $AlCl_3$

(iii) Sodium sulphide   (iv) Magnesium hydroxide

$$\underset{Na}{\overset{1+}{}}\times\underset{S}{\overset{2-}{}} \qquad \underset{Mg}{\overset{2+}{}}\times\underset{(OH)}{\overset{1-}{}}$$

Formula = Na_2S Formula = $Mg(OH)_2$

Question 2. Write down the names of compounds represented by the following formulae.

(i) $Al_2(SO_4)_3$ (ii) $CaCl_2$ (iii) K_2SO_4 (iv) KNO_3
(v) $CaCO_3$

Answer (i) Aluminium sulphate (ii) Calcium chloride (iii) Potassium sulphate (iv) Potassium nitrate (v) Calcium carbonate.

Question 3. What is meant by the term chemical formula?

Answer Chemical formula of a compound (or element) is the symbolic representation of its composition. It represents

(i) the number and kind of atoms present per molecule of the compound,
(ii) one mole of the compound,
(iii) molar mass of the compound.

Question 4. How many atoms are present in a
(i) H_2S molecule and (ii) PO_4^{3-} ion?

Answer

(i) 2 atom of hydrogen + 1 atom of sulphur
$\qquad\qquad\qquad$ = three (3) atoms (in a H_2S molecule).
(ii) 1 atom of phosphorus + 4 atoms of oxygen
$\qquad\qquad\qquad$ = five (5) atoms (in a PO_4^{3-} ion).

On Page 40

Question 1. Calculate the molecular masses of
$H_2, O_2, Cl_2, CO_2, CH_4, C_2H_6, C_2H_4, NH_3, CH_3OH.$

Answer

(i) Molecular mass of H_2 (hydrogen)
$\qquad\qquad\qquad$ = Atomic mass of hydrogen $\times$ 2
$\qquad\qquad\qquad$ = $1 \times 2 = 2\,u$
(ii) Molecular mass of O_2 (oxygen)
$\qquad\qquad\qquad$ = Atomic mass of oxygen $\times$ 2
$\qquad\qquad\qquad$ = $16 \times 2 = 32\,u$
(iii) Molecular mass of Cl_2 (chlorine)
$\qquad\qquad\qquad$ = Atomic mass of chlorine $\times$ 2
$\qquad\qquad\qquad$ = $35.5 \times 2 = 71\,u$
(iv) Molecular mass of CO_2 (carbon dioxide)
$\qquad\qquad\qquad$ = (Atomic mass of carbon $\times$ 1)
$\qquad\qquad\qquad\qquad$ + (Atomic mass of oxygen $\times$ 2)
$\qquad\qquad\qquad$ = $12 + (16 \times 2) = 12 + 32 = 44\,u$

(v) Molecular mass of CH_4 (methane)

$$= \text{(Atomic mass of carbon} \times 1)$$
$$+ \text{(Atomic mass of hydrogen} \times 4)$$
$$= 12 + (1 \times 4) = 12 + 4 = 16 \text{ u}$$

(vi) Molecular mass of C_2H_6 (ethane)

$$= \text{(Atomic mass of carbon} \times 2)$$
$$+ \text{(Atomic mass of hydrogen} \times 6)$$
$$= (12 \times 2) + (1 \times 6) = 24 + 6 = 30 \text{ u}$$

(vii) Molecular mass of C_2H_4 (ethene)

$$= \text{(Atomic mass of carbon} \times 2) + \text{(Atomic mass of hydrogen} \times 4)$$
$$= (12 \times 2) + (1 \times 4) = 24 + 4 = 28 \text{ u}$$

(viii) Molecular mass of NH_3 (ammonia)

$$= \text{(Atomic mass of nitrogen} \times 1)$$
$$+ \text{(Atomic mass of hydrogen} \times 3)$$
$$= (14 \times 1) + (1 \times 3) = 14 + 3 = 17 \text{ u}$$

(ix) Molecular mass of CH_3OH (methanol or methyl alcohol)

$$= \text{(Atomic mass of carbon} \times 1)$$
$$+ \text{(Atomic mass of hydrogen} \times 3)$$
$$+ \text{(Atomic mass of oxygen} \times 1)$$
$$+ \text{(Atomic mass of hydrogen} \times 1)$$
$$= 12 + 3 + 16 + 1 = 32 \text{ u}$$

Question 2. Calculate the formula unit masses of
ZnO, Na_2O, K_2CO_3. Given atomic masses of $Zn = 65$ u, $Na = 23$ u,
$K = 39$ u, $C = 12$ u and $O = 16$ u.

Answer

(i) Formula unit mass of ZnO (zinc oxide) $= 65 + 16 = 81$ u

(ii) Formula unit mass of Na_2O (sodium oxide) $= (23 \times 2) + (16 \times 1)$
$$= 46 + 16 = 62 \text{ u}$$

(iii) Formula unit mass of K_2CO_3 (potassium carbonate)
$$= (39 \times 2) + (12 \times 1) + (16 \times 3) = 78 + 12 + 48 = 138 \text{ u}$$

On Page 42

Question 1. If one mole of carbon atoms weighs 12 grams, what is the mass (in grams) of 1 atom of carbon?

Answer 1 mole carbon atom $= 6.022 \times 10^{23}$ atoms

Molar atomic mass $= 12$ g

$\because 6.022 \times 10^{23}$ carbon atoms weigh $= 12$ g

$\therefore$ 1 carbon atom weighs $\dfrac{12}{6.022 \times 10^{23}} = 1.99 \times 10^{-23}$ g

Question 2. Which has more number of atoms, 100 grams of sodium or 100 grams of iron (given, atomic mass of Na = 23 u, Fe = 56 u)?

Answer   Molar mass of sodium = 23 g

$$1 \text{ mol atom} = 6.022 \times 10^{23} \text{ atoms}$$

∵   23 g sodium contains 6.022×10^{23} atoms

∴   1 g sodium will contain $= \dfrac{6.022 \times 10^{23}}{23}$ atoms

∴   100 g sodium will Contain $= \dfrac{6.022 \times 10^{23} \times 100}{23}$

$$= 2.618 \times 10^{24} \text{ atoms}$$

Number of atoms of an element in a given mass

$$= \dfrac{\text{Given mass}}{\text{Gram atomic mass}} \times \text{Avogadro's number}$$

Thus, number of atoms in 100g Fe $= \dfrac{100\,\text{g}}{56\,\text{g}} \times 6.022 \times 10^{23}$

$$= 1.075 \times 10^{24} \text{ atoms}$$

Hence, 100 g of sodium has more number of atoms as compared to 100 g of iron.

Exercises

Question 1. A 0.24 g sample of compound of oxygen and boron was found by analysis to contain 0.096 g of boron and 0.144 g of oxygen. Calculate the percentage composition of the compound by weight.

Answer   Mass of the compound = 0.24 g

Mass of boron = 0.096 g

Mass of oxygen = 0.144 g

Percentage of boron $= \dfrac{\text{Mass of boron}}{\text{Mass of compound}} \times 100 = \dfrac{0.096\,\text{g}}{0.240\,\text{g}} \times 100 = 40\%$

Percentage of oxygen $= \dfrac{\text{Mass of oxygen}}{\text{Mass of compound}} \times 100$

$$= \dfrac{0.144\,\text{g}}{0.240\,\text{g}} \times 100 = 60\%$$

Alternative method

Percentage of oxygen = 100 − percentage of boron

$$= 100 - 40 = 60\%$$

Question 2. When 3.0 g of carbon is burnt in 8.00 g oxygen, 11.00 g of carbon dioxide is produced. What mass of carbon dioxide will be formed when 3.00 g of carbon is burnt in 50.00 g of oxygen? Which law of chemical combination will govern your answer?

Answer First we find the proportion of mass of carbon and oxygen in carbon dioxide.

In CO_2, $C : O = 12 : 32$ or $3 : 8$

In other words, we can say that

∵ 12.00 g carbon reacts with oxygen = 32.00 g

∴ 3.00 g carbon will react with oxygen = $\dfrac{32}{12} \times 3 = 8$ g

$$C + O_2 \longrightarrow CO_2$$

C	O_2	CO_2
12 g	32 g	$12 + 16 \times 2 = 44$ g
3 g	8 g	$3 + 8 = 11$ g

Therefore, 3.00 g of carbon will always react with 8.00 g of oxygen to form CO_2 (11g), even if large amount (50.00 g) of oxygen is present.

This answer will be governed by 'the law of constant proportions'.

Question 3. What are polyatomic ions? Give examples.

Answer The group of atoms which carry a fixed charge (either positive or negative) on them and behave as ions are called polyatomic ions.

For example

(i) Carbonate ion (CO_3^{2-})   (ii) Sulphate ion (SO_4^{2-})

(iii) Ammonium ion (NH_4^+)   (iv) Phosphate ion (PO_4^{3-})

Question 4. Write the chemical formulae of the following.

(i) Magnesium chloride   (ii) Calcium oxide

(iii) Copper nitrate   (iv) Aluminium chloride

(v) Calcium carbonate

Answer

(i) $\overset{2+}{Mg} \diagdown \overset{1-}{Cl}$

Formula = $MgCl_2$ (Magnesium chloride)

(ii) $\overset{2+}{Ca} \diagdown \overset{2-}{O}$

Formula = Ca_2O_2 or CaO (Calcium oxide)

(iii) $\overset{2+}{Cu} \diagdown \overset{1-}{NO_3}$

Formula = $Cu(NO_3)_2$ (Copper nitrate)

(iv) $\overset{3+}{Al} \diagdown \overset{1-}{Cl}$

Formula = $AlCl_3$ (Aluminium chloride)

(v) $\overset{2+}{Ca}\overset{2-}{CO_3}$

Fromula = $CaCO_3$ (Calcium carbonate)

Question 5. Give the names of the elements present in the following compounds.

(a) Quick lime   (b) Hydrogen bromide
(c) Baking powder   (d) Potassium sulphate

Note *First write the chemical name and chemical formula of the compound. Then, with the help of formula, name the elements.*

Answer

(a) **Quick lime** — Calcium oxide – CaO
  Elements — Calcium, oxygen.
(b) **Hydrogen bromide** — HBr
  Elements — Hydrogen, bromine.
(c) **Baking powder** — Sodium hydrogen carbonate —$NaHCO_3$
  Elements — Sodium, hydrogen, carbon, oxygen.
(d) **Potassium sulphate** —K_2SO_4
  Elements — Potassium, sulphur, oxygen.

Question 6. Calculate the molar mass of the following substances.

(a) Ethyne, C_2H_2
(b) Sulphur molecule, S_8
(c) Phosphorus molecule, P_4 (Atomic mass of phosphorus = 31)
(d) Hydrochloric acid, HCl
(e) Nitric acid, HNO_3

Answer

(a) Molar mass of C_2H_2 = (2 × Atomic mass of C) + (2 × Atomic mass of H)
    = (2 × 12) + (2 × 1)
    = 26 u
(b) Molar mass of S_8 = (8 × Atomic mass of S)
    = 8 × 32 = 256 u
(c) Molar mass of P_4 = 4 × Atomic mass of P
    = 4 × 31 = 124 u
(d) Molar mass of HCl = Atomic mass of hydrogen + Atomic mass of Cl
    = 1 + 35.5 = 36.5 u
(e) Molar mass of HNO_3 = Atomic mass of H + Atomic mass of N
    + (3 × Atomic mass of O)
    = 1 + 14 + (3 × 16) = 15 + 48 = 63 u

Question 7. What is the mass of
(a) 1 mole of nitrogen atoms?
(b) 4 moles of aluminium atoms (Atomic mass of aluminium = 27)?
(c) 10 moles of sodium sulphite (Na_2SO_3)?

Answer (a) Molar mass of N-atom = Atomic mass of N.
∴   Mass of 1 mol of N-atoms = 14 g
(b)   Mass of 1 mole Al-atoms = 27 g
∴   Mass of 4 moles of Al-atoms = 27 × 4 = 108 g
(c)   Mass of 1 mole of Na_2SO_3 = (23 × 2) + 32 + (16 × 3)
$$= 46 + 32 + 48 = 126 \text{ g}$$
Mass of 10 moles of Na_2SO_3 = 126 × 10 = 1260 g

Question 8. Convert into mole.
(a) 12 g of oxygen gas
(b) 20 g of water
(c) 22 g of carbon dioxide.

Answer   (a) **12 g of oxygen gas** (O_2)
Molar mass of oxygen (O_2) = 16 × 2 = 32 g
∵ 32 g oxygen gas = 1 mol
∴ 12 g oxygen gas = $\dfrac{1}{32 \text{ g}}$ × 12 g = 0.375 mol

(b) **20 g of water** (H_2O)
Molar mass of water (H_2O) = 2 + 16 = 18 g
∵ 18 g water = 1 mol
∴ 20 g water = $\dfrac{1}{18 \text{ g}}$ × 20 g = 1.11 mol

(c) **22 g of carbon dioxide** (CO_2)
Molar mass of carbon dioxide (CO_2) = 12 + 32 = 44 g
∵ 44 g CO_2 = 1 mol
∴ 22 g CO_2 = $\dfrac{1}{44 \text{ g}}$ × 22 g = 0.5 mol

Question 9. What is the mass of
(a) 0.2 mole of oxygen atoms?
(b) 0.5 mole of water molecules?

Answer   (a) Mass of 1 mole O-atoms = 16 g
Mass of 0.2 mole O-atoms = 16 × 0.2 = 3.2 g
(b) Mass of 1 mole of H_2O molecules = 18 g
Mass of 0.5 mole of H_2O molecules = 18 × 0.5 = 9.0 g

Question 10. Calculate the number of molecules of sulphur (S_8) present in 16 g of solid sulphur.

Answer   Molar mass of sulphur (S_8) = 32 × 8 = 256 g

Number of S_8 molecules in 256 g of solid sulphur = 6.022×10^{23}

Number of S_8 molecules in 16 g of solid sulphur = $\dfrac{6.022 \times 10^{23}}{256\,g} \times 16\,g$

$= 3.76 \times 10^{22}$ molecules

Question 11. Calculate the number of aluminium ions present in 0.051 g of aluminium oxide.

[**Hint** The mass of an ion is the same as that of an atom of the same element. Atomic mass of Al = 27 u.]

Answer   Molar mass of Al_2O_3 = (27 × 2) + (16 × 3) = 54 + 48 = 102 g

$$Al_2O_3 \rightleftharpoons \overset{3+}{2Al} + \overset{2-}{3O}$$

1 mol   2 mol
(102 g)

∵ 102 g Al_2O_3 contains Al^{3+} ions = $2 \times 6.022 \times 10^{23}$

∴ 0.051 g Al_2O_3 will contain Al^{3+} ions = $\dfrac{2 \times 6.022 \times 10^{23}}{102} \times 0.051$

$= 6.022 \times 10^{20}\ Al^{3+}$ ions

Selected NCERT Exemplar Problems
Multiple Choice Questions

Question 1. Which of the following correctly represents 360g of water?

(i) 2 moles of water

(ii) 20 moles of water

(iii) 6.022×10^{23} molecules of water

(iv) 1.2044×10^{25} molecules of water

(a) Only (i)   (b) (i) and (iv) (c) (ii) and (iii) (d) (ii) and (iv)

Answer (d)

(ii)   18 g (molar mass) of water = 1 mol

360 g (molar mass) of water = $\dfrac{1}{18} \times 360$ = 20 mol

(iv)   18 g of water = 6.022×10^{23} molecules

360 g of water = $\dfrac{6.022 \times 10^{23}}{18} \times 360$ = 1.2044×10^{25} molecules

Question 2. Which of the following statements is not true about an atom?

(a) Atoms are not able to exist independently.

(b) Atoms are the basic units from which molecules and ions are formed.

(c) Atoms are always neutral in nature.

(d) Atoms aggregate in large numbers to form the matter that we can see, feel or touch.

Answer (d) This statement is not true because atoms are very reactive. They combine together to form ions and molecules which in turn form the matter.

Question 3. The chemical symbol for nitrogen gas is

(a) Ni   (b) N_2 (c) N^+ (d) N

Answer (b) Nitrogen gas exists in the form of diatomic molecules, so it is N_2.

Question 4. The chemical symbol for sodium is

(a) So   (b) Sd   (c) NA   (d) Na

Answer (d) Sodium is known as **Natrium** in Latin language. First two letters **Na** are used as a symbol for sodium. First letter is written in capital and second in small letters.

Question 5. Which of the following would weigh the highest?

(a) 0.2 mole of sucrose ($C_{12}H_{22}O_{11}$)   (b) 2 moles of CO_2

(c) 2 moles of $CaCO_3$ (d) 10 moles of H_2O

Answer (c)

(a) Mass of 1 mole of sucrose ($C_{12}H_{22}O_{11}$)
$$= (12 \times 12) + (1 \times 22) + (16 \times 11) = 342 \text{ g}$$
Mass of 0.2 mole of sucrose $= 342 \times 0.2 = 68.4$ g

(b) Mass of 1 mole of $CO_2 = 12 + (16 \times 2) = 44$ g
Mass of 2 moles of $CO_2 = 44 \times 2 = 88$ g

(c) Mass of 1 mole of $CaCO_3 = 40 + 12 + (16 \times 3) = 100$ g
Mass of 2 moles of $CaCO_3 = 100 \times 2 = 200$ g

(d) Mass of 1 mole of $H_2O = 2 + 16 = 18$ g
Mass of 10 moles of $H_2O = 18 \times 10 = 180$ g
Therefore, Mass of 2 moles of $CaCO_3$ is the highest, i.e., 200 g.

Question 6. Which of the following has maximum number of atoms?

(a) 18 g of H_2O (b) 18 g of O_2

(c) 18 g of CO_2 (d) 18 g of CH_4

Answer (d) Number of atoms = $\dfrac{\text{Mass}}{\text{Molecular mass}} \times 6.022 \times 10^{23} \times P$

where, P = number of atoms in the molecule

(a) Number of atoms in 18 g of H_2O

$$= \dfrac{18}{18} \times 6.022 \times 10^{23} \times 3 = 18.066 \times 10^{23} = 1.8066 \times 10^{24}$$

(b) Number of atoms in 18 g of O_2

$$= \dfrac{18}{32} \times 6.022 \times 10^{23} \times 2 = 3.387 \times 10^{23} \times 2 = 6.774 \times 10^{23}$$

(c) Number of atoms in 18 g of $CO_2 = \dfrac{18}{44} \times 6.022 \times 10^{23} \times 3 = 7.390 \times 10^{23}$

(d) Number of atoms in 18 g of $CH_4 = \dfrac{18}{16} \times 6.022 \times 10^{23} \times 5 = 3.387 \times 10^{24}$

Thus, 18 g of CH_4 contains the maximum number of atoms.

Question 7. Which of the following contains maximum number of molecules?

(a) 1 g CO_2 (b) 1 g N_2
(c) 1 g H_2 (d) 1 g CH_4

Answer (c)

(a)   Number of molecules in 44g $CO_2 = 6.022 \times 10^{23}$

∴ Number of molecules in 1 g $CO_2 = \dfrac{6.022 \times 10^{23}}{44} = 1.37 \times 10^{22}$

(b)   Number of molecules in 28g $N_2 = 6.022 \times 10^{23}$

∴ Number of molecules in 1 g $N_2 = \dfrac{6.022 \times 10^{23}}{28} = 2.15 \times 10^{22}$

(c)   Number of molecules in 2g $H_2 = 6.022 \times 10^{23}$

∴ Number of molecules in 1 g $H_2 = \dfrac{6.022 \times 10^{23}}{2} = 3.011 \times 10^{23}$

(d)   Number of molecules in 16g $CH_4 = 6.022 \times 10^{23}$

∴ Number of molecules in 1 g $CH_4 = \dfrac{6.022 \times 10^{23}}{16} = 3.76 \times 10^{22}$

Thus, 1g H_2 contains the maximum number of molecules.

Question 8. Mass of one atom of oxygen is

(a) $\dfrac{16}{6.023 \times 10^{23}}$ g (b) $\dfrac{32}{6.023 \times 10^{23}}$ g

(c) $\dfrac{1}{6.023 \times 10^{23}}$ g (d) 8 u

Answer (a) 1 atom of an element $= \dfrac{1}{6.023 \times 10^{23}}$ mol

Mass of one O-atom $=$ Molar mass $\times$ Number of moles $= \dfrac{16}{6.023 \times 10^{23}}$ g

Question 9. 3.42 g of sucrose are dissolved in 18 g of water in a beaker. The number of oxygen atoms in the solution are

(a) 6.68×10^{23} (b) 6.09×10^{22}

(c) 6.022×10^{23} (d) 6.022×10^{21}

Answer (a)

    Step 1. Molar mass of sucrose, $C_{12}H_{22}O_{11} = 12 \times 12 + 1 \times 22 + 16 \times 11$

                                       $= 342$ g

or 342 g $= 1$ mole sucrose

                         3.42 g $= 0.01$ mol sucrose

    1 mol sucrose $(C_{12}H_{22}O_{11})$ contains O-atoms $= 11 \times 6.023 \times 10^{23}$

    0.01 mol sucrose will contain O-atoms

                         $= 0.01 \times 11 \times 6.023 \times 10^{23} = 6.6253 \times 10^{22}$

    Step 2. 18 g water $(H_2O) = 1$ mole O-atoms $= 6.023 \times 10^{23}$

    Step 3. By adding the number of O-atoms present in 3.42 g sucrose and 18 g water, we get

         $6.022 \times 10^{23} + 6.6253 \times 10^{22} = 10^{22}(60.22 + 6.6253)$

                                 $= 66.854 \times 10^{22}$

                                 $= 6.68 \times 10^{23}$

Question 10. A change in the physical state can be brought about

(a) only when energy is given to the system

(b) only when energy is taken out from the system

(c) when energy is either given to, or taken out from the system

(d) without any energy change

Answer (c) Energy change helps in changing the attraction forces between the particles, thus helps in changing the physical states (*i.e.*, solid, liquid, gas) of matter.

Short Answer Type Questions

Question 11. Which of the following represents a correct chemical formula? Name it.

    (a) $CaCl$ (b) $BiPO_4$ (c) $NaSO_4$ (d) NaS

Answer (b) $BiPO_4$, Bismuth phosphate.

Question 12. Write the molecular formulae for the following compounds.

(a) Copper (II) bromide   (b) Aluminium (III) nitrate

(c) Calcium (II) phosphate   (d) Iron (III) sulphide

(e) Mercury (II) chloride   (f) Magnesium (II) acetate

Answer

(a) $\overset{2+}{Cu}\diagdown\overset{-1}{Br} = CuBr_2$ (b) $\overset{3+}{Al}\diagdown\overset{-1}{NO_3} = Al(NO_3)_3$

(c) $\overset{2+}{Ca}\diagdown\overset{3-}{PO_4} = Ca_3(PO_4)_2$ (d) $\overset{3+}{Fe}\diagdown\overset{2-}{S} = Fe_2S_3$

(e) $\overset{2+}{Hg}\diagdown Cl^- = HgCl_2$ (f) $CH_3\overset{-1}{COO}\diagdown\overset{2+}{Mg} = (CH_3COO)_2Mg$

Question 13. Write the molecular formulae of all the compounds that can be formed by the combination of following ions.

$$Cu^{2+}, Na^+, Fe^{3+}, Cl^-, SO_4^{2-}, PO_4^{3-}$$

Answer

(a) Compounds of $Cu^{2+} = CuCl_2, CuSO_4, Cu_3(PO_4)_2$

(b) Compounds of $Na^+ = NaCl, Na_2SO_4, Na_3PO_4$

(c) Compounds of $Fe^{3+} = FeCl_3, Fe_2(SO_4)_3, FePO_4$

Question 14. Write the cations and anions present (if any) in the following compounds.

(a) CH_3COONa (b) $NaCl$ (c) H_2 (d) NH_4NO_3

Answer

S.No.	Compounds	Cation	Anion
(a)	CH_3COONa	Na^+	CH_3COO^-
(b)	$NaCl$	Na^+	Cl^-
(c)	H_2	—	—
(d)	NH_4NO_3	NH_4^+	NO_3^-

Question 15. Give the formulae of the compounds formed from the following sets of elements.

(a) Calcium and fluorine   (b) Hydrogen and sulphur

(c) Nitrogen and hydrogen   (d) Carbon and chlorine

(e) Sodium and oxygen   (f) Carbon and oxygen

Answer (a) $\overset{2+}{Ca}\diagdown\overset{-1}{F} = CaF_2$ (b) $\overset{+1}{H}\diagdown\overset{2-}{S} = H_2S$ (c) $\overset{-3}{N}\diagdown\overset{+1}{H} = NH_3$

(d) $\overset{+4}{C}\diagdown\overset{-1}{C} = CCl_4$ (e) $\overset{+1}{Na}\diagdown\overset{2-}{O} = Na_2O$ (f) $\overset{+4}{C}\diagdown\overset{-2}{O} = C_2O_4$ or CO_2

Question 16. Which of the following symbols of elements are incorrect? Give their correct symbols.

(a) Cobalt CO   (b) Carbon c

(c) Aluminium Al   (d) Helium He

(e) Sodium So

Answer

(a) Cobalt Co	(Second letter is small in symbol)
(b) Carbon C	(First letter is capital in symbol)
(c) Aluminium Al	(Second letter is small in symbol)
(d) Helium, He	(Correct symbol)
(e) Sodium Na	[Initial of Latin name (Natrium) is Na]

Question 17. Give the chemical formulae for the following compounds and compute the ratio by mass of the combining elements in each one of them.

(a) Ammonia   (b) Carbon monoxide

(c) Hydrogen chloride   (d) Aluminium fluoride

(e) Magnesium sulphide

Answer

(a) NH_3 (ammonia)	Ratio of N and H $= 14 : 3$
(b) CO_2 (carbon dioxide)	Ratio of C and O $= 12 : 32 = 3 : 8$
(c) HCl (hydrogen chloride or hydrochloric acid)	Ratio of H and Cl $= 1 : 35.5$
(d) AlF_3 (aluminium fluoride)	Ratio of Al and F $= 27 : 57 = 9 : 19$
(e) MgS (magnesium sulphide)	Ratio of Mg and S $= 24 : 32 = 3 : 4$

Question 18. State the number of atoms present in each of the following chemical species

(a) CO_3^{2-} (b) PO_4^{3-}

(c) P_2O_5 (d) CO

Answer

(a) Number of atoms in CO_3^{2-} = Number of C atoms + Number of O atoms
$$= 1 + 3 = 4$$

(b) Number of atoms in PO_4^{3-} = Number of P atoms + Number of O atoms
$$= 1 + 4 = 5$$

(c) Number of atoms in P_2O_5 = Number of P atoms + Number of O atoms
$$= 2 + 5 = 7$$

(d) Number of atoms in CO = Number of C atoms + Number of O atoms
$$= 1 + 1 = 2$$

Question 19. What is the fraction of the mass of water due to neutrons?

Answer   In water, number of neutrons = $0 \times 2 + 8 = 8$

Mass of 8 neutrons = $8 \times 1.00893 = 8.07$

($\because$ Mass of one neutron = 1.008934)

Molar mass of water = $1.008 \times 2 + 16.0 = 18.016\,u$

$\therefore$ Fraction of mass due to neutrons = $\dfrac{8.07}{18.016} \times 100 \cong 44.8\%$

Question 20. Classify each of the following on the basis of their atomicity.

(a) F_2	(b) NO_2	(c) N_2O	(d) C_2H_6
(e) P_4	(f) H_2O_2	(g) P_4O_{10}	(h) O_3
(i) HCl	(j) CH_4	(k) He	(l) Ag

Answer   **Monoatomic**   (*i.e.*, contain only one atom) He, Ag

Diatomic   (*i.e.*, contain two atoms, same or diferent) F_2, HCl

Polyatomic   (*i.e.*, contain more than two atoms)
NO_2, N_2O, C_2H_6, P_4, H_2O_2, P_4O_{10}, O_3, CH_4.

Question 21. Calculate the number of moles of magnesium present in a magnesium ribbon weighing 12 g. Molar atomic mass of magnesium is 24 g mol^{-1}.

Answer   Number of moles of Mg $= \dfrac{\text{Given mass}}{\text{Molar mass}} = \dfrac{12\,g}{24\,g\,mol^{-1}} = 0.5\,mol$

Long Answer Type Questions

Question 22. Verify by calculating that

(a) 5 moles of CO_2 and 5 moles of H_2O do not have the same mass.

(b) 240 g of calcium and 240 g magnesium elements have a mole ratio of 3 : 5.

Answer   (a) Mass of 5 mol CO_2 = $44 \times 5 = 220\,g$

Mass of 5 moles H_2O = $18 \times 5 = 90\,g$

$\therefore$ Both values are not equal.

(b) 240 g calcium = $\dfrac{240}{40} = 6\,mol$

240 g magnesium = $\dfrac{240}{24} = 10\,mol$

Ratio of 240 g Ca and 240 g Mg = $6 : 10 = 3 : 5$

Question 23. Find the ratio by mass of the combining elements in the following compounds.

(a) $CaCO_3$ (b) $MgCl_2$ (c) H_2SO_4 (d) C_2H_5OH

(e) NH_3 (f) $Ca(OH)_2$

Answer

(a) $Ca:C:O = 40:12:48 = 10:3:12$
(b) $Mg:Cl = 24:71$
(c) $H:S:O = 2:32:64 = 1:16:32$
(d) $C:H:O = 24:6:16 = 12:3:8$
(e) $N:H = 14:3$
(f) $Ca:O:H = 40:32:2 = 20:16:1$

Question 24. Calcium chloride when dissolved in water dissociates into its ions according to the following equation.

$$CaCl_2(aq) \longrightarrow Ca^{2+}(aq) + 2Cl^-(aq)$$

Calculate the number of ions obtained from $CaCl_2$ when 222 g of it is dissolved in water.

Answer Molar mass of $CaCl_2 = 40 + 2 \times 35.5 = 40 + 71 = 111\,g\,mol^{-1}$

$$CaCl_2(aq) \longrightarrow Ca^{2+}(aq) + 2Cl^-(aq)$$

1 mol   1 mol   2 mol

[111 g]   3 mol

111 g $CaCl_2$ produces ions = 3 mol = $3 \times 6.022 \times 10^{23}$ ions

222 g $CaCl_2$ produces ions = $\dfrac{3 \times 6.022 \times 10^{23}}{111} \times 222$

$= 36.132 \times 10^{23}$

$= 3.6132 \times 10^{24}$ ions

Question 25. Cinnabar (HgS) is a prominent ore of mercury. How many grams of mercury are present in 225 g of pure HgS? molar mass of Hg and S are $200.6\,gmol^{-1}$ and $32g\,mol^{-1}$ respectively.

Answer Molar mass of HgS $= 200.6 + 32 = 232.6\,g$

232.6 g HgS contains Hg $= 200.6$

225 g HgS contains Hg $= \dfrac{200.6 \times 225}{232.6} = 194.05$ g

Question 26. The mass of one steel screw is 4.11 g. Find the mass of one mole of these steel screws. Compare this value with the mass of the Earth (5.98×10^{24} kg). Which one of the two is heavier and by how many times?

Answer (a) 1 mol = 6.022×10^{23}

Mass of 1 mol screws = $6.022 \times 10^{23} \times 4.11g = 2.48 \times 10^{24}$ g

(b) $\dfrac{\text{Mass of 1 mol screw}}{\text{Mass of the earth}} = \dfrac{2.48 \times 10^{24} \text{ g}}{5.98 \times 10^{24} \times 10^3 \text{ g}} = \dfrac{1}{2.41 \times 10^3}$

Ratio = mass of 1 mole screw : mass of earth

= 1 : 2410

Mass of earth is heavier by 2410 times.

Question 27. A sample of vitamin C is known to contain 2.58×10^{24} oxygen atoms. How many moles of oxygen atoms are present in the sample?

Answer 6.022×10^{23} oxygen atoms = 1 mol

2.58×10^{24} oxygen atoms = $\dfrac{2.58 \times 10^{24}}{6.022 \times 10^{23}}$ = 4.28 mol

Question 28. Fill in the missing data in the following table.

Species / Property	H_2O	CO_2	Na atom	$MgCl_2$
No. of moles	2	—	—	0.5
No. of particles	—	3.011×10^{23}	—	—
Mass	36 g	—	115 g	—

Answer For H_2O

Given, no. of moles = 2 and mass = 36 g

∴ Number of particles = No. of moles $\times 6.022 \times 10^{23}$

$= 2 \times 6.022 \times 10^{23}$

$= 1.2044 \times 10^{24}$

For CO_2

Given, no. of particles = 3.011×10^{23}

∴ Number of moles of CO_2 = $\dfrac{\text{Number of particles}}{6.022 \times 10^{23}}$

$= \dfrac{3.011 \times 10^{23}}{6.022 \times 10^{23}}$ = 0.5 mol

Mass of CO_2 = Moles $\times$ Molar mass

$= 0.5 \times 44 = 22$ g

($\because$ Molar mass of $CO_2 = 12 + 2 \times 16 = 44$)

For Na atom

Given, mass = 115 g

Number of moles = $\dfrac{\text{Mass}}{\text{Molar mass}} = \dfrac{115}{23} = 5$ mol

∴ Number of particles = $5 \times 6.022 \times 10^{23} = 3.011 \times 10^{24}$

For MgCl$_2$

Given, no. of moles = 0.5

∴ Number of particles = $0.5 \times 6.022 \times 10^{23} = 3.011 \times 10^{23}$

Mass = Number of moles × Molar mass

(Molar mass of $MgCl_2 = 24 + 2 \times 35.5 = 24 + 71 = 95$)

= $0.5 \times 95 = 47.5$ g

Thus, the completed table is as

Species Property	H_2O	CO_2	Na atom	$MgCl_2$
No. of moles	2	**0.5**	5.0	0.5
No. of particles	**1.2044 × 10^{24}**	3.011 × 10^{23}	**3.011 × 10^{24}**	**3.011 × 10^{23}**
Mass	36 g	**22 g**	115 g	**47.5 g**

Question 29. The visible universe is estimated to contain 10^{22} stars. How many moles of stars are present in the visible universe?

Answer 6.022×10^{23} stars = 1 mole stars.

$$10^{22} \text{ stars} = \dfrac{1 \times 10^{22}}{6.022 \times 10^{23}} = 1.67 \times 10^{-2} \text{ mol}$$

Question 30. What are ionic and molecular compounds? Give examples.

Answer **Ionic compounds** are made up of ions. Ionic bond/electrovalent bond is present in ionic compounds.

Examples NaCl, CaO etc.

Molecular compounds are made up of molecules. Covalent bond is present in molecular compounds.

Examples H_2O, CH_4 etc.

4

Structure of the Atom

Important Concepts

1. JJ Thomson is credited for the discovery of electron and Eugen Goldstein for that of proton.

2. JJ Thomson proposed a christmas pudding model for an atom in which 'electrons were embedded in the sphere of a positive charge.'

3. Alpha particles are nuclei of helium having + 2 charge and 4 mass.

4. Gold foil is exclusively used for α-particle scattering experiment as gold is having extraordinary malleability *i.e.,* very thin foil (1000 atom thick) can be made from it.

5. Ernest Rutherford discovered nucleus of an atom by α-particle scattering experiment.

6. Rutherford's model of an atom does not describe the stability of the atom.

7. Neils Bohr said that electrons revolve around the nucleus at definite paths (orbits/shells/energy levels) having definite energy too.

8. The maximum number of electrons in a shell is given by $2n^2$ rule.

9. The combining capacity of an element is known as its **valency.**

10. Presence of complete octet (8 electrons in outermost shell) provides an atom a stable configuration.

[Helium is the exception as it has a duplet (K shell).]

11. Atomic number = Number of protons

    Mass number = Number of protons + Number of neutrons
12. Atoms having same number of protons (same atomic number) but different number of neutrons are called **isotopes** of an element.
13. **Isobars** are the atoms with same mass number but different atomic number.
14. Atomic mass of an element is taken as the average mass of all the naturally occurring atoms of that element. During the calculation, the percentage of isotopes is also considered.
15. James Chadwick discovered neutrons, the neutral particle in the atom.
16. Hydrogen $_1H^1$ (or protium) has no neutron.

Electronic Configuration of Some Elements

S.No.	Element	Symbol	Atomic number	Configuration			
				K	L	M	N
1.	Hydrogen	H	1	1			
2.	Helium	He	2	2			
3.	Lithium	Li	3	2	1		
4.	Berrylium	Be	4	2	2		
5.	Boron	B	5	2	3		
6.	Carbon	C	6	2	4		
7.	Nitrogen	N	7	2	5		
8.	Oxygen	O	8	2	6		
9.	Fluorine	F	9	2	7		
10.	Neon	Ne	10	2	8		
11.	Sodium	Na	11	2	8	1	
12.	Magnesium	Mg	12	2	8	2	
13.	Aluminium	Al	13	2	8	3	
14.	Silicon	Si	14	2	8	4	
15.	Phosphorus	P	15	2	8	5	
16.	Sulphur	S	16	2	8	6	
17.	Chlorine	Cl	17	2	8	7	
18.	Argon	Ar	18	2	8	8	
19.	Potassium	K	19	2	8	8	1
20.	Calcium	Ca	20	2	8	8	2

Intext Questions

On Page 47

Question 1. What are canal rays?

Answer Canal rays or anode rays are the positively charged rays which are seen moving from the anode towards cathode in a specially designed dischage tube (with a porous cathode), when a high voltage is applied across the electrodes.

Question 2. If an atom contains one electron and one proton, will it carry any charge or not?

Answer No, the charge (– 1) on an electron and that on a proton (+1) balance and neutralise each other.

On Page 49

Question 1. On the basis of Thomson's model of an atom, explain how the atom is neutral as a whole?

Answer As the magnitude of positive and negative charges is equal, the atom is electrically neutral.

Question 2. On the basis of Rutherford's model of an atom, which subatomic particle is present in the nucleus of an atom?

Answer Nucleus is positively charged according to Rutherford's model of an atom, *i.e.*, proton is present inside the nucleus.

Question 3. Draw a sketch of Bohr's model of an atom with three shells.

Answer

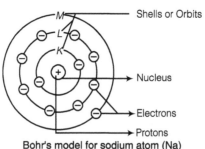

Bohr's model for sodium atom (Na)

$[_{11}Na = 2, 8, 1]$

Question 4. What do you think would be the observation if the α-particle scattering experiment is carried out using a foil of a metal other than gold?

Answer Rutherford used gold for α-particle scattering experiment because gold is the **most malleable** metal. A very thin foil of 10^{-7}m thickness (or 1000 atoms thick) can be made with gold. Malleability of silver is next to gold (10^{-6} m thick foil can be made). More thick foils can be made by other metals like platinum. As the thickness of the foil increases, the possibility of correctness of the experiment decreases. So use of gold in this case is preferred.

Question 5. Name the three sub-atomic particles of an atom.

Answer The subatomic particles in an atom are protons, electrons and neutrons.

Question 6. Helium atom has an atomic mass of 4 u and two protons in its nucleus. How many neutrons does it have?

Answer Atomic mass of helium   = 4 u
Number of protons   = 2
Let the number of neutrons = x
Number of protons + Number of neutrons = Atomic mass
$$x + 2 = 4$$
$$x = 4 - 2 = 2$$

On Page 50

Question 1. Write the distribution of electrons in carbon and sodium atoms.

Answer

S.No.	Element	Alomic number	Electronic configuration
			K, L, M
1.	Carbon (C)	6	2, 4
2.	Sodium (Na)	11	2, 8, 1

Question 2. If K and L shells of an atom are full, then what would be the total number of electrons in the atom?

Answer Maximum number of electrons in K-shell = 2
Maximum number of electrons in L-shell = 8
Total number of electrons in the atom   = 2 + 8 = 10

On Page 52

Question 1. How will you find the valency of chlorine, sulphur and magnesium?

Answer Magnesium is a metal while chlorine and sulphur are non-metals.
Valency of a metal = number of valence electrons
(*i.e.*, number of electrons present in outermost shell.)
Valency of a non-metal = 8 – number of valence electrons.

(a) $_{12}Mg$ = 2, 8, 2   Valency of magnesium = 2
(b) $_{16}S$ = 2, 8, 6   Valency of sulphur = 8 − 6 = 2
(c) $_{17}Cl$ = 2, 8, 7   Valency of chlorine = 8 − 7 = 1

Question 2. If number of electrons in an atom is 8 and number of protons is also 8, then

(i) what is the atomic number of the atom? and
(ii) what is the charge on the atom?

Answer

(i) Atomic number = number of protons = 8.
(ii) The charge on the atom is zero because number of electrons and number of protons is equal.

Question 3. Find the mass number of oxygen and sulphur atom.

Answer   Mass number = No. of protons + No. of neutrons

(a) In oxygen, protons = 8, neutrons = 8
Mass number of oxygen = 8 + 8 = 16
(b) In sulphur, protons = 16, neutrons = 16
Mass number of sulphur = 16 + 16 = 32

On Page 53

Question 1. For the symbol H, D and T tabulate three sub-atomic particles found in each of them.

Answer

Symbol	Protons	Neutrons	Electrons
$_1H^1$	1	0	1
$_1D^2$	1	1	1
$_1T^3$	1	2	1

Question 2. Write the electronic configuration of any one pair of isotopes and isobars.

Answer   Isotopes   *e.g.*, $_{17}Cl^{35}$ and $_{17}Cl^{37}$.

Electronic configuration of both the isotopes of chlorine is same as their atomic number is same.

$$_{17}Cl = \begin{matrix} K & L & M \\ 2 & 8 & 7 \end{matrix}$$

Isobars   *e.g.*, $_{20}Ca^{40}$ and $_{18}Ar^{40}$.

Electronic configuration

$$\begin{matrix} & K & L & M & N \\ _{20}Ca = & 2 & 8 & 8 & 2 \\ _{18}Ar = & 2 & 8 & 8 \end{matrix}$$

Exercises

Question 1. Compare the properties of electrons, protons and neutrons.

Answer

Property	Electron	Proton	Neutron
Location	Extra nuclear portion (orbit)	Inside nucleus	Inside nucleus
Absolute charge	$(-)1.6 \times 10^{-19}$ C	$(+)1.6 \times 10^{-19}$ C	Nil
Relative charge	-1	$+1$	Nil
Absolute mass	9.1×10^{-31} kg	1.67×10^{-27} kg	1.675×10^{-27} kg
Relative mass	1/1840	1	1

Question 2. What are the limitations of JJ Thomson's model of the atom?

Answer Limitations of Thomson's model of atom

1. Thomson's model could not explain the experimental results of other scientists such as Rutherford, as there is no nucleus in the atomic model proposed by Thomson.
2. It does not have any experimental evidence in its support.

Question 3. What are the limitations of Rutherford's model of the atom?

Answer Limitations of Rutherford's model of an atom

1. It could not explain the stability of the atom.

   Reason When a charged particle revolves in a circular orbit, it radiates energy continuously due to accelerated motion. This makes atom highly unstable. But we know that the atom is stable.
2. Rutherford's model could not explain the distribution of electrons in the extra nuclear portion of the atom.

Question 4. Describe Bohr's model of the atom.

Answer Bohr's model of atom

1. Electrons revolve in well defined paths, known as orbits or shells around the nucleus.
2. These orbits are also called energy levels.
3. These are named as K, L, M, N ..... or 1, 2, 3, 4 ..... and so on.
4. The order of energy increases from K onwards. It means $K < L < M < N$....
5. While revolving in an orbit, the electron neither loses or gains energy. As the energy of an orbit is stationary, these are also known as stationary states.

Question 5. Compare all the proposed models of an atom given in this chapter.

S.No.	Thomson's model	Rutherford's model	Bohr's model
1.	Nucleus not present.	Nucleus present.	Nucleus present.
2.	Positive charge present in the form of a sphere.	Positive charge (protons) present inside the nucleus.	Positive charge (protons) present inside the nucleus.
3.	Electrons embedded in the positive sphere (uniform distribution).	Electrons revolve around the nucleus.	Electrons revolve around the nucleus in well defined orbits with definite energy.

Question 6. Summarise the rules for writing of distribution of electrons in various shells for the first eighteen elements.

Answer   Rules for writing the electronic configuration

1. The maximum number of electrons in a shell is given by $2n^2$ rule, where n is the shell number (1, 2, 3 ...). Thus, K shell can accomodate maximum 2 electrons, $L = 8$, $M = 18$ and N shell can have a maximum number of 32 electrons.
2. The outermost or valence shell of an atom can accomodate only 8 electrons (or less) but not more than 8.
3. Electrons are not accomodated in a given shell untill the inner shells are filled.
   That is the shells are filled in a stepwise manner.

Question 7. Define valency by taking examples of silicon and oxygen.

Answer   **Valency**   The combining capacity of the atom of an element with the atom (s) of other element (s) in order to complete its octet is called the valency of that element.
   Valency of metal = number of valence electrons,
Valency of non-metal = 8 – number of valence electrons.

Examples

(i) $_{14}Si = 2, 8, 4$;   Valency $= 8 - 4 = 4$.
(ii) $_8O = 2, 6$;   Valency $= 8 - 6 = 2$.

Question 8. Explain with examples
   (i) atomic number, (ii) mass number, (iii) isotopes and, (iv) isobars.
   Give any two uses of isotopes.

Answer

(i) **Atomic number** The number of protons present in the nucleus of the atom of an element is called its atomic number.
   Atomic number = Number of protons

   For example   Sodium atom has 11 protons. Thus, its atomic number is 11. It is represented as $_{11}Na$.

(ii) **Mass number** (or atomic mass) The total number of protons and neutrons (nucleons) present in an atom is called its mass number.

Mass number = no. of protons + no. of neutrons

For example Sodium atom has 11 protons and 12 neutrons. Its mass number is 23. It is represented as ^{23}Na.

(iii) **Isotopes** Atoms of an element that have same atomic number but different mass number are called isotopes of that element.

For example Hydrogen has 3 isotopes $_1H^1, _1H^2$ and $_1H^3$.

(iv) **Isobars** Atoms of different elements that have same mass number but different atomic number are called isobars.

For example $^{40}_{18}Ar$ and $^{40}_{20}Ca$ are isobars.

Uses of Isotopes

1. Radioactive isotope of iodine (I^{131}) is used in the treatment of goitre.
2. Radioactive uranium (U^{235}) is used as a fuel in the nuclear reactors.
3. Radioactive isotope of cobalt (Co^{60}) releases γ-radiations so it is used in the treatment of cancer.

Question 9. Na$^+$ has completely filled K and L shells. Explain.

Answer K, L, M

Na (atom) = 2, 8, 1

When an atom loses one electron, it acquires a positive charge. Thus, Na atom will have lose one electron from its M shell to get converted into Na$^+$ ion.

Na$^+$ (ion) = 2, 8

As the maximum capacity of K shell is 2 electrons and that of L shell is 8 electrons, Na$^+$ has completely filled K and L shells.

Question 10. If bromine atom is available in the form of, say, two isotopes $^{79}_{35}Br$ (49.7%) and $^{81}_{35}Br$ (50.3%), calculate the average atomic mass of bromine atom.

Answer Average atomic mass of an element

$$= \left[\left(\text{Atomic mass of I isotope} \times \frac{\% \text{ of I isotope}}{100} \right) + \left(\text{Atomic mass of II isotope} \times \frac{\% \text{ of II isotope}}{100} \right) \right]$$

Average atomic mass of bromine

$$= \left[\left(79 \times \frac{49.7}{100} \right) + \left(81 \times \frac{50.3}{100} \right) \right]$$

$$= 39.263 + 40.743$$

$$= 80.006$$

Question 11. The average atomic mass of a sample of an element X is 16.2 u. What are the percentages of isotopes $_8^{16}X$ and $_8^{18}X$ in the sample?

Answer Let the percentage of $_8^{16}X = x$

Then, the percentage of $_8^{18}X = (100 - x)$ ...(i)

Average atomic mass of X = 16. 2 u

According to the given data,

$$16 \times \frac{x}{100} + 18 \times \frac{(100 - x)}{100} = 16.2 \qquad \text{...(ii)}$$

$$\frac{16x}{100} + \frac{1800 - 18x}{100} = 16.2$$

$$16x + 1800 - 18x = 1620$$

$$-2x = -1800 + 1620$$

$$x = \frac{180}{2} = 90\%$$

Placing the value of x in Eq. (i)

$$\% \text{ of } _8^{18}X = 100 - 90 = 10\%$$

Isotope $_8^{16}X$ = 90% ; Isotope $_8^{18}X$ = 10%

Question 12. If $Z = 3$, what would be the valency of the element? Also, name the element.

Answer Electronic configuration of element $Z = \overset{K,\ L}{2,\ 1}$

Valeny of the element = Number of valence electrons.

$$= 1$$

Name of the element = Lithium

Question 13. Composition of the nuclei of two atomic species X and Y are given as under.

$$X \quad Y \text{ ; Protons} = 6 \quad 6 \text{ ; Neutrons} = 6 \quad 8$$

Give the mass numbers of X and Y. What is the relation between the two species?

Answer Mass number = Number of protons + Number of neutrons.

Mass number of X = 6 + 6 = 12

Mass number of Y = 6 + 8 = 14

To find the relation between X and Y,

Atomic number of X = Number of protons = 6

Atomic number of Y = Number of protons = 6

As it is obvious that the atomic numbers of both elements X and Y are same (6) but their mass numbers are different, X and Y are isotopes of the same element (carbon).

X and Y are $_6^{12}C$ and $_6^{14}C$ respectively.

Question 14. For the following statements, write T for (True) and F for (False).
- (a) JJ Thomson proposed that the nucleus of an atom contains only nucleons.
- (b) A neutron is formed by an electron and a proton combining together. Therefore, it is neutral.
- (c) The mass of an electron is about $\dfrac{1}{2000}$ times that of proton.
- (d) An isotope of iodine is used for making tincture iodine, which is used as a medicine

Note *Put tick (✓) against correct choice and cross (×) against wrong choice in questions 15, 16, 17 and 18.*

Answer (a) F. Because in J.J. Thomson model nucleus was not present.

(b) T. $\underset{\text{electron}}{{}_{-1}e^{0}} + \underset{\text{proton}}{{}_{1}H^{1}} \longrightarrow \underset{\text{neutron}}{{}_{0}n^{1}}$

(c) T. Mass of electron is $\dfrac{1}{1840}$ times *i.e.*, about $\dfrac{1}{2000}$ times that of the proton.

(d) F. Tincture is made by dissolving iodine in alcohol, not from the isotope of iodine.

Question 15. Rutherford's alpha-particle scattering experiment was responsible for the discovery of
- (a) atomic nucleus
- (b) electron
- (c) proton
- (d) neutron

Answer (a) On the basis of his experiment Rutherford predicted that centre part of the atom is solid, positively charged and is responsible for the mass of the atom. He called this portion atomic nucleus.

Question 16. Isotopes of an element have
- (a) the same physical properties
- (b) different chemical properties
- (c) different number of neutrons
- (d) different atomic numbers

Answer (c) Isotopes have similar chemical properties, same atomic number but different mass number.

Question 17. Number of valence electrons in Cl^{-} ion are
- (a) 16
- (b) 8
- (c) 17
- (d) 18

Answer (b) Valence electron are the electron present in outermost shell of an atom.

$${}_{17}Cl \text{ (atom)} = 2, 8, \underline{7}; \quad \text{Valence electrons} = 7$$
$$Cl^{-} \text{ (ion)} = 2, 8, \underline{8}; \quad \text{Valence electrons} = 8$$

Question 18. Which one of the following is a correct electronic configuration of sodium?
- (a) 2, 8
- (b) 8, 2, 1
- (c) 2, 1, 8
- (d) 2, 8, 1

Answer   (d) Atomic number of Na is 11.

Electronic configuration $_{11}$Na = 2, 8, 1

Question 19. Complete the following table.

Atomic number	Mass number	Number of neutrons	Number of protons	Number of electrons	Name of the atomic species
9	—	10	—	—	—
16	32	—	—	—	Sulphur
—	24	—	12	—	—
—	2	—	1	—	—
—	1	0	1	0	—

Answer

Atomic number	Mass number	Number of neutrons	Number of protons	Number of electrons	Name of the atomic species
9	19	10	9	9	Fluorine
16	32	16	16	16	Sulphur
12	24	12	12	12	Magnesium
1	2	1	1	1	Deuterium
1	1	0	1	0	Hydrogen ion

Explanation

(i) **Fluorine** ($_9F^{19}$)   Atomic number = 9 ; Number of neutrons = 10

Mass number = atomic no. + number of neutrons = 9 + 10 = 19

Number of protons = Atomic number = Number of electrons = 9

Thus the element is fluorine ($_9F^{19}$).

(ii) **Sulphur** ($_{16}S^{32}$)   Atomic number = 16

Number of protons = Number of electrons = 16

Number of neutrons = Mass number − Atomic number = 32 − 16 = 16

(iii) **Magnesium** ($_{12}Mg^{24}$)   Number of protons = 12

Atomic number = Number of proton = 12

Number of electrons = Number of protons = 12

Number of neutrons = Mass number − Atomic number = 24 − 12 = 12

(iv) **Deuterium** ($_1D^2$)   Number of protons = Number of electrons = 1

∴ Atomic number = 1 ;   Mass number = 2

Number of neutrons = 2 − 1 = 1

(v) **Hydrogen ion** ($_1H^+$)   Mass number = 1

Number of protons = 1 ; Number of neutrons = 0

Number of electrons = 1 − 1 = 0.

Atomic number = Number of protons = 1

Because, number of electrons is zero, so the species is hydrogen ion, not hydrogen atom.

Selected NCERT Exemplar Problems

Multiple Choice Questions

Question 1. Which of the following correctly represent the electronic distribution in the Mg atom?

    (a) 3, 8, 1   (b) 2, 8, 2   (c) 1, 8, 3   (d) 8, 2, 2

Answer (b) Atomic number and the number of electrons in magnesium atom is 12. So, electronic configuration is 2, 8, 2 (because 12 = 2 + 8 + 2).

Question 2. Rutherford's alpha (α) particles scattering experiment resulted into discovery of

    (a) electron   (b) proton

    (c) nucleus in the atom   (d) atomic mass

Answer (c) Rutherford discovered nucleus of the atom by his α particle scattering experiment.

Question 3. The number of electrons in an element X is 15 and the number of neutrons is 16. Which of the following is the correct representation of the element?

    (a) $^{31}_{15}X$ (b) $^{31}_{16}X$ (c) $^{16}_{15}X$ (d) $^{15}_{16}X$

Answer (a) Atomic number = Number of protons

                     = Number of electrons in neutral atom = 15

    Mass number = Number of protons + Number of neutrons.

               = 15 + 16 = 31

    Thus, the atom is represented as $^{31}_{15}X$.

Question 4. Dalton's atomic theory successfully explained

    (i) law of conservation of mass

   (ii) law of constant composition

  (iii) law of radioactivty

  (iv) law of multiple proportion

        (a) (i), (ii) and (iii)   (b) (i), (iii) and (iv)

        (c) (ii), (iii) and (iv)   (d) (i), (ii) and (iv)

Answer (d) No point is mentioned by Dalton in his theory about radioactivity.

Question 5. Which of the following statements about Rutherford's model of atom are correct?

    (i) Considered the nucleus as positively charged.

   (ii) Established that the α-particles are four times as heavy as a hydrogen atom.

  (iii) Can be compared to solar system.

(iv) Was in agreement with Thomson's model.

    (a) (i) and (ii)   (b) (ii) and (iii)

    (c) (i) and (iv)   (d) Only (i)

Answer (d) According to Rutherford model, a central positively charged nucleus is present in the atom and electron revolve around it. This model is similar to solar system so also called planetary model.

Question 6. Which of the following are true for an element?

  (i) Atomic number = number of protons + number of electrons.

 (ii) Mass number = number of protons + number of neutrons.

(iii) Atomic number = number of protons = number of neutrons.

(iv) Atomic number = number of protons = number of electrons.

    (a) (i) and (ii)   (b) (i) and (iii)

    (c) (ii) and (iii)   (d) (ii) and (iv)

Answer (d)

Question 7. In the Thomson's model of atom, which of the following statements are correct?

  (i) The mass of the atom is assumed to be uniformly distributed over the atom.

 (ii) The positive charge is assumed to be uniformly distributed over the atom.

(iii) The electrons are uniformly distributed in the positively charged sphere.

(iv) The electrons attract each other to stabilise the atom.

    (a) (i), (ii) and (iii)   (b) (i) and (iii)

    (c) (i) and (iv)   (d) (i), (iii) and (iv)

Answer (a)

Question 8. Rutherford's α-particle scattering experiment shows that

  (i) electrons have negative charge.

 (ii) the mass and positive charge of the atom is concentrated in the nucleus.

(iii) neutron exists in the nucleus.

(iv) most of the space in atom is empty.

    Which of the above statements are correct?

    (a) (i) and (iii)   (b) (ii) and (iv)   (c) (i) and (iv)   (d) (iii) and (iv)

Answer (b)

Question 9. The ion of an element has 3 positive charges. Mass number of the atom is 27 and the number of neutrons is 14. What is the number of electrons in the ion.

    (a) 13   (b) 10   (c) 14   (d) 16

Answer (b)   Number of protons = Atomic number

    Alomic number = Mass number − Number of neutrons = 27 − 14 = 13
    This element is aluminium (Al).
    Number of electrons in the Al atom = 13
    Number of electrons in the Al^{3+} ion = 13 − 3 = 10

Question 10. Identify the Mg^{2+} ion from the figure where, n and p represent the number of neutrons and protons respectively.

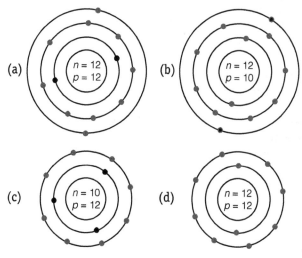

Answer (d)

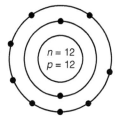

        K, L, M
    $_{12}$Mg atom = 2, 8, 2
     Mg^{2+} ion = 2, 8

Question 11. In a sample of ethyl ethanoate ($CH_3COOC_2H_5$) the two oxygen atoms have the same number of electrons but different number of neutrons, which of the following is the correct reason for it?
  (a) One of the oxygen atoms have gained electrons
  (b) One of the oxygen atoms has gained two neutrons
  (c) The two oxygen atoms are isotopes
  (d) The two oxygen atoms are isobars

Answer (c) Isotopes of an element have same number of protons (and electrons) but different number of neutrons.

Question 12. Elements with valency 1 are
  (a) always metals
  (b) always metalloids
  (c) either metals or non-metals
  (d) always non-metals

Answer (c)
        Metals, whose valence electron is 1.
        Non-metals, whose valence electrons are 7, both have valency 1.

Question 13. The first model of an atom was given by
  (a) N Bohr   (b) E Goldstein
  (c) Rutherford   (d) JJ Thomson

Answer (d)

Question 14. An atom with 3 protons and 4 neutrons will have a valency of
  (a) 3   (b) 7   (c) 1   (d) 4

Answer (c)
              K, L
        $_3$Li = 2, 1
        As valence electron is 1, valency is also 1.

Question 15. The electron distribution in an aluminium atom is
  (a) 2, 8, 3   (b) 2, 8, 2
  (c) 8, 2, 3   (d) 2, 3, 8

Answer (a)
              K, L, M
        $_{13}$Al = 2, 8, 3

Question 16. Which of the following in figure do not represent Bohr's model of an atom correctly?

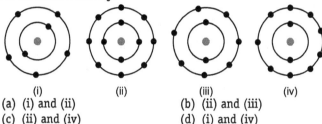

| (i) | (ii) | (iii) | (iv) |

(a) (i) and (ii)   (b) (ii) and (iii)
(c) (ii) and (iv)   (d) (i) and (iv)

Answer (c)
Maximum number of electrons in K shell is 2, not 4, so (ii) is wrong.
Maximum capacity of L shell is 8 electrons, not 9. So, (iv) is also wrong.

Question 17. Which of the following statement is always correct?
(a) An atom has equal number of electrons and protons
(b) An atom has equal number of electrons and neutrons
(c) An atom has equal number of protons and neutrons
(d) An atom has equal number of electrons, protons and neutrons

Answer (a) Atom is electrically neutral. It is possible only due to the presence of equal number of protons and electrons.

Question 18. Atomic models have been improved over the years. Arrange the following atomic models in the order of their chronological order.
(i) Rutherford's atomic model   (ii) Thomson's atomic model
(iii) Bohr's atomic model
(a) (i), (ii) and (iii)   (b) (ii), (iii) and (i)
(c) (ii), (i) and (iii)   (d) (iii), (ii) and (i)

Answer (c)

Short Answer Type Questions

Question 19. Is it possible for the atom of an element to have one electron, one proton and no neutron. If so, name the element.

Answer Yes, hydrogen's isotope protium $(_1H^1)$ has one electron, one proton and no neutron.

Question 20. Write any two observations which support the fact that atoms are divisible.

Answer 1. Formation of ionic compounds is possible due to the formation of ions which involves the transfer of electrons.

2. Presence of isotopes for the same element is possible due to the difference in the number of neutrons.

Above observations show that atom is formed by different particles as electrons, protons and neutrons, *i.e.*, atom is divisible.

Question 21. Will ^{35}Cl and ^{37}Cl have different valencies? Justify your answer.

Answer No, ^{35}Cl and ^{37}Cl are the isotopes. So, they have same number of protons and electrons. Hence their electronic configuration and valencies are also the same.

$$K, L, M$$
$$_{17}Cl = 2, 8, 7$$

Valency of ^{35}Cl and $^{37}Cl = 8 - 7 = 1$

Question 22. Why did Rutherford select a gold foil in his α-ray scattering experiment?

Answer Because gold is the best malleable metal. A very thin foil ($\approx$ 1000 atoms thick) can be made from gold, hence the observations are very clear.

Question 23. One electron is present in the outermost shell of the atom of an element X. What would be the nature and value of charge on the ion formed if this electron is removed from the outermost shell?

Answer An element X (1 valence electron) is metal. When this valence electron is removed from the outermost shell, a cation (positive ion) will be formed with a charge +1.

Question 24. Write down the electron distribution of chlorine atom. How many electrons are there in the L-shell? Atomic number of chlorine is 17.

Answer　　　　K, L, M
$$_{17}Cl = 2, 8, 7$$

L-shell of chlorine contains 8 electrons.

Question 25. In the atom of an element X, 6 electrons are present in the outermost shell. If it acquires noble gas configuration by accepting requisite number of electrons, then what would be the charge on the ion so formed?

Answer In order to complete its octet element X require 2 electrons, so, the charge on the anion (X^{2-}) formed is -2.

Question 26. Calculate the number of neutrons present in the nucleus of an element X which is represented as $^{31}_{15}X$.

Answer   Mass number of $X = 31$
Atomic number of $X = 15$
Number of neutrons = Mass number – Atomic number
$$= 31 - 15$$
$$= 16$$

Question 27. In response to a question, a student stated that in an atom, the number of protons is greater than the number of neutrons, which in turn is greater than the number of electrons. Do you agree with the statement? Justify your answer.

Answer   No, this statement is not correct.
According to this statement $p > n > e$.

But actually $p \gtrless e$ and $n > p$.

(where p = protons, n = neutrons, e = electrons)

Question 28. The atomic number of calcium and argon are 20 and 18 respectively, but the mass number of both these elements is 40. What is the name given to such a pair of elements.

Answer   A pair of elements having same mass number but different atomic number is called **isobars**.

Question 29. Helium atom has 2 electrons in its valence shell but its valency is not 2. Explain.

Answer   Atomic number of helium is 2. K is its valence shell, so it can accomodate only 2 electrons (maximum capacity). It means that its valence shell is complete. So, its valency is zero instead of two.

Question 30. An element X has a mass number 4 and atomic number 2. Write the valency of this element.

Answer $_2^4He$ is the element X. Its valency is zero.

(For details, consult the answer of Q. 29.)

Long Answer Type Questions

Question 31. Why do helium, neon and argon have a zero valency?

Answer   Because their outermost shell is complete.

$$
\begin{array}{l}
\phantom{_{18}Ar = } K \;\; L \;\; M \\
_2He = 2 \\
_{10}Ne = 2, \;\; 8 \\
_{18}Ar = 2, \;\; 8, \;\; 8
\end{array}
$$

Question 32. The ratio of the radii of hydrogen atom and its nucleus is $\sim 10^5$. Assuming the atom and the nucleus to be spherical,

(i) What will be the ratio of their sizes?

(ii) If atom is represented by planet earth $'R_e' = 6.4 \times 10^6 \, m$, estimate the size of the nucleus.

Answer

(i) Atomic size is represented in terms of atomic radius. Hence, the ratio of nucleus to atomic size $= 1 : 10^5$

(ii) If atomic size $= 6.4 \times 10^6 \, m$

Then let the size of the nucleus be x m.

According to the ratio given above, $\dfrac{x}{6.4 \times 10^6} = \dfrac{1}{10^5}$

$$x = \dfrac{6.4 \times 10^6}{10^5}$$

$$x = 64 \, m$$

Thus, size of the nucleus would be 64 m.

Question 33. Enlist the conclusions drawn by Rutherford from his α-ray scattering experiment.

Answer Conclusion of Rutherford's α-ray scattering experiment

1. Most of the space inside the atom is empty because most of the α-particles passed through the gold foil without getting deflected.
2. Very few particles were deflected from their path, indicating that the positive charge of the atom occupies very little space.
3. A very small fraction of α-particles were deflected by 180°, indicating that all the positive charge and mass of the gold atom were concentrated in very small volume within the atom.

Question 34. In the Gold foil experiment of Geiger and Marsden, that paved the way for Rutherford's model of an atom ~1.00% of the α- particles were found to deflect at angles > 50°. If one mole of α-particles were bombarded on the gold foil, compute the number of α-particles that would deflect at angles less than 50°.

Answer 1 mol $= 6.022 \times 10^{23}$ particles.

Number of α-particles deflected at angles (>50°) greater than

$$50° = 1 \% \text{(Given)}$$

∴ Number of α- particles deflected at the angles less than

$$50° = 100 - 1 = 99 \%$$

∴ Actual number of α-particles deflected at the angles less than

$$50° = \dfrac{99}{100} \times 6.022 \times 10^{23} = 5.96 \times 10^{23}$$

5

The Fundamental Unit of Life

Important Concepts

1. **Robert Hooke** (1665) observed honey comb-like structures or boxes from a thin slice of cork through his self-designed microscope. He called these boxes as **cells**.
2. The word 'cell' in Latin means 'a little room'.
3. The invention of magnifying glasses led to the discovery of microscopic world.
4. **Leewenhoek** in 1674 discovered the free living cells in pond water for the first time with the help of improved microscope.
5. **Robert Brown** in 1831 discovered the nucleus in the cell.
6. **Purkinje** in 1839 coined the term 'protoplasm' for the fluid substance of the cell.
7. **Schleiden** (1838) and **Schwann** (1839) proposed the cell theory. According to this theory
   (i) All plants and animals are composed of cells.
   (ii) The cell is the basic unit of life.
8. **Virchow** further expanded this theory suggesting that all cells arise from pre-existing cells.
9. The small organisms like *Amoeba, Chlamydomonas, Paramecium* and bacteria are made of single cell called as unicellular organisms.

10. In multicellular animals such as some fungi, plants and animals, many cells group together in a single body and perform different functions to form various body parts.

11. The shape and size of cells are related to the specific function they perform. Some cells like *Amoeba* have changing shapes while nerve cells have a typical shape.

12. Each living cell has the capacity to perform certain basic functions that are characteristic of all living forms besides some special functions.

13. Division of labour is also present in each cell. It contains certain specific components within it known as **cell organelles.**

14. Each kind of cell organelle performs a special function, such as making new material in the cell, etc.

15. One interesting point about cell is that all cells are found to have the same organelles, no matter what their function is or what organism they are found in.

16. Cells can be classified as
    (i) **Prokaryotic cells** These are simple cells and do not have nuclear membrane and the membrane bound organelles like mitochondria, endoplasmic reticulum, Golgi apparatus, lysosomes.
    (ii) **Eukaryotic cells** These are complex cells and possess a nuclear membrane and membrane bound organelles.

17. Plasma membrane or cell membrane is the outermost covering of cell that separates the contents of the cell from its external environment.

18. The plasma membrane is extremely thin, elastic and selectively permeable. It is made up of lipids and proteins.

19. The functions of plasma membrane are
    (i) It provides definite shape to the cell.
    (ii) It is selectively permeable.
    (iii) It provides mechanical support for the protection of internal structure of a cell.

20. Cell wall is present in plant cells only. It is non-living and mainly contains cellulose. It has following functions
    (i) It provides rigidity to the plant cell.
    (ii) It is selectively permeable.
    (iii) It provides mechanical support for the protection of internal structures of a call.

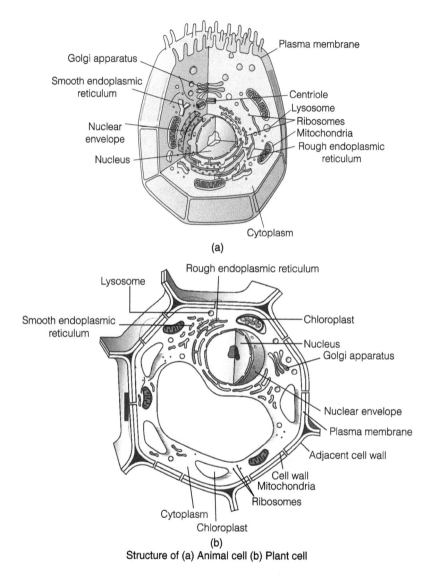

Structure of (a) Animal cell (b) Plant cell

21. Nucleus is the largest cell organelle which controls all the cell activities. It has a double-layered porous covering called **nuclear membrane**.

22. The nucleus contains rod-shaped structures called **chromosomes**. They are composed of DNA and protein.

23. DNA (Deoxyribonucleic acid) contain the information necessary for constructing and organising cells. The functional segments of DNA are called **genes.**

24. In a cell, which is not dividing, this DNA is present as part of chromatin material which is a thread-like entangled mass. Whenever, the cell is about to divide, the chromatin material gets organised into chromosomes.

25. The functions of nucleus are :
    (i) It controls all the functions of cell directly or indirectly.
    (ii) It controls cell division.

26. Cytoplasm is viscous, homogeneous, colloidal fluid that contains various molecules of water, amino acids, carbohydrates, protein and lipids, etc.

27. It contains many cell organelles which perform specific functions. The main functions of cytoplasm are:
    (i) it is a physical basis of metabolic activities.
    (ii) the cell organelles perform specific functions in the cytoplasm.
    (iii) it provides turgidity to the cell.

28. Cell organelles are visible mostly only within an electron microscope. These are membrane bound structures within themselves. This feature distinguishes eukaryotic cells from prokaryotic cells. The important cell organelles are endoplasmic reticulum. Golgi apparatus, lysosomes, mitochondria, plastids and vacuoles.

29. Endoplasmic Reticulum (ER) is a large network of membrane-bound tubes and sheets. It is an irregular, interconnected network of flattened sacs made up of double membrane and are interconnected with each other.

30. The endoplasmic reticulum is of two types :
    (i) Rough Endoplasmic Reticulum (RER)
    (ii) Smooth Endoplasmic Reticulum (SER)

31. The functions of ER are :
    (i) it is associated with synthesis, storage and transport of metabolic products.
    (ii) it gives internal support to the colloidal matrix.
    (iii) RER is involved in protein synthesis.

32. **Ribosomes** are the smallest cell organelles without a membrane present freely or attached to the RER. It is present

both in cytoplasm as well as inside the nucleus, where it is called **nucleolus**. Ribosomes are present in all the cells.

33. The function of ribosome is that they are the site of protein synthesis in the cell.

34. Golgi apparatus or Golgi bodies or Golgi complex was first described by **Camillo Golgi**. It consists of membrane bound fluid filled vesicles, vacuoles and stack of many flattened closed sacs (cisternae).

35. In plant cells, they are distributed throughout the cytoplasm and are called **dictyosomes**. In animal cells, they are larger and one or two in number while in plants they are smaller and more in number. The membranes of Golgi apparatus often have connections with the membranes of endoplasmic reticulum through ER vesicles.

36. The functions of Golgi complex are :
    (i) it helps in synthesis and modifications of proteins, lipids and carbohydrates.
    (ii) it helps in the synthesis of lysosomes and peroxisomes.
    (iii) it is involved in the formation of cell plate during cell division.
    (iv) it also forms complex sugars from simple sugars.
    (v) the material synthesized near ER is packaged and dispatched to various targets inside and outside the cell through the Golgi apparatus.
    (vi) it also helps in storage, modification and packaging of products in vesicles.

37. Lysosomes are small sized hydrolytic enzyme (digestive enzymes) containing vesicles which are bounded by a single membrane. These are also known as 'suicidal bags' or 'digestive bags'.

38. The functions of lysosomes are :
    (i) they cause digestion of worn out cell organelles.
    (ii) they help in intercellular and intracellular digestion of food particles.
    (iii) they destroy foreign substances.
    (iv) they help in the digestion of bones by digesting cartilage.

39. Mitochondria are double membraned bag-like structures. Their outer membrane is smooth and the inner membrane is folded inwards to form **cristae**. They contain enzymes required for aerobic oxidation of glucose.

40. The functions of mitochondria are:
    (i) they help in cellular respiration and release of energy in the form of ATP molecules.
    (ii) mitochondria are popularly known as 'power house of the cell'.

41. **Plastids** are present only in plant cells. The internal organisation of plastids consists of numerous membrane layers embedded in a material called the stroma. Like the mitochondria, plastids also have their own DNA and ribosomes.

42. The plastids are of following three types:
    (i) **Leucoplasts** They are colourless and store food in the form of starch, protein and fats.
    (ii) **Chromoplasts** They are colourful plastids like red, orange, yellow, etc., except green.
    (iii) **Chloroplasts** They are green-colour plastids because of the presence of chlorophyll. They trap the solar energy and perform the function of photosynthesis.

43. The various functions of plastids are:
    (i) They provide bright colours to fruits and flower which helps in pollination and dispersal.
    (ii) They perform the functions of photosynthesis.

44. Centrosome is present in animal cells only which is located near the nucleus. It contains centrioles. The centrioles are surrounded by centrosphere and involved in spindle fibre formation during cell division.

45. The centrosome initiates and regulates cell division and produces basal bodies from which arise **cilia** and **flagella**.

46. Vacuoles are storage sacs for solids or liquid contents. They are small sized in animal cells while plant cells have very large vacuoles.

47. The outermost covering of vacuoles is **tonoplast**. The functions of tonoplast are:
    (i) they help in storage of food, water and other waste substances.
    (ii) they provide turgidity and rigidity to the cell.
    (iii) in *Amoeba*, the food vacuole contains the food items.
    (iv) in some unicellular organisms, specialised vacuoles also play important roles in expelling excess water and some wastes from the cell.

48. Each cell thus, acquires its structure and ability to function because of the organisation of its membrane and organelles in specific ways. Thus, the cell has a **basic structural organisation.**

49. The basic structural organisation of cell helps to perform functions like respiration obtaining nutrition, excretion or forming new proteins.

Intext Questions

On Page 59

Question 1. Who discovered cells and how?

Answer Robert Hooke discovered cells with the help of his self-designed microscope. He examined a thin slice of cork and saw that the cork resembled the structure of a honey comb consisting of many compartments.

Question 2. Why is the cell called the structural and functional unit of life?

Answer Living cells have certain specific components within it known as cell organelles. Each kind of cell organelle performs a specific function, such as making new materials in the cells, release of waste, transportation, etc. Thus, a cell can perform all its functions with the help of these organelles. That is why the cells are called structural and functional unit of life.

On Page 61

Question 1. How do substances like CO_2 and water move in and out of the cell? Discuss.

Answer Substances like CO_2 (a cellular waste) accumulates in high concentration inside the cell. In the cell's external environment, the concentration of CO_2 is low as compared to that inside the cell. As soon as there is a difference of concentration of CO_2 inside and outside a cell, CO_2 moves out of the cell, from a region of high concentration to a region of low concentration outside the cell by the process of diffusion.

Question 2. Why is the plasma membrane called a selectively permeable membrane?

Answer The plasma membrane selectively allows the entry and exit of some materials in and out of the cell. It also prevents movement of some other materials. Therefore, it is called a selectively permeable membrane.

On Page 63

Question 1. Fill in the gaps in the following table illustrating differences between prokaryotic and eukaryotic cells.

S.No.	Prokaryotic Cell	Eukaryotic Cell
1.	Size : generally small (1 - 10 µm) $1\,\mu m = 10^{-6}\,m$	Size : generally large (5 - 100 µm).
2.	Nuclear region : .... and known us	Nuclear region : well defined and surrounded by a nuclear membrane
3.	Chromosome : single	More than one chromosome
4.	Membrane bound cell organelles absent	....

Answer

S.No.	Prokaryotic Cell	Eukaryotic Cell
1.	Size : generally small (1 - 10 µm) $1\,\mu m = 10^{-6}\,m$	Size : generally large (5 - 100 µm).
2.	Nuclear region : undefined nuclear region containing only nucleic acids (genetic material) and known as nucleoid	Nuclear region : well defined and surrounded by a nuclear membrane.
3.	Chromosome : single	More than one chromosome
4.	Membrane-bound cell organelles absent	Membrane bound cell organelles present

On Page 65

Question 1. Can you name the two organelles we have studied that contain their own genetic material?

Answer Mitochondria and plastids.

Question 2. If the organisation of a cell is destroyed due to some physical or chemical influence, what will happen?

Answer Living cells are capable of performing certain basic functions due to the presence of cell organelles present in it. If this organisation of cell is destroyed, then cell will not be able to perform its basic functions and will die after sometime.

Question 3. Why are lysosomes known as suicide bags?

Answer The lysosomes contain hydrolytic enzymes which are capable of breaking down organic matter in case of any disturbance in cellular metabolism. For example, when a cell gets damaged, then lysosomes burst and enzymes digest their own cell. Hence, the lysosomes are known as 'suicide bags' of cells.

Question 4. Where are protein synthesised inside the cell?

Answer Protein is synthesised in cells in ribosomes. The ribosomes are attached to the surface of endoplasmic reticulum.

Exercises

Question 1. Make a comparison and write down ways in which plant cells are different from animal cells.

Answer Comparison of plant cell and animal cell

S.No.	Plant Cell	Animal Cell
1.	Cell wall is present outside the plasma membrane.	Cell wall is absent.
2.	Generally regular in shape.	Generally irregular in shape.
3.	Larger in size than animal cells.	Smaller in size than animal cells.
4.	Plastids are present.	Plastids are absent except in *Euglena*.
5.	A permanent and large vacuole is present.	Vacuoles are many, small and temporary.
6.	Many simple units of Golgi apparatus called dictyosome is present.	A single, highly complex and prominent Golgi apparatus is present.
7.	Centrosome and centrioles are absent, instead polar caps are present.	Centrosome and centrioles are present.

Question 2. How is a prokaryotic cell different from a eukaryotic cell?

Answer Refer to Ans. of Question 1 (Intext Questions Page 63).

Question 3. What would happen if the plasma membrane ruptures or breaks down?

Answer In case of plasma membrane ruptures or breaks down:
   (i) All the useful substances will move out of the cell because plasma membrane is selectively permeable.
   (ii) There will be no difference between cell content and its external environment.
   (iii) The cell will close its normal shape.

Question 4. What would happen to the life of a cell if there was no Golgi apparatus?

Answer Effect of absence of Golgi apparatus on life of a cell
   (i) The packaging and dispatching of different types of proteins to various targets inside and outside the cell will be influenced.
   (ii) The products of cell cannot be stored and modified later.
   (iii) There will be effect on lysosomes formation. This will cause accumulation of worn out and dead cell organelles within the cell which may cause cell death.

Question 5. Which organelle is known as the power house of the cell? Why?

Answer Mitochondria are called power house of the cell. These contain oxidative enzymes which oxidises the food and convert it into energy currency of the cell in the form of ATP (Adenosine Triphosphate). This energy is used by body for making new chemical compounds and for doing other works. This is the reason, mitochondria are called power house of the cell.

Question 6. Where do the lipids and proteins constituting the cell membrane get synthesised?

Answer The synthesis of lipids occur in Smooth Endoplasmic Reticulum (SER). The proteins are synthesised in the ribosomes which are attached to the Rough Endoplasmic Reticulum (RER).

Question 7. How does an *Amoeba* obtain its food?

Answer *Amoeba* acquires its food through endocytosis. Endocytosis is the process of ingestion of food through the plasma membrane. This occurs due to flexible nature of plasma membrane which enable the *Amoeba* to engulf in food and other materials from its surroundings.

Question 8. What is osmosis?

Answer The movement of solvent from a region of its high concentration to a region of its low concentration through a semipermeable membrane is called osmosis. During osmosis, the water molecules (solvent) are free to cross the plasma membrane in both the directions.

Question 9. Carry out the following osmosis experiments

Take four peeled potato halves and scoops each one out to make potato cups. One of these potato cups should be made from a boiled potato. Put each potato cup in a trough containing water. Now

(a) Keep cup *A* empty

(b) Put one tea spoon sugar in cup *B*.

(c) Put one tea spoon salt in cup *C*.

(d) Put one tea spoon sugar in the boiled potato cup *D*.

Keep these for two hours. Then observe the four potato cups and answer the following:

(i) Explain why water gathers in the hollowed portion of *B* and *C*?

(ii) Why is potato *A* necessary for this experiment?

(iii) Explain why water does not gather in the hollowed out portion of *A* and *D*?

Answer

(i) The water gathers in the hollowed portion of *B* and *C* due to the process of osmosis. Since, the concentration of solute (sugar in cup *B* and salt in cup *C*) is higher inside the cup as compared to the water, which is outside the cup. Hence, water from its higher concentration (outside the cup) will move towards the lower concentration (inside the cup). This process of osmosis (moving in of solvent) is called **endosmosis**.

(ii) Potato *A* acts as a control for the experiment. This is required for comparing the results of the experiment.

(iii) Water does not gather in the hollowed out portions of *A* and *D* because of the following reasons:

• The hollowed portion of potato *A* is empty. So, because of no concentration difference, no osmosis can occur.

• The hollowed portion of potato *D* contains sugar in it but it is boiled. So, osmosis cannot occur as its semipermeable membrane is destroyed by boiling.

Question 10. Which type of cell devision is required for growth and repair of body and which type is involved in formation of gametes?

Answer

For growth and repair, mitosis cell division is required while in formation of gametes meiosis cell division is required.

Selected NCERT Exemplar Problems

Multiple Choice Questions

Question 1. Which of the following can be made into crystal?

(a) A bacterium   (b) An *Amoeba*

(c) A virus   (d) A sperm

Answer (c) Viruses are considered neither living nor non-living. A living thing is made up of organic compounds so can be decomposed into simple materials. Virus having a non-living feature, so it can be crystallized.

Question 2. A cell will swell up if

(a) the concentration of water molecules in the cell is higher than the concentration of water molecules in surrounding medium

(b) the concentration of water molecules in surrounding medium is higher than water molecules concentration in the cell

(c) the concentration of water molecules is same in the cell and in the surrounding medium

(d) concentration of water molecules does not matter

Answer (b) When a cell is placed in hypotonic solution, it swells up building pressure against the cell membrane or cell wall in case of plant cell.

Question 3. Chromosomes are made up of

(a) DNA   (b) protein

(c) DNA and protein   (d) RNA

Answer (c) Chromosomes contain DNA molecules and necessary proteins for constructing and organising cells.

Question 4. Which of these options are not a function of ribosomes?

I. It helps in manufacture of proteins molecules

II. It helps in manufacture of enzymes

III. It helps in manufacture of hormones

IV. It helps in manufacture of molecules

(a) I and II   (b) II and III   (c) III and IV   (d) IV and I

Answer (c) Ribosomes help in protein synthesis of cell.

Question 5. Which of these is not related to endoplasmic reticulum?

(a) It behaves as transport channel for proteins between nucleus and cytoplasm

(b) It transports materials between various regions in cytoplasm.

(c) It can be the site of energy generation

(d) It can be the site of some biochemical activities of the cell

Answer (c) Site of energy generation are mitochondria in cells. Rest of the functions given in options a, b and d are related to ER.

Question 6. Following are a few definitions of osmosis. Read carefully and select the correct definition.

(a) Movement of water molecules from a region of higher concentration to a region of lower concentration through a semipermeable membrane.

(b) Movement of solvent molecules from its higher concentration to lower concentration.

(c) Movement of solvent molecules from higher concentration to lower concentration of solution through a permeable membrane.

(d) Movement of solute molecules from lower concentration to higher concentration of solution through a semipermeable membrane.

Answer (a) In osmosis, the movement of solvent occurs from a region of its high concentration to a region of low concentration through a semipermeable membrane.

Question 7. Plasmolysis in a plant cell is defined as

(a) breakdown (lysis) of plasma membrane in hypotonic medium

(b) shrinkage of cytoplasm in hypertonic medium

(c) shrinkage of nucleoplasm

(d) None of the above

Answer (b) When a living plant cell loses water through osmosis, there is shrinkage or contraction of the protoplasm away from the cell wall.

Question 8. Which of the following are covered by a single membrane?

(a) Mitochondria (b) Vacuole   (c) Lysosomes   (d) Plastid

Answer (b) Vacuoles are bound by a single membrane called tonoplast.

Question 9. Find out the correct sentence.

(a) Enzymes packed in lysosomes are made through RER (Rough Endoplasmic Reticulum).

(b) Rough endoplasmic reticulum and smooth endoplasmic reticulum produce lipid and protein respectively.

(c) Endoplasmic reticulum is related with the destruction of plasma membrane.

(d) Nucleoid is present inside the nucleoplasm of eukaryotic nucleus.

Answer (a) Lysosomal enzymes are made by RER.

Question 10. Which cell organelle plays a crucial role in detoxifying many poisons and drugs in a cell?

(a) Golgi apparatus   (b) Lysosomes
(c) Smooth endoplasmic reticulum (d) Vacuoles

Answer (c) SER is involved in the process of detoxification of many poisons and drugs in liver cells of vertebrates.

Question 11. The proteins and lipids, essential for building the cell membrane are

(a) rough endoplasmic reticulum   (b) Golgi apparatus
(c) plasma membrane   (d) mitochondria

Answer (a) ER with ribosomes (RER) is involved in the manufacture of proteins.

Question 12. The undefined nuclear region of prokaryotes are also known as

(a) nucleus   (b) nucleolus
(c) nucleic acid   (d) nucleoid

Answer (d) Lack of nuclear membrane in prokaryotic cells leads to the formation of undefined nuclear region. The genetic material is localized in a region of cytoplasm called nucleoid.

Question 13. The cell organelle involved in forming complex sugars from simple sugars are

(a) endoplasmic reticulum   (b) ribosomes
(c) plastids   (d) Golgi apparatus

Answer (d) Golgi apparatus is specialized to modify, package and secrete complex biomolecules.

Question 14. Which out of the following is not a function of vacuole?

(a) Storage
(b) Providing turgidity and rigidity to the cell
(c) Waste excretion
(d) Locomotion

Answer (d) Vacuoles are mostly present in plant cells having all the a, b, c, (given options) function. Plants do not show locomotion.

Question 15. *Amoeba* acquires its food through a process, termed

(a) exocytosis
(b) endocytosis
(c) plasmolysis
(d) exocytosis and endocytosis both

Answer (b) Endocytosis is the process of ingestion of food particles by the cells through plasma membrane.

Question 16. Cell wall of which one of these is not made up of cellulose?

(a) Bacteria   (b) *Hydrilla*

(c) Mango tree   (d) Cactus

Answer (a) In bacteria, cell wall is made up of peptidogly can (a polysaccharide).

Question 17. Silver nitrate solution is used to study

(a) endoplasmic reticulum   (b) Golgi apparatus

(c) nucleus   (d) mitochondria

Answer (b) Camillo Golgi developed silver nitrate solution as a staining method for individual nerve and cell structures.

Question 18. Organelle other than nucleus, containing DNA is

(a) endoplasmic reticulum   (b) Golgi apparatus

(c) mitochondria   (d) lysosomes

Answer (c) Mitochondria have their own circular DNA and 70 S ribosomes which helps to make some of its own proteins.

Question 19. Kitchen of the cell is

(a) mitochondria

(b) endoplasmic reticulum

(c) chloroplast

(d) Golgi apparatus

Answer (c) Chloroplasts present in leaves are green coloured plastids which contain chlorophyll. Chlorophylls trap sunlight and carryout photosynthesis.

Question 20. Lipid molecules in the cell are synthesized by

(a) smooth endoplasmic reticulum   (b) rough endoplasmic reticulum

(c) Golgi apparatus   (d) plastids

Answer (a) SER does not contain ribosomes. It helps in synthesis of lipids.

Question 21. Cell arises from pre-existing cell was stated by

(a) Haeckel   (b) Virchow

(c) Hooke   (d) Schleiden

Answer (b) Rudolf Virchow (1855) expanded the cell theory and suggested that 'all cells arise from pre-existing cells'.

Question 22. Cell theory was given by
   (a) Schleiden and Schwann
   (b) Virchow
   (c) Hooke
   (d) Haeckel

Answer   (a) Schleiden (1838) and Schwann (1839) proposed the cell theory.

Question 23. The only cell organelle seen in prokaryotic cell is
   (a) mitochondria   (b) ribosomes
   (c) plastids   (d) lysosomes

Answer   (b) Ribosomes are found in both eukaryotic and prokaryotic cells except in mature sperms and RBCs. In prokaryotic cells they are found floating freely in cytoplasm.

Question 24. Organelle without a cell membrane is
   (a) ribosome   (b) Golgi apparatus
   (c) chloroplast   (d) nucleus

Answer   (a) Ribosomes are membrane less, dense, spherical and granular particles.

Question 25. 1 μm is
   (a) 10^{-6} m   (b) 10^{-9} m
   (c) 10^{-10} m   (d) 10^{-3} m

Answer   (a) 1 micrometer or micron (μm) = 10^{-6}m

Question 26. Lysosome arises from
   (a) endoplasmic reticulum
   (b) Golgi apparatus
   (c) nucleus
   (d) mitochondria

Answer   (b) Golgi apparatus is involved in the formation of lysosomes.

Question 27. Living cells were discovered by
   (a) Robert Hooke
   (b) Purkinje
   (c) Leeuwenhoek
   (d) Robert Brown

Answer   (c) Leeuwenhoek (1674) with the improved microscope, discovered the free living cells in pond water for the first time.

Question 28. Select the odd one out.

(a) The movement of water across a semipermeable membrane is affected by the amount of substances dissolved in it
(b) Membranes are made of organic molecules like proteins and lipids
(c) Molecules soluble in organic solvents can easily pass through the membrane
(d) Plasma membrane contain chitin sugar in plants

Answer (d) Plasma membrane is made up of phospholipids and proteins. It contains glycolipids and glycoprotein.

Short Answer Type Questions

Question 29. Why does the skin of your finger shrink when you wash clothes for a long time?

Answer Soap solution is a hypertonic solution. While washing clothes, through the process of osmosis water moves out of the finger cells causing their shrinkage.

Question 30. A person takes concentrated solution of salt, after sometime, he starts vomiting. What is the phenomenon responsible for such situation? Explain.

Answer Exosmosis is responsible for this situation. Salt solution is hypertonic. When taken by a person, it withdraws water from a cell or system through exosmosis.

Question 31. We eat food composed of all the nutrients like carbohydrates, proteins, fats, vitamins, minerals and water. After digestion, these are absorbed in the form of glucose, amino acids, fatty acids and glycerol, etc. What mechanisms are involved in absorption of digested food and water?

Answer The mechanisms involved in absorption of digested food and water are diffusion and osmosis respectively. Diffusion is the spontaneous movement of substances or molecules from a region of their higher concentration to lower concentration.
Osmosis is the movement of solvent (water from high concentration to a region of lower concentration) through a semipermeable membrane.
In this case, from small intestine (high concentration) to blood (low concentration).

Question 32. If you are provided with some vegetables to cook, you generally add salt into the vegetables during cooking process. After adding salt, vegetables release water. What mechanism is responsible for this?

Answer Exosmosis.

Question 33. Match the following A and B

S.No.	A	B	
1.	Smooth endoplasmic reticulum	A.	Amoeba
2.	Lysosome	B.	Nucleous
3.	Nucleoid	C.	Bacteria
4.	Food vacuoles	D.	Detoxification
5.	Chromatin material and nucleolus	E.	Suicidal bags

Answer 1 – D, 2 – E, 3 – C, 4 – A, 5 – B

Question 34. How do substances like carbon dioxide (CO_2) and water (H_2O) move in and out of the cell?

Answer By diffusion (CO_2) and osmosis (water). When CO_2 accumulates in high concentration inside the cell, diffusion occurs. CO_2 moves out of the cell from a region of high concentration to a region of lower concentration. In the same way, oxygen enters the cells.

When a cell is placed in a solution with a different solute concentration, the water tends to move either in or out of the cell by the process of osmosis.

Question 35. How are chromatin, chromatid and chromosomes related to each other?

Answer The chromosomes consist of two arms called chromatids. The chromatids are made up of chromatin. The chromatin fibres are very fine thread like coiled filaments uniformly distributed in the nucleoplasm.

Long Answer Type Questions

Question 36. Differentiate between rough and smooth endoplasmic reticulum. How is endoplasmic reticulum important for membrane biogenesis?

Answer Differences between rough and smooth endoplasmic reticulum

S.No.	Smooth Endoplasmic Reticulum	Rough Endoplasmic Reticulum
1.	SER has no ribosomal particles on the surface, hence look smooth.	RER has particles of ribosome on the surface.
2.	It helps in manufactures of lipids and fat molecules.	They are the sites of protein synthesis.

Lipids, cholesterol from SER and some proteins from RER help in building the cell membrane. This process is called membrane biogenesis.

Question 37. Draw a neat diagram of plant cell and label any three parts which differentiate it from animal cell.

Answer Structure of a plant cell.

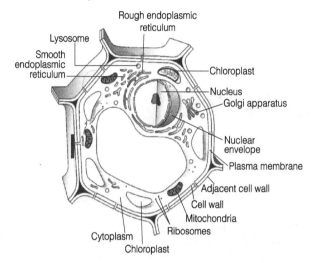

The chloroplast, big-sized vacuole and cell wall are not present in a plant cell.

6

Tissues

Important Concepts

1. **Tissue** is a group of cells that are similar in structure and/or work together to perform a particular function. All the cells of tissue have a common origin. Blood muscles, phloem and xylem are examples of some tissues.

2. **Differences between Plant and Animal Tissues**

S.No.	Plant Tissue	Animal Tissue
1.	The dead supportive tissues are more abundant as compared to living tissues. They provide structural and mechanical strength.	Living tissues are more abundant as compared to dead tissues.
2.	Some tissues divide throughout life. Growth is limited to certain regions.	Growth in animals occurs throughout life.
3.	Tissue organisation is towards stationary habit.	Tissue organisation is towards mobility.
4.	They are differentiated into meristematic and permanent tissues.	Such differentiation is not present.
5.	They need less energy for maintenance.	They need more energy for maintenance.

3. Plant organs like root, stem, leaves, flowers and fruits are made up of different kinds of tissues to perform specific functions.

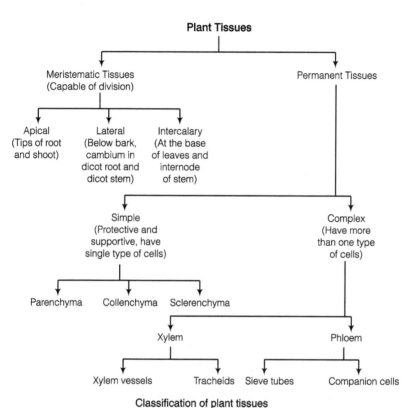

Classification of plant tissues

4. **Meristematic tissue** occurs only in certain specific regions. Depending on their location, meristematic tissues can be classified as

(i) Apical (ii) Lateral (iii) Intercalary

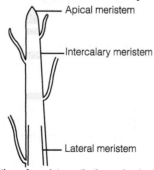

Location of meristematic tissue in plant body

(i) **Apical meristem** is situated at the growing tips of stems and roots. It is responsible for increase in height of the plant called as **primary growth**.

(ii) **Lateral meristem** occurs on the sides and helps in increasing the girth of the stem. This is called **seconary growth**.

(iii) **Intercalary meristem** is located at the base of the leaves or internodes on twigs, *e.g.*, stems of grasses and other monocots. It helps in growth of leaves and elongation of internodes.

5. **Permanent tissues** are formed when meristematic tissues take up a specific role and lose the ability to divide. This process of taking up a permanent shape, size and a function is called **differentiation**.

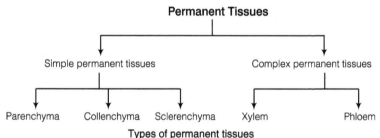

Types of permanent tissues

6. **Simple permanent tissues** are made up of structurally and functionally similar cells. On the basis of nature of cells, these are further divided as parenchyma, collenchyma and sclerenchyma.

7. **Parenchyma** (*Para*–beside; *enchyma*–tissue) are present in stem, roots, leaves, flowers and fruits.

(i) They form the basic packing tissue of the plant body.

(ii) The cells are living and have large intercellular spaces between them.

(iii) Its main function is to store and assimilate food. It also provides mechanical strength to the plant.

(iv) If chloroplast is present in parenchyma, it is called chlorenchyma to carry out photosynthesis.

(v) In aquatic plants, large cavities are present in parenchyma to give buoyancy to the plants to help them float. This type of parenchyma is called aerenchyma.

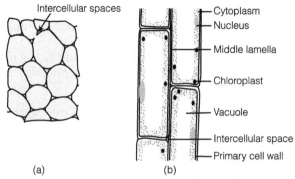

Parenchyma (a) Transverse section (b) Longitudinal section

8. **Collenchyma** (*Kolla*–glue; *enchyma*–tissue) is a kind of living tissue like parenchyma. It is present below the epidermis of green dicotyledonous stem and leaf stalk (petiole). These are absent in monocot roots, stems and leaves.

   (i) It provides flexibility to the plant without breaking. It also provides mechanical support to the plant.

   (ii) The cells are circular, oval, elongated, longitudinally and irregularly thickened at the corners by the deposition of extra pectin and cellulose. These cells have very little intercellular space between them.

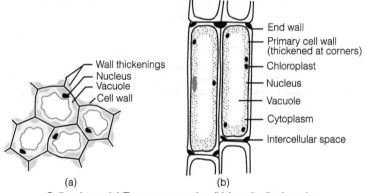

Collenchyma (a) Transverse section (b) Longitudinal section

9. **Sclerenchyma** (*Scleros*–hard; *enchyma*–tissue) is a dead, simple permanent tissue, which makes the plant hard and stiff.

   (i) The cells are long, narrow and closely packed without any intercellular spaces.

   (ii) The cells of sclerenchyma are of two types–sclereids and fibres.

(iii) It occurs in stems, roots, veins of leaves, hard covering of seeds and nuts. The husk of coconut is made up of sclerenchyma tissue.

(iv) Sclerenchyma gives strength and rigidity to the plant body. A number of fibres commercially used are jute, flax, hemp, etc.

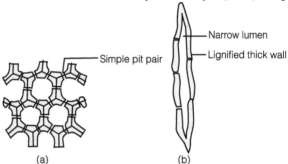

Sclerenchyma (a) Transverse section (b) Longitudinal section

10. **Epidermis** is the outermost, protective layer of cells. It is usually made up of single layer of cells.

(i) In plants living in very dry habitats, the epidermis may be thicker since protection against water loss is critical.

(ii) Epidermal cells on the aerial parts of the plant often secrete a waxy, water resistant layer on their outer surface. This is to protect against loss of water.

(iii) Most epidermal cells are relatively flat often their outer and side walls are thicker than the inner wall.

(iv) In the epidermis of leaves, small pores called stomata are present. Stomata are enclosed by kidney-shaped cells called guard cells. These help in exchange of gases and transpiration.

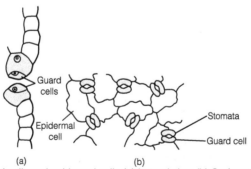

Guard cells and epidermal cells (a) Lateral view (b) Surface view

(v) Epidermal cells of roots, whose function is water absorption, commonly bear long hair like parts that greatly increase the total absorptive surface area.

(vi) In some desert plants, epidermis has a thick waxy coating of cutin on its outer surface.

(vii) As plants grow older, a strip of secondary meristem replaces the epidermis of the stem. Cells on the outside are cut off from this layer. This forms the several layer **thick cork** or the bark of the tree. Cork cells have a chemical called **suberin** in their walls that makes them impervious to gases and water.

11. Complex permanent tissues are made up of more than one type of cells. For example, **xylem** and **phloem**. They are both conducting tissues and constitute a vascular bundle.

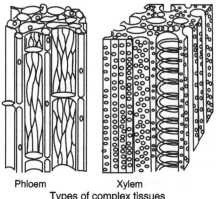

Phloem   Xylem
Types of complex tissues

12. **Xylem** consists of tracheids, vessels, xylem parenchyma and xylem fibres. The cells have thick walls and many of them are dead cells.

(i) Tracheids and vessels are tubular structures. This allows them to transport water and minerals vertically.

(ii) Parenchyma stores food and helps in the sideways conduction of water.

(iii) Fibres are mainly supportive in function.

(iv) Xylem helps in conduction of water and minerals from roots to all parts of the shoot.

(v) It also provides mechanical support.

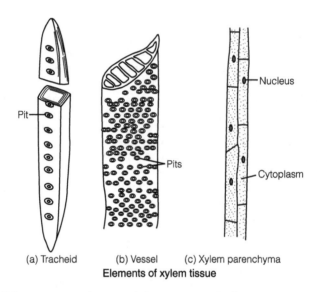

(a) Tracheid   (b) Vessel   (c) Xylem parenchyma
Elements of xylem tissue

13. **Phloem** is made up of four types of elements, sieve tubes, companion cells, phloem fibres and the phloem parenchyma.
    (i) Sieve tubes are tubular cells with perforated end walls.
    (ii) In phloem, unlike xylem, materials can move in both directions.
    (iii) Phloem cells are living cells, except for phloem fibres.
    (iv) It transports food from leaves to other parts of the plant.
    (v) Phloem parenchyma helps in storage of food.

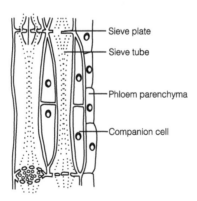

Section of a phloem tissue

14. **Animal tissues** can be classified as following based on their functions :

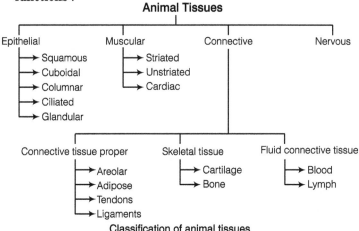

Classification of animal tissues

15. **Epithelial tissue** forms the outer covering and the lining of all the organs and their cavities. The shape of their cells is flattened, cuboidal and columnar. The tissue helps in protection, secretion, absorption and excretory activities of the cells. Epithelial tissue can be squamous, cuboidal, columnar, ciliated and glandular.

16. **Squamous epithelium** is present on the skin, lining of alveoli of lungs, blood vessels, cheeks, etc. The cells are flat and polygonal arranged in the form of tiles. These play important role in protection, osmosis and diffusion.

17. **Cuboidal epithelium** is present in glands, ducts and germinal layers of ovary. The cells are cube like or isodimetric. The function of cuboidal epithelium is secretion and absorption.

18. **Columnar epithelium** forms the lining of stomach, intestine and genital ducts. The cells are piller like resting on a thin membrane. This tissue helps in protection absorption and secretion.

19. **Ciliated epithelium** lines the respiratory tract, Fallopian tube and nephrons. The cells are cuboidal, columnar with fine hair-like cilia. Their function is protection, spreading of mucus. Cilia help in movement of gases and liquid.

20. **Glandular epithelium** is present in glands. The cells are cubical, branched or unbranched. The main role of glandular epithelium is secretion.

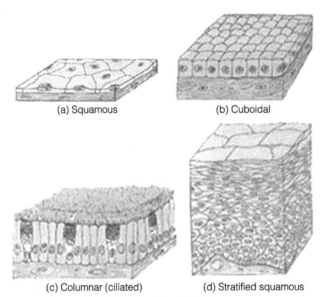

(a) Squamous (b) Cuboidal

(c) Columnar (ciliated) (d) Stratified squamous

Different types of epilthelial tissues

21. **Connective tissue connects** various body tissues or organs. It connects bones to bones, muscles to bones and also binds tissues. The main function of connective tissue is binding, supporting and packing of different tissues and organs of the body. The various types of connective tissues are areolar tissue, cartilage, bone, tendon, ligament and blood.

22. **Areolar tissue** is present between other tissues and organs. The cells are embedded in a matrix of elastic and in inelastic fibres. The functions of areolar tissue are binding and repair of body tissues.

23. **Cartilage** forms the covering of the edges of bones and supporting wind pipe, nose and pinna. It consists of clear ground matrix having chondroblasts in lacunae. Cartilage is flexible and provides firm support due to this feature.

24. **Bone** forms the skeleton of vertebrate animals. It consists of osteoblasts embedded in a hard matrix of calcium and phosphorus with circular canals called **Haversian canals**. Its functions are:

    (i) Provide support and shape to the body.

    (ii) Protect internal organs and a site of blood corpuscles.

25. **Tendons** are located between muscles and bones. These are non-elastic fibres of white colour. Their function is to connect muscles with bones.

26. **Ligaments** are present at the joints of long bones. Their cells and matrix have elastic fibres of yellow colour. The ligaments connect one bone to the other bone.

27. **Blood** flows through the heart and blood vessels, *i.e.*, arteries and veins. It contains plasma and blood corpuscles. The blood corpuscles are of following three types.

    (i) Erythrocytes (Red blood cells – RBCs)

    (ii) Leucocytes (White blood cells – WBCs)

    (iii) Thrombocytes (Platelets)

    The functions of blood are transport of food, oxygen, carbon dioxide, waste and hormones.

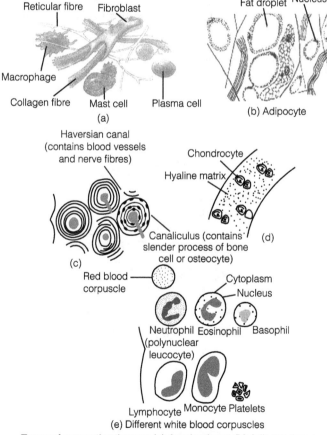

Types of connective tissues: (a) Areolar tissue (b) Adipose tissue
(c) Compact bone (d) hyaline cartilage (e) Types of blood cells

28. **Muscular tissue** is attached to bones, forms the wall of internal organs and in the heart. It is a contractile tissue made up of different kinds of muscle fibres. The function of muscular tissue is to give support to the body and help in movement. The skeletal tissue can be of three types :

   (i) **Striated** or skeletal muscles are attached to the bones. These are long, cylindrical, multinucleated cells with alternated dark and light bands. This assists in voluntary movement of the body.

  (ii) **Non-striated** or smooth muscles are located in the lining of blood vessels, respiratory tract, digestive organs, urinary bladder, reproductive organs, etc. They have spindle-shaped, uninucleated structure without striations. Their function is related to the involuntary movement and peristaltic movements.

 (iii) **Cardiac muscles** are located in heart. These are cylindrical, branched fibres with faint striations having one or two nuclei in each cell. These are related to beating of heart.

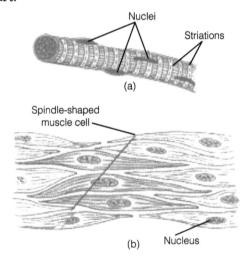

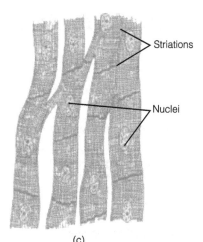

(c)
Types of muscles fibres: (a) Striated muscle
(b) Smooth muscle (c) Cardiac muscle

29. **Nervous tissue** is present in brain, spinal cord and nerves. It contains neurons containing glandular cytoplasm and distinct nuclei with dendrons, dendrites and axon. Nervous tissue controls all the body activities, conduction of impulse and to stimulate other tissues for activity.

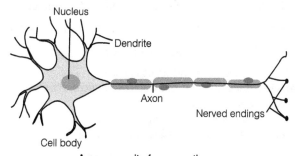

A neuron unit of nervous tissue

30. The functional combination of nerve and muscle tissue is fundamental to most animals. This combination enables animals to move rapidly in response to stimuli.

Intext Questions

On Page 69

Question 1. What is a tissue?

Answer A group of cells that are similar in structure and/or work together to achieve a particular function is called tissue.

Question 2. What is the utility of tissues in multicellular organisms?

Answer In multicellular organisms, the body system is based on the division of labour. It means the cells performing a specific function are grouped together to form a particular tissue. The different tissues are organized in a way to provide highest efficiency in functioning of the body.

On Page 73

Question 1. Name types of simple tissues.

Answer The three main types of simple tissues are:
(i) Parenchyma   (ii) Collenchyma   (iii) Sclerenchyma

Question 2. Where is apical meristem found?

Answer Apical meristem is present in growing tips of stems and roots of plants. It helps in increasing the length of the stem and the root.

Question 3. Which tissue makes up the husk of coconut?

Answer The husk of coconut is made up of sclerenchymatous tissue.

Question 4. What are the constituents of phloem?

Answer The constituents of phloem tissue are:
(i) Sieve tubes (tubular living cells with perforated end walls)
(ii) Companion cell (living cells)
(iii) Phloem parenchyma (living cells)
(iv) Phloem fibres (non-living and sclerenchyma cells)

On Page 77

Question 1. Name the tissue responsible for movement in our body.

Answer The movement of our body depends on muscular tissue. It consists of elongated cells (muscle fibres).

Question 2. What does a neuron look like?

Answer A neuron consists of a cell body with a nucleus and cytoplasm from which long, thin hair-like parts arise. Each neuron has a single long part, called the axon and many short, branched parts called dendrites. Many nerve fibres bound together by connective tissue to make up a nerve.

Question 3. Give three features of cardiac muscles:

Answer Features of cardiac muscles :
  (i) These are involuntary, show rhythmic contraction and relaxation throughout life.
  (ii) The cells are cylindrical, branched, uninucleate having faint cross striations.
  (iii) These muscles do not get fatigued under normal conditions.

Question 4. What are the functions of areolar tissue?

Answer Functions of areolar tissue :
  (i) It fills the space inside the organs, thus acts as a packing tissue between the organs.
  (ii) It supports many delicate organs in the body.
  (iii) It plays role in repair of tissues.

Exercises

Question 1. Define the term 'tissue'.

Answer A group of cells that are similar in structure and/or work together to achieve a particular function is called tissue..

Question 2. How many types of elements together make up the xylem tissue? Name them.

Answer The following four types of elements make up xylem tissue:
  (i) Xylem tracheids (tubular unicellular).
  (ii) Xylem vessels (multicellular).
  (iii) Xylem parenchyma (stores food and helps in sideways conduction of water).
  (iv) Xylem fibres (provide mechanical support).

Question 3. How are simple tissues different from complex tissues in plants?

Answer

S.No.	Simple Tissue	Complex Tissues
1.	Made up of only one type of cells.	Made up of more than one type of cells.
2.	Mainly responsible for storage and mechanical support.	Mainly responsible for the transport of water, minerals, sugars and other metabolites.
	Examples Parenchyma, collenchyma and sclerenchyma.	**Examples** Xylem and phloem.

Question 4. Differentiate between parenchyma, collenchyma and sclerenchyma on the basis of their cell wall.

Answer Differences between parenchyma, collenchyma and sclerenchyma

S.No.	Parenchyma	Collenchyma	Sclerenchyma
1.	These are living cells with thin walls.	These are living cells with slightly thick walls.	These are dead cells with thick cell walls.
2.	Cells are uniformly thin	Cells are elongated.	Cells are long and narrow.
3.	The cells are loosely packed with large intercellular spaces.	The cells are irregularly thickened at the corners with very little intercellular spaces.	The cells are thickened due to lignin. These are so thick that there is no internal space inside the cell.

Question 5. What are the functions of the stomata?

Answer Functions of stomata :
   (i) They are essential for gas exchange with the atmosphere.
   (ii) They help in transpiration in the form of water vapour through leaves.

Question 6. Diagrammatically show the difference between the three types of muscle fibres.

Answer

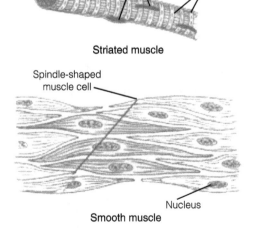

Striated muscle

Smooth muscle

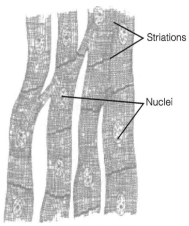

Cardiac muscle

Question 7. What is the specific function of the cardiac muscles?

Answer Specific function of cardiac muscles is rhythmic contraction and relaxation throughout life without tiring under normal conditions.

Question 8. Differentiate between striated, unstriated and cardiac muscles on the basis of their structure and site/location in the body.

Answer

Features	Striated Muscles	Unstriated Muscles	Cardiac Muscles
Structure	These are made up of long, cylindrical, unbranched and multinucleate cells.	These muscles are made up of long uninucleate cells with pointed ends.	These are made up of cells which are cylindrical branched and uninucleate.
	These show alternate light and dark striations.	These do not show striations.	These muscles show faint striations.
Site/ Location	These are located in limbs and are mostly attached to bones to help in body movement.	These are mostly present in walls of alimentary canal, blood vessels, ureters, bronchi of the lungs and in the iris of eyes.	These are present only in the walls of heart.

Question 9. Draw a labelled diagram of a neuron.

Answer

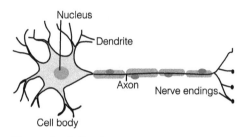

Question 10. Name the following.

(a) Tissue that forms the inner lining of our mouth.

(b) Tissue that connects muscle to bone in humans.

(c) Tissue that transports food in plants.

(d) Tissue that stores fat in our body.

(e) Connective tissue with a fluid matrix.

(f) Tissue present in the brain.

Answer

(a) Squamous epithelium   (b) Tendons

(c) Phloem   (d) Adipose tissue

(e) Blood   (f) Nervous tissue

Question 11. Identify the type of tissue in the following skin, bark of tree, bone, lining of kidney tubule and vascular bundle.

Answer

(a) Skin—Squamous epithelium.

(b) Bark of tree—Epidermal tissue with a chemical called suberin, *i.e.*, cork.

(c) Bone—Connective tissue.

(d) Lining of kidney tubule—Cubical epithelium.

(e) Vascular bundle—Conductive tissue (xylem and phloem).

Question 12. Name the regions in which parenchyma tissue is present.

Answer Parenchyma tissue is mainly found in all soft parts of the plant such as root, stem, leaves, flowers, fruits, etc. It is also present in ground tissue of petioles, mesophyll cells of leaves and in vascular bundles.

Question 13. What is the role of epidermis in plants?

Answer Role of epidermis in plants.

(i) It is protective in function.

(ii) It becomes thick and prevent water loss in plants living in very dry habitats.

(iii) These cells secrete a waxy, water-resistant layer on the outer surface which protect against loss of water, mechanical injury and infections.

(iv) Leaf epidermis have stomata to help in gas exchange and transpiration.

(v) In roots, epidermal cells help in the absorption of water.

(vi) In old plants, epidermal layer becomes thick and forms cork. Cork cells contain a chemical called suberin in their walls which makes them impervious to gases and water.

Question 14. How does the cork act as a protective tissue?

Answer Cork is made up of several layers of epidermal cells. These cells of cork are dead and compactly arranged without intercellular spaces. They also have a chemical called suberin in their walls which makes cork impervious to gases and water.

Question 15. Complete the following chart.

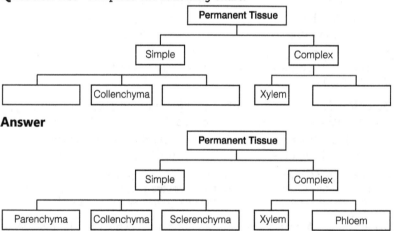

Answer

Selected NCERT Exemplar Problems

Multiple Choice Questions

Question 1. Which of the following has dead cells?
- (a) Parenchyma
- (b) Sclerenchyma
- (c) Collenchyma
- (d) Epithelial tissue

Answer (b) The sclerenchyma tissue consists of dead cells which make the plant hard and stiff. For example, husk of coconut is a sclerenchymatous tissue.

Question 2. Find out incorrect sentence.
  (a) Parenchymatous tissues have intercellular spaces.
  (b) Collenchymatous tissues are irregularly thickened at corners.
  (c) Apical and intercalary meristems are permanent tissues.
  (d) Meristematic tissues, in its early stage, lack vacuoles.

Answer (c) Apical and intercalary meristems are meristematic tissues.

Question 3. Girth of stem increases due to
  (a) apical meristem   (b) lateral meristem
  (c) intercalary meristem   (d) vertical meristem

Answer (b) Lateral meristem occurs on the sides and helps in increasing the girth of the stem.

Question 4. Which cell does not have perforated cell wall?
  (a) Tracheids   (b) Companion cells
  (c) Sieve tubes   (d) Vessels

Answer (b) Companion cells are elements of phloem. These lie on the sides of perforated sieve tubes and are associated with them through plasmodesmata.

Question 5. Intestine absorbs the digested food materials. What type of epithelial cells are responsible for that?
  (a) Stratified squamous epithelium (b) Columnar epithelium
  (c) Spindle fibres   (d) Cuboidal epithelium

Answer (b) Columnar epithelium is present in the walls of intestine. Sometimes, these cells have microvilli on their free ends to increase the absorptive surface area for the absorption of digested food materials.

Question 6. A person met with an accident in which two long bones of hand were dislocated. Which among the following may be the possible reason?
  (a) Tendon break   (b) Break of skeletal muscle
  (c) Ligament break   (d) Areolar tissue break

Answer (c) Ligaments are elastic structures which connect one bone to another.

Question 7. While doing work and running, you move your organs like hands, legs, etc. Which among the following is correct?
  (a) Smooth muscles contract and pull the ligament to move the bones
  (b) Smooth muscles contract and pull the tendons to move the bones
  (c) Skeletal muscles contract and pull the ligament to move the bones
  (d) Skeletal muscles contract and pull the tendon to move the bones

Answer (d) Tendons are strong, inelastic, white fibrous tissues that join skeletal muscles to the bones.

Question 8. Which muscles act involuntarily?
  I. Striated muscles
  II. Smooth muscles
  III. Cardiac muscles
  IV. Skeletal muslces
  (a) I and II   (b) II and III
  (c) III and IV   (d) I and IV

Answer (b) Smooth muscles are present in the walls of hollow visceral organs except heart. They occur in walls of alimentary canal, urinogenital organs, blood vessels, etc. Cardiac muscles are present only in heart. Both of these are involuntary in action.

Question 9. Meristematic tissues in plants are
  (a) localised and permanent   (b) not limited to certain regions
  (c) localised and dividing cells (d) growing in volume

Answer (c) Meristematic tissues are responsible for growth of cells. These are localized in root and shoot tips, the growth region of plant.

Question 10. Which is not a function of epidermis?
  (a) Protection from adverse condition
  (b) Gaseous exchange
  (c) Conduction of water
  (d) Transpiration

Answer (c) Conduction of water in plant is a function of a permanent tissue called xylem.

Question 11. Select the incorrect sentence.
  (a) Blood has matrix containing proteins, salts and hormones.
  (b) Two bones are connected with ligament.
  (c) Tendons are non-fibrous tissue and fragil.
  (d) Cartilage is a form of connective tissue.

Answer (c) Tendons are strong, inelastic, white fibrous tissues which join the skeletal tissues to bones.

Question 12. Cartilage is not found in
  (a) nose   (b) ear
  (c) kidney   (d) larynx

Answer (c) Cartilage is a soft, firm, flexible connective tissue. It is found mainly in nose, ear and larynx.

Question 13. Fats are stored in human body as

    (a) cuboidal epithelium   (b) adipose tissue

    (c) bones   (d) cartilage

Answer   (b) Adipose tissue is a group of several oval fat cells or adipocytes. Fat is stored in the form of adipose tissue in human body.

Question 14. Bone matrix is rich in

    (a) fluoride and calcium   (b) calcium and phosphorus

    (c) calcium and potassium   (d) phosphorus and potassium

Answer   (b) Bone matrix contains various inorganic minerals including calcium and phosphorus.

Question 15. Contractile proteins are found in

    (a) bones   (b) blood

    (c) muscles   (d) cartilage

Answer   (c) Muscles form contractile tissue made up of contractile proteins.

Question 16. Voluntary muscles are found in

    (a) alimentary canal   (b) limbs

    (c) iris of the eye   (d) bronchi of lungs

Answer   (b) Voluntary muscles are attached to bones and are responsible for voluntary movements.

Question 17. Nervous tissue is not found in

    (a) brain   (b) spinal cord

    (c) tendons   (d) nerves

Answer   (c) Tendons are a type of connective tissue. These join skeletal tissue to bones.

Question 18. Nerve cell does not contain

    (a) axon   (b) nerve endings

    (c) tendons   (d) dendrites

Answer   (c) Tendons do not belong to nervous tissue. These are connective tissues.

Question 19. Which of the following helps in repair of tissue and fills up the space inside the organ?

    (a) Tendon   (b) Adipose tissue

    (c) Areolar   (d) Cartilage

Answer   (c) Areolar tissue is a loose connective tissue. It acts as a packing tissue between the organs lying in the body cavity.

Question 20. The muscular tissue which functions throughout the life continuously without fatigue is

   (a) Skeletal muscle   (b) Cardiac muscle
   (c) Smooth muscle   (d) Voluntary muscle

Answer   (b) Cardiac muscles are exclusively present in the walls of heart. They show rhythmic contraction throughout life without fatigue.

Question 21. Which of the following cells is found in the cartilaginous tissue of the body?

   (a) Mast cells   (b) Basophils
   (c) Osteocytes   (d) Chondrocytes

Answer   (d) Chondrocytes are found in cartilaginous tissue, *i.e.*, cartilage of the body. These are living cartilage cells, present in a fluid filled space called lacunae within the matrix of cartilage.

Question 22. The dead element present in the phloem is

   (a) companion cells   (b) phloem fibres
   (c) phloem parenchyma   (d) sieve tubes

Answer   (b) Phloem fibres or bast fibres are dead sclerenchymatous fibres which provide mechanical strength.

Question 23. Which of the following does not lose their nucleus at maturity?

   (a) Companion cells   (b) Red blood cells
   (c) Vessel   (d) Sieve tube cells

Answer   (a) Companion cells contain a large elongated nucleus and dense cytoplasm. Sieve tube elements do not have nuclei. They depend on companion cells for their requirements. Thus, these two cells together form the functional unit of phloem.

Question 24. In desert plants, rate of water loss gets reduced due to the presence of

   (a) cuticle   (b) stomata   (c) lignin   (d) suberin

Answer   (a) Cuticle is a waterproof layer of a waxy substance called cutin. This protects against the loss of water.

Question 25. A long tree has several branches. The tissue that helps in the side ways conduction of water in the branches is

   (a) collenchyma
   (b) xylem parenchyma
   (c) parenchyma
   (d) xylem vessels

Answer (d) Xylem vessels are arranged in a row placed upon the other forming long tube-like structures for long distance transport. This forms a continuous system from bottom to top of the plant, for the vertical transport of water and minerals.

Question 26. If the tip of sugarcane plant is removed from the field, even then it keeps on growing in length. It is due to the presence of

(a) cambium   (b) apical meristem
(c) lateral meristem   (d) intercalary meristem

Answer (d) Intercalary meristem helps in growth of leaves and elongation of internodes.

Question 27. A nail is inserted in the trunk of a tree at a height of 1 metre from the ground level. After three years the nail will

(a) move downwards   (b) move upwards
(c) remain at the same position   (d) move sideways

Answer (c) This is because the trunk of a tree contains permanent tissue. The meristematic tissue loses its ability to divide after sometime and forms permanent tissue. So, the trunk of tree will not change and the nail will remain at the same place.

Question 28. Parenchyma cells are

(a) relatively unspecified and thin-walled
(b) thick-walled and specialised
(c) lignified
(d) None of the above

Answer (a) The parenchyma cells are living relatively unspecified and thin-walled.

Question 29. Flexibility in plants is due to

(a) collenchyma   (b) sclerenchyma
(c) parenchyma   (d) chlorenchyma

Answer Collenchyma is a living mechanical tissue which provides elasticity and flexibility to the young dicot stem.

Question 30. Cork cells are made impervious to water and gases by the presence of

(a) cellulose   (b) lipids
(c) suberin   (d) lignin

Answer (c) The suberin present in the walls of cork cells makes them impervious to gases and water. This way it protects plant from dessication, infection or mechanical injury.

Question 31. Survival of plants in terrestrial environment has been made possible by the presence of

    (a) intercalary meristem   (b) conducting tissue

    (c) apical meristem   (d) parenchymatous tissue

Answer   (c) Conducting tissues are xylem and phloem. In terrestrial plants, xylem helps in the conduction of water and phloem transports food synthesized by leaves throughout the plant body.

Question 32. Choose the wrong statement.

    (a) The nature of matrix differs according to the function of the tissue.

    (b) Fats are stored below the skin and in between the internal organs.

    (c) Epithelial tissues have intercellular spaces between them.

    (d) Cells of striated muscles are multinucleate and unbranched.

Answer   (c) The cells of epithelial tissues are tightly packed and form a continuous sheet over the entire body surface.

Question 33. The water conducting tissue generally present in gymnosperm is

    (a) vessels   (b) sieve tube

    (c) tracheids   (d) xylem fibres

Answer   (c) Tracheids are elongated dead single cells with hard lignified walls. They conduct water and do not have open ends like the vessels, so water has to pass from cell to cell *via* the pits (small unthickened areas in the cell wall).

Short Answer Type Questions

Question 34. Animals of colder regions and fishes of cold water have thicker layer of subcutaneous fat, Describe why?

Answer   The subcutaneous fat is an adipose tissue. It acts as an insulator and reduces heat loss from the body and thereby regulates the body temperature. Due to this, animals of colder regions and fishes are rich in adipose tissue.

Question 35. If a potted plant is covered with a glass jar, water vapours appear on the wall of glass jar. Explain why?

Answer   The plants continuously release water vapour by transpiration process. The stomata present in the epidermis layer of leaves regulate. This loss of water in the form of water vapours. These water vapours accumulate on the wall of glass jar.

Question 36. Water hyacinth float on water surface. Explain.

Answer In aquatic plants, large cavities are present in parenchyma which give buoyancy to the plants and help them to float in water. This kind of parenchyma is called aerenchyma.

Long Answer Type Questions

Question 37. Give reasons for

(i) Meristematic cells have a prominent nucleus and dense cytoplasm but they lack vacuole.

(ii) Intercellular spaces are absent in sclerenchymatous tissue.

(iii) We get a crunchy and granular feeling when we chew pear fruit.

(iv) Branches of a tree move and bend freely in high wind velocity.

(vi) It is difficult to pull out the husk of a coconut tree.

Answer

(i) The meristematic cells lack vacuole because they are metabolically active. They do not need vacuoles for storage.

(ii) The sclerenchymatous tissues are dead, simple permanent tissue which make the plants hard and stiff. That is why these are closely packed without any intercellular spaces.

(iii) This is due to the presence of sclerenchyma tissue in pear and guava which provides crunchiness to the fruits. This tissue makes the plant hard and stiff.

(iv) Branches of tree move and bend freely due to the presence of collenchyma tissue. It provides mechanical support and elasticity to the young stem. This leads to easy bending in various parts without breaking.

(vi) Husk of a coconut tree contains sclerenchyma tissues. These are dead cells, closely packed and without intercellular spaces. Their thick walls make the cell hard, strong and impermeable to water.

Question 38. List the characteristic of cork. How they are formed? Mention their role.

Answer Characteristics of Cork

(i) Its cells are dead and compactly arranged without intercellular spaces.

(ii) They have a chemical called suberin in their walls which makes them impervious to gases and water.

Formation of Cork

As plant grows old, the outer protective tissue, *i.e.*, epidermis undergoes certain changes. The epidermis of young stem is replaced by a strip of secondary meristem called cork cambium or phellogen. The layer of cells which is cut by cork cambium on the outer side ultimately becomes several layered thick cork.

Role of Cork

(i) It provides protection against mechanical injury, dryness, extreme temperature, etc.

(ii) Cork protects plant from harmful microorganisms.

(iii) It prevents loss of water by evaporation.

Question 39. Why are xylem and phloem called complex tissues? How are they different than others?

Answer   Both xylem and phloem consist of more than one type of cells. This feature makes them complex tissue. All these type of cells coordinate to perform a common function in plants.

S.No.	Xylem	Phloem
1.	Consists of tracheids, vessels, xylem parenchyma and xylem fibres.	Consist of sieve tubes, companion cell, phloem parenchyma and phloem fibres.
2.	They transport water and minerals vertically from soil to aerial parts of the plant.	They transport food from leaves to other parts of the plant.
3.	Most of the cells except xylem parenchyma are dead cells.	Most of the cells except phloem fibres are living cells.

Question 40. (i) Differentiate between meristematic and permanent tissues in plants.

(ii) Define the process of differentiation.

(iii) Name any two simple and two complex permanent tissues in plants.

Answer   (i)

S.No.	Meristematic	Permanent
1.	Cells of this tissue divide throughout their life.	They lose the ability to divide to take up a specific function.
2.	They are located at specific regions of the plant viz; apical, lateral, intercalary.	They are distributed throughout the plant body.
3.	Cells of this tissue are very active, have dense cytoplasm, thin walls and prominent nuclei. They lack vacuoles.	They are vacuolated, vary in shape and size. Their cell walls may be thick.
4.	Cell wall is cellulosic.	Cell wall is made up of cellulose/lignin/suberin.

(ii) The loss of ability to divide by taking up a permanent shape, size and function is called differentiation.

(iii) **Simple   permanent   tissue** Parenchyma/collenchyma/sclerenchyma. **Complex permanent** tissue Phloem/xylem.

7

Diversity in Living Organisms

Important Concepts

1. Classification is arranging the living organisms into groups or sub-groups on the basis of similarities and differences.

2. To make relevant groups, the basic characteristics are selected which explain more fundamental differences among the organisms. This helps in creating broad groups and sub-groups will be divided based on less important characteristics.

3. The basis of classification used for hierarchial classification is/are:

   (i) The presence or absence of membrane bound cell organelles including a nucleus.

      (a) The **eukaryotic cells** have membrane-bound organelles and a nucleus which allow the cellular processes to be carried out efficiently in isolation from each other.

      (b) The **prokaryotic cells** do not have a clearly demarcated nucleus and other organelles. This feature allows them to have their biochemical pathway organised in very different ways.

      (c) The nucleated cells are capable of making a multicellular organism because they can take up specialised functions.

   (ii) The presence of single cell in an organism (unicellular) or many cells grouped together (multicellular). This creates very basic difference between body designs.

(a) In single-celled organism, *e.g., Ameoba,* all the functions are carried out by a cell.

(b) In cells that grouped together to form a single organism use the principle of division of labour. These groups of cells take up specialised functions. For example, a body of worm is made up of group of cells if compared to *Ameoba.*

(iii) Ability of producing their own food (producers) or acquiring food from others (consumers). This feature would make very different body designs.

4. **Classification** and **evolution** states that the life forms will be closely related to their evolution, Due to evolution, the changes accumulate in their body design that allow them to survive better.

5. **Charles Darwin** first described this idea of evolution in 1859 the **Origin of Species.**

6. Based on the idea of evolution, some ancient group of animals are referred as 'primitive' or 'lower' groups and the relatively recent groups are called 'advanced' or 'higher' groups.

7. Evolutionary idea states that there is a possibility that complexity in design will increase over the time. Here, we can say that older organisms are simple while younger organisms are more complex.

8. **The hierarchy of classification** is based on separating organisms on the basis of hierarchy of characteristics into smaller and smaller groups.

9. **Ernst Haeckel** (1894), **Robert Whittaker** (1959) and **Carl Woese** (1977) tried to classify all the living organisms into broad categories called kingdoms.

10. Whittaker proposed five kingdoms :
    (i) Monera
    (ii) Protista
    (iii) Fungi
    (iv) Plantae
    (v) Animalia

11. This classification is based on their cell structure, mode and source of nutrition and body organisation. Whittaker's classification is widely used.

12. Woese modified it by dividing Monera into archaebacteria (archea) and eubacteria (or bacteria).

13. A brief outlines of five kingdom classification:

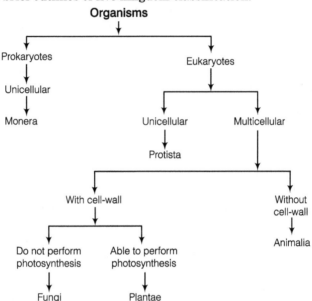

The five kingdom classification

14. Further classification is done by naming the sub-groups in various levels as given.

15. **Kingdom–Monera**

   (i) Monerans do not have a well-defined nucleus or organelles. They also do not have multicellular body designs.

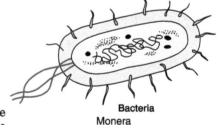

Bacteria
Monera

   (ii) Some of them have cell walls while some do not have.

   (iii) The mode of nutrition can be either synthesising their own food (autotrophic) or acquiring it from other sources (heterotrophic).

   (iv) This group includes bacteria, blue-green algae or cyanobacteria and mycoplasma.

Diversity in Living Organisms

16. **Kingdom–Protista**
    (i) This group includes many kinds of unicellular eukaryotic organisms.
    (ii) Some of them have appendages like hair-like cilia or whip-like flagella for moving around.
    (iii) These can be autotrophs or heterotrophs.
    (iv) Examples are unicellular algae, diatoms and protozoans such as *Amoeba, Paramecium, Euglena, Trypanosoma, Entamoeba,* etc.

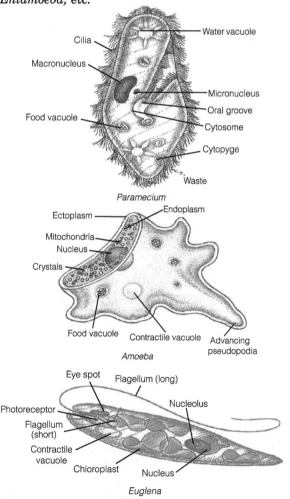

Paramecium

Amoeba

Euglena

Protozoa

17. **Kingdom–Fungi**

  (i) These are heterotrophic eukaryotic organisms.

  (ii) They are also called saprophytes as they feed on dead and decaying organic materials as food.

  (iii) Many fungi have the capacity to become multicellular organisms at certain stages in their lives.

  (iv) Their cell walls are made up of a tough complex sugar called **chitin**.

  (v) Examples are yeast and mushrooms.

  (vi) Some fungi show symbiotic relationship with blue-green algae. These symbiotic life forms are called **lichens**.

18. **Kingdom–Plantae**

  (i) These are multicellular eukaryotes with cell walls.

  (ii) They are autotrophs and use chlorophyll for the photosynthesis.

19. **Kingdom–Animalia**

  (i) These are multicellular eukaryotes without cell walls.

  (ii) They are heterotrophs.

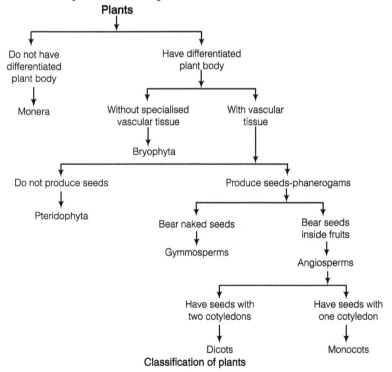

Classification of plants

20. A brief outline of classification of plants :
21. Levels of classification among plants
    (i) The first level of classification depends on whether the plant body has well-differentiated, distinct components.
    (ii) The second level is whether the differentiated plant body has special tissues for the transport of water and other substances within it.
    (iii) The third level is based on their ability to bear seeds and whether the seeds are enclosed within fruits.
22. **Thallophyta**
    (i) These plants, commonly called algae do not have well-differentiated body designs.
    (ii) These are mainly aquatic.
    (iii) Examples are *Spirogyra, Ulothrix, Cladophora* and *Chara*.

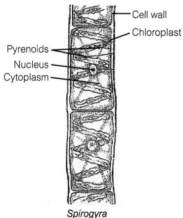

Spirogyra
Thallophyta–Algae

23. **Bryophyta**
    (i) These are called 'amphibians of plant kingdom'.
    (ii) The plant body is differentiated to form stem and leaf-like structure.
    (iii) There is no specialised tissue for the conduction of water and other substances from one part of plant body to another.
    (iv) Examples are moss (*Funaria*) and liverworts (*Marchantia* and *Riccia*).

Funaria
Bryophytes

24. **Pteridophyta**
    (i) The plant body is differentiated into roots, stem and leaves and has specialised tissue for the conduction of water and other substances from one part to another.
    (ii) Spores are present on the undersurface of leaves.
    (iii) Examples are *Marsilea*, ferns and horsetails.

Fern
Pteridophyta

Note *The thallophytes, the bryophytes and the pteridophytes have naked embryos that are called spores. The reproductive organs of plants in all these three groups are very inconspicuous, therefore they are called as 'cryptogamae' or 'both hidden reproductive organs'.*

25. **Gymnosperms** (Gr. *Gymno*–naked; *sperma*–seed)
    (i) These bear naked seeds and are usually perennial, evergreen and woody.
    (ii) Examples are *Cycas*, *Pinus* and *Deodar*, etc.

26. **Angiosperms** (Gr. *Angio*–covered; *sperma*–seed)
    (i) The seeds develop inside an organ which is modified to become a fruit.
    (ii) These are also called flowering plants.
    (iii) These have cotyledons in their seeds.
    (iv) Based on the number of cotyledons, these are divided as:
    (a) **Monocots** consist of single cotyledon.
    (b) **Dicots** consist of two cotyledons.

27. Monocots have only one cotyledon. They have fibrous root system and leaves have parallel venation. Examples are cereals, grasses, banana, onion, coconut, lily, etc.

28. Dicots have two cotyledons. They have tap root system and leaves consist of reticulate venation. Examples are mango, orange, sunflower, pulses, etc.
29. An outline of classification of animals.

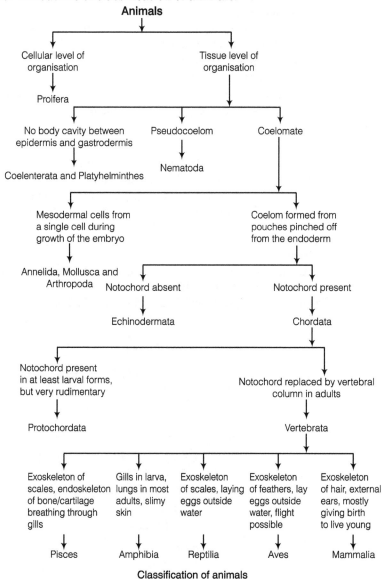

Classification of animals

30. Kingdom–Animalia have eukaryotic, multicellular and heterotrophic organisms. They are further classified based on the extent and type of body design differentiation found.

31. **Phylum–Porifera**
    (i) Porifera means pore (hole) bearing organisms.
    (ii) The pores lead to canal system that helps in circulating water to bring in food and oxygen.
    (iii) They are commonly called as sponges.
    (iv) They are mostly found in marine habitats.
    (v) The body is covered with a hard outside layer or skeleton.
    (vi) Examples are *Sycon*, *Euplectela*, *Spongilla*, etc.

32. **Phylum–Coelenterata**
    (i) These live in water.
    (ii) They show more body design differentiation.
    (iii) The body have a cavity called coelenteron.
    (iv) The body is covered with two layers of cells. One layer makes up cells on the outside of the body and the other one makes the inner lining of the body.
    (v) Some of these live in colonies (corals) while others have a solitary lifespan (*Hydra*).
    (vi) Tentacles are present around the mouth which contain special stringing cells called **cnidoblasts**.
    (vii) Examples are *Hydra*, jellyfish and sea anemone.

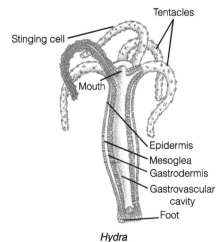

Hydra

33. Phylum–Platyhelminthes (Flatworms).

(i) The body of animals in this group is bilaterally symmetrical (left and right halves of the body have same design).

(ii) The body is triploblastic, *i.e.,*there are three layers of cells from which differentiated tissues can be made. This allows outside and inside body linings as well as some organs to be made.

(iii) There is some degree of tissue formation. However, there is no true internal body cavity or coelom in which well developed organs can be accomodated.

(iv) The body is flattened dorsiventrally (from top to bottom), that is why these animals are called **flatworms**.

(v) They are either free living or parasitic.

(vi) Some examples are *Planaria*, liverfluke and tape worm, etc.

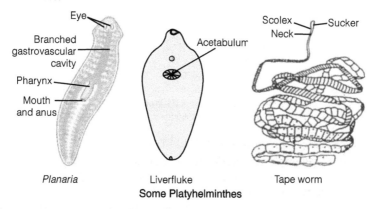

Planaria   Liverfluke   Tape worm

Some Platyhelminthes

34. Phylum–Nematoda (Round or Thread Worms)

(i) Their body is bilaterally symmetrical and triploblastic. However, the body is cylindrical rather than flattened.

(ii) There are tissues but no real organs. A sort of body cavity or **pseudocoelom** is present.

(iii) These are commonly known as parasitic worms causing diseases, such as elephantiasis (filarial worms) or the worms in the intestines (round worm or pinworms).

35. Phylum–Annelida (Segmented Worms)

(i) Annelids are also bilaterally symmetrical and triploblastic but, in addition they have a true body cavity. This allows true organs to be packaged in the body structure.

(ii) There is extensive organ differentiation. This differentiation occurs in segmental fashion, with the segments lined up one after the other from head to tail.

(iii) These are found in habitats like freshwater, marine water as well as land.

(iv) Example are earthworms, *Nereis* and leechs.

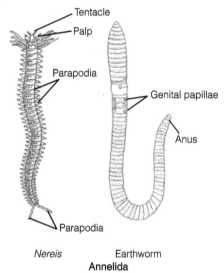

Nereis   Earthworm
Annelida

36. **Phylum–Arthropoda** (Jointed Legs)

(i) This phylum includes largest group of animals.

(ii) These animals have bilaterally symmetrical and segmented body.

(iii) There is an open circulatory system present so that blood does not flow in well defined blood vessels.

(iv) The coelomic cavity is blood-filled called haemocoel.

(v) They have jointed legs.

(vi) Examples are prawns, butterflies, houseflies, spiders, scorpions, centipedes and crabs.

37. **Phylum–Mollusca** (Soft-Bodied Animals)

(i) The animals belonging to this phylum have bilateral symmetry.

(ii) The coelomic cavity is reduced.

(iii) There is little segmentation.

(iv) They have an open circulatory system and kidney-like organs for excretion.

(v) They have a foot that is used for moving around.

(vi) Examples are *Octopus*, chiton, snails and mussels.

38. **Phylum–Echinodermata** (Spiny-Skinned Animals)

(i) These are exclusively free living marine animals.

(ii) They are triploblastic and have a coelomic cavity.

(iii) They also have a peculiar water-driven tube system that have used for moving around.

(iv) They have hard calcium carbonate structures that they use as a skeleton.

(v) Examples are starfish, sea urchin, sea cucumber, feather star, etc.

39. **Phylum–Protochordata**

(i) These animals are bilaterally symmetrical, triploblastic and have a coelom.

(ii) They show a new feature of body design, namely a notochord, at least at some stages during their lives.

(iii) They are marine animals.

(iv) Respiration is through gill slits.

(v) Examples are *Balanoglossus, Herdemania* and *Amphioxus*.

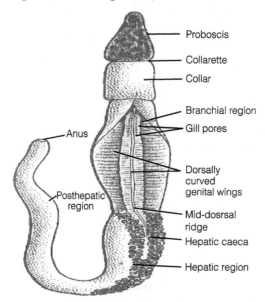

A protochordata : *Balanoglossus*

40. **Phylum–Vertebrata**

   (i) These animals have a true vertebral column and internal skeleton, it allows a completely different distribution of muscle attachment points to be used for movement.

   (ii) Vertebrates are bilaterally symmetrical, triploblastic, coelomic and segmented with complex differentiation of body tissues and organs.

   Note *All chordates possess following features :*
   (i) They have a notochord and a dorsal nerve cord.
   (ii) They are triploblastic.
   (iii) They have paired gill pouches and are coelomate.

41. Vertebrates are grouped into following five classes :

   (i) Pisces   (ii) Amphibia   (iii) Reptilia

   (iv) Aves   (v) Mammalia

42. **Class–Pisces**

   (i) Pisces comprise fishes which are exclusively aquatic animals.

   (ii) Their skin is covered with scales/plates.

   (iii) They obtain oxygen dissolved in water by using gills.

   (iv) The body is streamlined and a muscular tail is used for movement.

   (v) They are cold-blooded and their hearts have only two chambers.

   (vi) They lay eggs.

   (vii) The skeleton of some fishes is entirely made of cartilage such as sharks and of some made of both bone and cartilage, such as tuna or rohu.

   (viii) Some examples of pisces are scoliodon (dog fish), electric ray, sting ray, angler fish, rohu, sea horse, *Anabas*, etc.

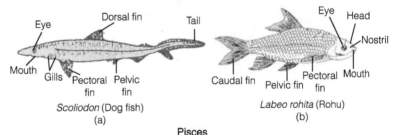

Scoliodon (Dog fish) — Eye, Dorsal fin, Tail, Mouth, Gills, Pectoral fin, Pelvic fin
(a)

Labeo rohita (Rohu) — Eye, Head, Nostril, Mouth, Pectoral fin, Pelvic fin, Caudal fin
(b)

Pisces

43. **Class–Amphibia**

   (i) These animals do not have scales but have mucus glands in the skin.

(ii) Heart is three-chambered.

(iii) Respiration is through either gills or lungs.

(iv) They lay eggs.

(v) These inhabit both land and water.

(vi) Examples are common frog, *Hyla* load and salamander, etc.

44. **Class–Reptilia**

(i) These are cold-blooded animals, have scales and breathe through lungs.

(ii) Most of them have three-chambered heart, except crocodiles have four-chambers in heart.

(iii) They lay eggs with tough coverings and do not need to lay their eggs in water, unlike amphibians.

(iv) For example, snakes, turtles, lizards and crocodiles.

45. **Class–Aves**

(i) These are warm-blooded animals and have four-chambered heart.

(ii) They lay eggs.

(iii) There is an outside covering of feathers and two forelimbs are modified for flight.

(iv) They breathe through lungs.

(v) Examples are all birds, such as ostrich, sparrow, crow, pigeon, etc.

46. **Class–Mammalia**

(i) Mammals are warm-blooded animals.

(ii) They have four-chambered heart.

(iii) They have mammary glands for the production of milk to nourish their young.

(iv) The skin is covered with hairs, sweat and oil glands.

(v) They produce young ones. However, a few of them like platypus and echidna lay eggs and some like kangaroos give birth to very poorly developed young ones.

(vi) Examples of mammals are dog, cat, rat, bat, human, etc.

47. **Nomenclature** is a system of giving scientific names to the plants and animals. The scientific name of an organism is the result of the process of classification which puts it along with organisms it is most related to. But, when we actually name the species, we do not list the whole hierarchy of groups it belongs to. Instead, we only write the name of the genus and species of that particular organism. Both these names will be used in Latin forms.

48. Certain conventions are followed while writing the scientific names:
    (i) The name of the genus begins with a capital letter.
    (ii) The name of the species begins with a small letter.
    (iii) When printed, the scientific name is given in italics.
    (iv) When written by hand, the genus name and the species name have to be underlined separately.

49. **Carolus Linnaeus**, The Father of Taxonomy proposed the binomial nomenculature. In this system, the name of every organism is composed of two components, the first one is genus (generic name) and second is the species (specific name).

    For example, man is known as *Homo sapiens*. *Homo* is the genus and *sapiens* is the species. Linnaeus classified all organisms into two kingdoms—the plant kingdom and animal kingdom. Eichler (1883) further divided plant kingdom into two sub-kingdoms–Cryptogamae and Phanerogamae.

Intext Questions

On Page 80

Question 1. Why do we classify organisms?

Answer There are several variety of living things on the Earth. It is not easy to study all of them one by one. For this, we keep them in different groups based on similarities and differences. This make their study systematic, easy and quick. Thus, the method of placing living organisms into groups or sub-groups on the basis of similarities and differences is called classification.

Question 2. Give three examples of the range of variations that you see in life forms around you.

Answer We can see following range of variations in different life forms :
  (i) **Variation in size** The bacteria are so small in size that they cannot be seen without observing under microscope. On the other hand, blue whale and red wood trees of California are such a giant living structures.
  (ii) **Variation in lifespan** The insects like fruit flies live for few hours while some trees-like pine live for several years.
  (iii) **Variations in body colours** Some living things are colourless, such as worms, whereas birds, insects, flowers are colourful.

On Page 82

Question 1. Which do you think is a more basic characteristic for classifying organisms?

(i) The place where they live.

(ii) The kind of cells they are made of why?

Answer The basic characteristic for all living organisms is the kind of cells they are made of. This is because :

(i) All eukaryotic cells have membrane-bound organelles. These have a nucleus which controls the cellular processes to be carried out systematically.

(ii) These cells grow and become multicellular organisms and take up their specific functions.

Question 2. What is the primary characteristic on which the first division of organisms is made?

Answer The primary characteristic on which first division of organisms is based on whether the cells occur singly (unicellular) or they are grouped together and function as individual group (multicellular).

Question 3. On what bases are plants and animals put into different categories?

Answer Plants can make their own food, whereas animals cannot. Their body designs are also different based on this characteristic. So, they are put into different categories.

On Page 83

Question 1. Which organisms are called primitive and how are they different from the so called advanced organisms?

Answer The organisms which have ancient body designs that have not changed much are called **primitive organisms** or **lower organisms**. These are simple life forms. On the other hand, the organisms that have acquired their particular body designs relatively recently, they are called **advanced organisms** or **higher organisms**. These are more complex life forms.

Question 2. Will advanced organisms be the same as complex organisms? Why?

Answer The advanced organisms will be the same as complex organisms. This is because there is a possibility that complexity in design will increase over evolutionary time.

On Page 85

Question 1. What is the criterion for classification of organisms as belonging to kingdom– Monera and Protista?

Answer **Kingdom–Monera**
(i) These organisms do not have a well-defined nucleus or cell organelles.
(ii) They do not have multicellular body.
(iii) Cell wall is present in some of them only.
(iv) The mode of nutrition can be autotrophic or heterotrophic.
(v) The organisms belong to Monera are bacteria, blue-green algae and mycoplasma.

Kingdom–Protista
(i) The kingdom–Protista includes many kinds of unicellular eukaryotic organisms.
(ii) Their mode of nutrition can be autotrophic or heterotrophic.
(iii) The organisms have appendages like cilia or flagella for the movement.
(iv) The organisms belong to Protista are algae, diatoms and protozoans.

Question 2. In which kingdom will you place an organism which is single celled, eukaryotic and photosynthetic?

Answer Kingdom–Protista.

Question 3. In the hierarchy of classification, which grouping will have the smallest number of organisms with a maximum common characteristics and which will have the largest number of organisms?

Answer In the hierarchy of classification, the **species** is the grouping which will have the smallest number of organisms with a maximum of characteristics in common. The grouping which will have the largest number of organisms with a maximum characteristics common is **kingdom**.

On Page 88

Question 1. Which division among plants has the simplest organisms?

Answer The division 'Thallophyta' of plant kingdom has the simplest organisms. These oranisms do not have well-differentiated body design.

Question 2. How are pteridophytes different from the phanerogams?

Answer Differences between pteridophytes and phanerogams

S.No.	Pteridophytes	Phanerogams
1.	These include ferns, *Marsilea* and horse tails.	This group includes gymnosperms and angiosperms.
2.	They have hidden reproductive organs. So, also called as cryptogams.	They have well-differentiated reproductive tissues.
3.	They have naked embryos.	They have embryo along with stored food that are called seeds.

Question 3. How do gymnosperms and angiosperms differ from each other?

Answer Differences between gymnosperms and Agiosperms

S.No.	Gymnosperms	Angiosperms
1.	The plants of this group bear naked seeds.	The plants of this group bear seeds enclosed inside an organ which further becomes a fruit.
2.	The plant embryo contains many cotyledons.	Cotyledons present are only one or two.
3.	Plants are usually perennial, evergreen and woody.	Plants may be annual, biennial, perennial, woody or non-woody.

On Page 94

Question 1. How do poriferan animals differ from coelenterate animals?

Answer Differences between poriferan and coelenterate animals

S.No.	Poriferan Animals	Coelenterate Animals
1.	These organisms have holes (pores) over their body.	These organisms have body cavity called coelenteron with a single opening.
2.	Their body is made up of single layer of cells.	Their body is made up of two layer of cells.
3.	The body design of these animals have very minimum differentiation and division into tissues.	They show more body design differentiation.
4.	These have a characteristic canal system to helps in circulating water throughout the body to bring in food and oxygen.	These have a characteristic feature of cavity in the body.
5.	These are non-motile attached to some solid support.	Some of these live in colories (e.g., corals) while some have solitary lifespan (Hydra).

Question 2. How do annelid animals differ from arthropods?

Answer Differences between annelids and arthropods

S.No.	Annelids	Arthropods
1.	The body is segmented, lined up one after the other from head to tail. This is called metameric segmentation.	Their body also have segments but lack complete metameric segmentation.
2.	The true body cavity called 'coelom' is present.	The body cavity is present. It contains blood, so called 'haemocoel'.
3.	These are also called segmented worms.	These are commonly called 'animals with jointed legs'.
4.	Breathing occurs through the skin.	Breathing by gill, trachea, book lungs, etc.
5.	A majority of annelids are hermaphrodites.	Sexes are separate.
6.	Example–Earthworm, Nereis, etc.	Examples–Crab, prawn, housefly, etc.

Question 3. What are the differences between amphibians and reptiles?

Answer Differences between amphibians and Reptiles

S.No.	Amphibians	Reptiles
1.	These are aquatic or terrestial.	These have terrestrial habitat.
2.	They breathe through lungs or gills.	They breathe only through lungs.
3.	They have smooth, slimy, non-scaly exoskeleton.	Their body is covered by waterproof scaly exoskeleton.
4.	Heart is three-chambered.	Heart is three chambered (except crocodiles).
5.	Their eggs are without coverings.	Their eggs have tough coverings.
6.	Exampels – Frog, food, newt, etc.	Examples – Wall, lizard, snakes crocodiles, etc.

Question 4. What are the differences between animals belonging to the Aves group and those in the mammalia group?

Answer Differences between Aves and Mammalia

S.No.	Aves	Mammalia
1.	The body is covered with feathers.	Their body is covered by skin with hair.
2.	The forelimbs are modified for flight.	The forelimbs are modified for climbing or for some other purposes.
3.	Mammary glands are absent.	Mammary glands are present. These produce milk to feed their young ones.
4.	Bones are light and hollow.	Bones are solid, hard and filled with bone marrow.
5.	They lay eggs (oviparous).	They produce young ones (viviparous). However, platypus and echidna lay eggs and some like Kangaroos give birth to very poorly developed young ones.

Exercises

Question 1. What are the advantages of classifying organisms?

Answer Advantages of classification
  (i) It gives information regarding the diversity of plants and animals.
  (ii) It makes the study convenient of wide variety of organisms.
  (iii) It helps to understand the pattern of evolution.
  (iv) If forms the basis for the development of other biological sciences like Ecology, Biogeography, Biochemistry and other disciplines of Biology.

Question 2. How would you choose between two characteristics to be used for developing a hierarchy in classification?

Answer The characteristics taken for developing a hierarchy in classification are :

(i) The cell has membrane-bound organelles or without membrane. Because this could lead to different biochemical pathway influencing every aspect of cell design.

(ii) The cells occur singly or they are in groups. This leads to very basic difference in basic body organisation of organisms.

(iii) The organisms are autotrophs (make their own food) or heterotrophs (acquire food from others).

These are the basis of developing hierarchy in classifying organisms.

Question 3. Explain the basis for grouping organisms into five kingdoms.

Answer The basis for grouping organisms into five kingdoms depends on their

(i) Cell shape and structure

(ii) Body organisation

(iii) Mode of nutrition

Question 4. What are the major divisions in the Plantae? What is the basis for these divisions?

Answer Major divisions of kingdom–Plantae are :

(i) Thallophyta

(ii) Bryophyta

(iii) Pteridophyta

(iv) Gymnosperms

(v) Angiosperms

Basis of divisions in Plantae

(i) Well-differentiated plant body with distinct parts.

(ii) Presence of special tissues for the transport of water and other substances.

(iii) Ability to bear seeds.

(iv) Seeds are enclosed within fruits or not.

Question 5. How are the criteria for deciding divisions in plants different from the criteria for deciding the sub-groups among animals?

Answer The body design of plants is very different than animals. The plants have body design based on their need to prepare their own food, whereas animals obtain their food from plants and animals. Hence, in animals other body features like presence of skeleton, etc., is used to make sub-groups rather than making broad groups. Both plants and animals have different body designs so the criteria for deciding divisions in sub-groups is totally different from animals.

Question 6. Explain how animals in Vertebrata are classified into futher sub-groups.

Answer Characteristics for classifying bacteria into further sub-groups (classes) :

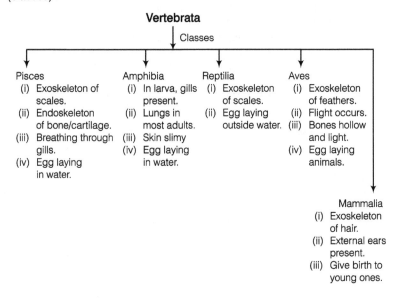

Vertebrata

↓ Classes

Pisces
(i) Exoskeleton of scales.
(ii) Endoskeleton of bone/cartilage.
(iii) Breathing through gills.
(iv) Egg laying in water.

Amphibia
(i) In larva, gills present.
(ii) Lungs in most adults.
(iii) Skin slimy
(iv) Egg laying in water.

Reptilia
(i) Exoskeleton of scales.
(ii) Egg laying outside water.

Aves
(i) Exoskeleton of feathers.
(ii) Flight occurs.
(iii) Bones hollow and light.
(iv) Egg laying animals.

Mammalia
(i) Exoskeleton of hair.
(ii) External ears present.
(iii) Give birth to young ones.

Selected NCERT Exemplar Problems

Multiple Choice Questions

Question 1. Find out incorrect sentences.
(a) Protista includes unicellular eukaryotic organisms.
(b) Whittaker considered cell structure, mode and source of nutrition for classifying the organisms in five kingdoms.
(c) Both Monera and Protista may be autotrophic and heterotrophic.
(d) Monerans have well-defined nucleus.

Answer (d) Monerans do not have a defined nucleus or cell organelles.

Question 2. Which among the following has specialised tissue for conduction of water?

(i) Thallophyta   (ii) Bryophyta
(iii) Pteridophyta   (iv)Gymnosperms
  (a) (i) and (ii)   (b) (ii) and (iii)
  (c) (iii) and (iv)   (d) (i) and (iv)

Answer (c) The plants of these groups have differentiated body into roots, stem, leaves and have specialised tissue (xylem) for the conduction of water.

Question 3. Which among the following produce seeds?

  (a) Thallophyta   (b) Bryophyta
  (c) Pteridophyta   (d) Gymnosperms

Answer (d) The gymnosperms produce naked seeds. The thallophytes, bryophytes and pteridophytes have naked embryo called spores.

Question 4. Which one is a true fish?

  (a) Jellyfish   (b) Starfish   (c) Dogfish   (d) Silverfish

Answer (c) Dogfish (*Scoliodon*) belongs to the class–Pisces, so it is a true fish.

Question 5. Which among the following is exclusively marine?

  (a) Porifera   (b) Echinodermata
  (c) Mollusca   (d) Pisces

Answer (b) Echinoderms are exclusively free-living marine animals.

Question 6. Which among the following have open circulatory system?

(i) Arthropoda   (ii) Mollusca
(iii) Annelida   (iv) Coelenterata
  (a) (i) and (ii)   (b) (iii) and (iv)
  (c) (i) and (iii)   (d) (ii) and (iv)

Answer (a) Arthropoda and Mollusca have an open circulatory system so the blood does not flow in well-defined vessels.

Question 7. In which group of animals, coelom is filled with blood?

  (a) Arthropoda   (d) Annelida
  (c) Nematoda   (d) Echinodermata

Answer (a) In Arthropoda, body cavity is reduced and filled with blood called haemocoel.

Question 8. Elephantiasis is caused by

  (a) *Wuchereria*   (b) pinworm
  (c) planarians   (d) liver flukes

Answer (a) *Wuchereria* is a filaria worm which belongs to phylum–Nematoda. It is a parasitic worm causes elephantiasis in humans.

Question 9. Which one is the most striking or (common) character of the vertebrates?

  (a) Presence of notochord
  (b) Presence of triploblastic condition
  (c) Presence of gill pouches
  (d) Presence of coelom

Answer (a) The striking feature of vertebrates is presence of notochord. The bones called vertebrae develop around the notochord and the nerve cord.

Question 10. Which among the following have scales?

  (i) Amphibians   (ii) Pisces
 (iii) Reptiles   (iv) Mammals
    (a) (i) and (iii)   (b) (iii) and (iv)
    (c) (ii) and (iii)   (d) (i) and (ii)

Answer (c) Class–Pisces and Reptiles have scales. The amphibians and mammals have skin as an outermost covering.

Question 11. Find out the false statement.

  (a) Aves are warm blooded, egg laying and have four-chambered heart.
  (b) Aves have feather covered body, fore limbs are modified as wing and breathe through lungs.
  (c) Most of the mammals are viviparous.
  (d) Fishes, amphibians and reptiles are oviparous.

Answer (d) Fishes, amphibians and reptiles lay eggs, so they are oviparous.

Question 12. Pteridophyta do not have

  (a) root   (b) stem
  (c) flowers   (d) leaves

Answer (c) Pteridophytes do not have roots, stems and leaves. They are not flowering plants.

Question 13. Identify a member of Porifera

(a) *Spongilla*   (b) *Euglena*   (c) *Penicillium*   (d) *Hydra*

Answer   (a) *Spongilla* belongs to Porifera. *Euglena* is a protozoan, *Penicillum* is a fungi and *Hydra* is a coelentrate.

Question 14. Which is not an aquatic animal?

(a) *Hydra*   (b) Jelly fish   (c) Corals   (d) Filaria

Answer   (d) Filaria (*Wuchereria*) is a parasitic worm which belongs to Nematoda.

Question 15. Amphibians do not have the follwoing

(a) three-chambered heart   (b) gills or lungs
(c) scales   (d) mucus glands

Answer   (c) Amphibians have moist skin which also helps in gas exchange in aquatic habitats.

Question 16. Organisms without nucleus and cell organelles belongs to

(i) fungi   (ii) Protista
(iii) cyanobacteria   (iv) archaebacteria
  (a) (i) and (ii)   (b) (iii) and (iv)
  (c) (i) and (iv)   (d) (ii) and (iii)

Answer   (b) Cyanobacteria and archae bacteria belongs to Monera. Monerans do not have a defined nucleus and cell organelles.

Question 17. Which of the following is not a criterian for classification of living organisms?

(a) Body design of the organism
(b) Ability to produce one's own food
(c) Membrane bound nucleus and cell organelles
(d) Height of the plant

Answer   (d) Height is not a basic differentiating characteristic in living organisms.

Question 18. The feature that is not a characteristic of protochordata?

(a) Presence of notochord
(b) Bilateral symmetry and coelom
(c) Jointed legs
(d) Presence of circulatory system

Answer   (c) Jointed legs is a characteristic of phylum–Arthropoda.

Question 19. The locomotory organs of Echinodermata are
- (a) tube feet
- (b) muscular feet
- (c) jointed legs
- (d) parapodia

Answer   (a) Tube feet are used for the movement in echinoderms.

Question 20. Corals are
- (a) Poriferans attached to some solid support
- (b) Cnidarians, that are solitary living
- (c) Poriferans present at the sea bed
- (d) Cnidarians that live in colonies

Answer   (d) Cnidarians are aquatic; solitary and colonial forms.

Question 21. Who introduced the system of scientific nomenclature of organisms?
- (a) Robert Whittaker
- (b) Carolus Linnaeus
- (c) Robert Hooke
- (d) Ernst Haeckel

Answer   (b) Carolus Linnaeus introduced the binomial system of nomenclature in 1812 century.

Question 22. Two-chambered heart occurs in
- (a) crocodiles
- (b) fish
- (c) aves
- (d) amphibians

Answer   (b) Fish have two-chambers, amphibians have three-chambers, crocodiles and aves have four-chambers in their heart.

Question 23. Skeleton is made entirely of cartilage in
- (a) sharks
- (b) tuna
- (c) rohu
- (d) None of these

Answer   (a) Sharks are cartilaginous fish belonging to the sub-class–Chondrichthyes of class–Pisces.

Question 24. One of the following is not an annelid
- (a) *Nereis*
- (b) Earthworm
- (c) leech
- (d) urchins

Answer   (d) Urchins belong to Echinodermata.

Question 25. The book *Systema Naturae* was written by
- (a) Linnaeus
- (b) Haeckel
- (c) Whittaker
- (d) Robert Brown

Answer   (a) *Systema Naturae* was written by Linnaeus from which all the fundamental taxonomical researches have taken of.

Question 26. Karl Von Linne was involved with which branch of science?

(a) Morphology (b) Taxonomy (c) Physiology (d) Medicine

Answer (b) Karl Von Linne or Carolus Linnaeus was involve with Taxonomy. Taxonomy is a branch of science which deals with the classification of living organisms.

Question 27. Real organs are absent in

(a) Mollusca (b) Coelenterata
(c) Arthropoda (d) Echinodermata

Answer (b) These animals have cavity in body. Their body is with no head and segmentation. The body is diploblastic. One layer makes up cells on the outside of the body and the other makes the inner lining of the body. These lack real organs.

Question 28. Hard calcium carbonate structures are used as skeleton by

(a) Echinodermata (b) Protochordata
(c) Arthropoda (d) Nematoda

Answer (a) Echinoderms have hard, calcareous exoskeleton. For example, starfish.

Question 29. Differentiation in segmental fashion occurs in

(a) Leech (b) Starfish (c) Snails (d) *Ascaris*

Answer (a) In leech (annelid), body is metamerically segmented, *i.e.*, a series of similar segments.

Question 30. In taxonomic hierarchy family, comes between

(a) Class and Order (b) Order and Genus
(c) Genus and Species (d) Divison and Class

Answer (a) In hierarchial classification, family comes between order and genus.

Question 31. Five-kingdom classification has given by

(a) Morgan (b) R Whittaker
(c) Linnaeus (d) Haeckel

Answer (b) R. Whittaker (1959) proposed the five kingdom system of classification.

Question 32. Well-defined nucleus is absent in

(a) Blue-green algae (b) Diatoms
(c) Algae (d) Yeast

Answer (a) Blue-green algae belong to the kingdom–Monera which lack a well-defined nucleus.

Question 33. The *'Origin of Species'* is written by

(a) Linnaeus　　(b) Darwin　　(c) Haeckel　　(d) Whittaker

Answer (b) Charles Darwin (1859) wrote '*Origin of Species*' in which he described the idea of evolution of living organisms.

Question 34. Meena and Hari observed an animal in their garden. Hari called it an insect while Meena said it was an earthworm. Choose the character from the following which confirms that it is an insect.

(a) Bilateral symmetrical body　　(b) Body with jointed legs
(c) Cylindrical body　　(d) Body with little segmentation

Answer (b) Body with jointed legs is present in insects. Insects belong to the phylum–Arthropoda.

Short Answer Type Questions

Question 35. Classify the following organisms based on the absence/presence of true coelom (*i.e.,* acoelomate, pseudocoelomate and coelomate).

> *Spongilla,* Sea anemone, *Planaria* and Liverfluke
> *Wuchereria, Ascaris, Nereis,* Earthworm
> Scorpion, Birds, Fishes and Horse

Answer *Spongilla,* sea anemone, *Planaria* and liverfluke are coelomates. *Wuchereria* is a peudocoelomate. *Nereis,* scorpion, earthworm, birds, fishes and horses are coelomates.

Long Answer Type Questions

Question 36. Thallophyta, Bryophyta and Pteridophyta are called as 'cryptogams'. Gymnosperms and angiosperms are called as 'phanerogams'. Discuss why? Draw one example of Gymnosperm.

Answer The Thallophyta, Bryophyta and Pteridophyta are called 'cryptogams' because the reproductive organs of these groups are inconspicuous or hidden. Seeds are absent. On the other hand, 'phanerogams' include gymnosperms and angiosperms which have well-differentiated reproductive tissue and the embryo with stored food. Embyro develops into seed.

Pinus   *Cycas*

Question 37. Define the terms and give one example of each.

(i) Bilateral symmetry   (ii) Coelom

(iii) Triploblastic

Answer

(i) **Bilateral Symmetry** The left and right halves of the body have same design in bilaterally symmetrical organims, *e.g.,* liverfluke.

(ii) **Coelom** It is an internal body cavity between visceral organs and body wall in which well-developed organ can be accomodated, *e.g.,* butterfly.

(iii) **Triploblastic** Animals having three layers of cells from which differentiated tissue can be made are called triploblasitc *e.g.,* starfish.

Question 38. You are given leech, *Nereis, Scolopendra,* prawn and scorpion; and all have segmented body organisation. Will you classify them in one group? If no, give the important characters based on which you will separate these organisms into different groups.

Answer The organisms given here do not belong to the same group. Leech and *Nereis* belong to phylum–Annelida because they have metamerically segmented body *i.e.,* body is divided into many segments internally by septa.

Body segments are lined up one after the other from head to tail. *Scolopendra,* prawn and scorpion belong to the phylum–Arthropoda as these have jointed legs and open circulatory system.

Question 39. Which organism is more complex and evolved among bacteria, mushroom and mango tree. Give reasons.

Answer Mango tree is a eukaryote, multicellular, autotrophic, terrestrial with covered seeds. So, it is more complex. The bacteris is a unicellular prokaryote and fungi are heterotrophic, simple thallophyte with no body differentiation in tissues. So, both of these are simple organisms.

Question 40. Differentiate between flying lizard and bird. Draw the diagram.

Answer Differences between flying lizard and bird

S.No.	Flying Lizard	Bird
1.	It belongs to group–Reptilia.	It belongs to Aves.
2.	It is cold-blooded.	Warm-blooded.
3.	Body is covered with scales.	Body is covered with feathers.
4.	It has three-chambered heart.	Heart is four-chambered in birds.

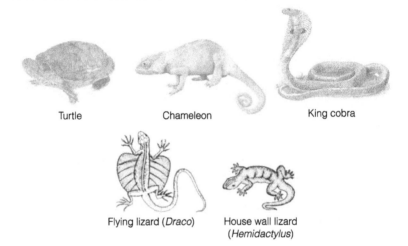

Turtle   Chameleon   King cobra

Flying lizard (*Draco*)   House wall lizard (*Hemidactylus*)

Question 41. List out some common features in cat, rat and bat.

Answer Bat, rat and cat belong to the class–Mammalia and have following common features.
  (i) All have notochord at some stage of life cycle.
  (ii) All are warm-blooded.
  (iii) All have four-chambered heart.
  (iv) All have skin covered with hair and wilth sweat and oil glands.

Question 42. Why do we keep both snake and turtle in the same class?

Answer Both snake and turtle are kept in same class, because both
  (i) are cold-blooded.
  (ii) have scales as outer covering.
  (iii) have lungs for breathing.
  (iv) have three-chambered heart.
  (v) lay eggs with tough outer covering.

8

Motion

Important Concepts

1. **Motion** An object is said to be in motion if its position changes with time.

   Motion is a relative term, an object may appear to be moving for one person but can be stationary for other person.

2. **Describing Motion** Motion of an object is always described with respect to a reference point which is called origin.

   Note *The point from which the motion of the object is to be observed, is called origin.*

3. **Terms Required to Describe Motion**

   (i) **Distance** The total length of the path covered by a moving object is called distance.

   - Distance is a scalar quantity, it require only magnitude for representation.
   - SI unit of distance is 'metre (m)'.
   - Distance covered by a moving object can never be zero.
   - Distance covered by a moving object is always positive.

     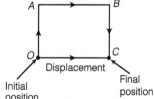

   e.g., An object starts from point O and reaches to C through A and B.

   In this case, distance travelled by the object $= OA + AB + BC$

(ii) **Displacement** The shortest distance between the initial and final position of the moving object is called the **displacement** of the object.

- Displacement is a vector quantity, it requires both magnitude and direction for representation.
- SI unit of displacement is 'metre (m)'.
- If the object comes back to its initial position, then displacement of the object is zero.
- Displacement of the object can be positive and negative both.
- In the given figure in part (i), displacement $= C$

Note *Displacement of a moving object can never be greater than the distance travelled by it.*

$$Displacement \le Distance$$

$$\therefore \quad \frac{Displacement}{Distance} \le 1$$

i.e., ratio of displacement and distance is always less than or equal to 1.

4. **Uniform Motion and Non-Uniform Motion**

(i) If an object covers equal distances in equal intervals of time, then its motion is said to be **uniform motion**.

(ii) If an object covers unequal distance in equal intervals of time, then its motion is said to be **non-uniform motion**.

5. **Rate of Motion**

The ratio of distance travelled by an object and time taken is called the **rate of motion**.

Different objects may take different amounts of time to cover a given distance.

6. **Terms Required to Measure the Rate of Motion**

(i) **Speed** Speed of an object is defined as the distance travelled by it per unit time.

$$\text{Speed} = \frac{\text{Distance}}{\text{Time}} \text{ or } s = \frac{D}{t}$$

- Speed is a scalar quantity.
- SI unit of speed is metre per second (ms^{-1} or m/s). Other units of speed are cms^{-1}, kmh^{-1} etc.
- Speed can never be zero.
- Speed is always positive.

(ii) **Uniform Speed (Constant Speed)** If a moving object covers equal distances in equal intervals of time, then its speed is said to be **uniform speed**.

(iii) **Non-Uniform Speed** If a moving object covers unequal distances in equal intervals of time, then its speed is said to be **non-uniform**.

(iv) **Average Speed** It is defined as the ratio of the total distance travelled by the object and total time taken.

$$\text{Average speed} = \frac{\text{Total distance travelled}}{\text{Total time taken}}$$

(v) **Instantaneous Speed** The speed of an object at any instant during its motion is called **instantaneous speed**. The speedometer of a vehicle indicates the instantaneous speed of the vehicle.

(vi) **Velocity** Velocity of an object is defined as the displacement of the object per unit time.

$$\text{Velocity} = \frac{\text{Displacement}}{\text{Time}}$$

$$v = \frac{\vec{\mathbf{D}}}{t}$$

- Velocity is a vector quantity.
- SI unit of velocity is ms^{-1}.
- Velocity of an object can be zero, positive or negative.
- Velocity of an object can be changed by changing the object's speed, direction of motion or both.

(vii) **Uniform or Constant Velocity** If an object covers equal displacements in equal intervals of time, then its velocity is said to be uniform or constant velocity.

(viii) **Non-Uniform or Variable Velocity** If an object covers unequal displacement in equal intervals of time, then its velocity is said to be non-uniform or variable velocity.

(ix) **Average Veloci`ty** It is defined as the ratio of total displacement of the object and total time taken.

$$\text{Average velocity} = \frac{\text{Total displacement}}{\text{Total time taken}}$$

If velocity of the object changes at a uniform rate, then

$$\text{Average velocity} = \frac{\text{Initial velocity} + \text{Final velocity}}{2}$$

$$v_{\text{av}} = \frac{u + v}{2}$$

where, u is initial velocity and v is final velocity.

Note 1. *If a body is moving in a single straight line, then the magnitude of its speed and velocity will be equal.*
2. *Average speed of an object can never be zero, but the average velocity of a moving object can be zero.*

7. **Rate of Change of Velocity : Acceleration**
The change in velocity per unit time is called the acceleration

$$\text{Acceleration} = \frac{\text{Change in velocity}}{\text{Time taken}}$$

If a body starts with velocity u and after time t its velocity become v, then acceleration $a = \dfrac{v-u}{t}$

Acceleration is a vector quantity. Its SI unit is m s^{-2}.

(i) **Positive Acceleration** If the velocity of an object increases with time in the direction of motion, then the acceleration of the object is said to be positive.

(ii) **Negative Acceleration** If the velocity of an object decreases with time, then the acceleration of the object is said to be negative. Negative acceleration is also called **retardation**.

Note *If only the direction of motion (not the magnitude of velocity) of the object changes, then also the object has acceleration.*

8. **Graphical Representation of Motion**
Motion of an object can be described using line graphs, following graphs can be drawn for motion of an object.

(i) **Distance-Time Graphs** The change in position of an object with time can be represented by distance-time graph. Time is taken along x-axis and distance is taken along y-axis.

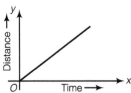

- Distance-time graph can be drawn under various conditions, where object moves with uniform speed, non-uniform speed, remains rest etc.
- If an object moves with uniform speed, then distance-time graph is a straight line.
- Distance-time graph of a body can be used to calculate the speed/velocity of the body, slope of distance-time graph indicates speed.

If an object moves with non-uniform speed, then distance-time graph is a curved line.

(ii) **Velocity-time graph** The change in velocity with time for an object moving in a straight line can be represented by velocity-time graph. Time is taken along x-axis and velocity is taken along y-axis.

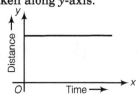

- If object moves with uniform velocity, velocity-time graph will be a straight line parallel to x-axis.
- The area enclosed by velocity-time graph and time axis will be equal to the magnitude of the displacement.
- For uniformly accelerated motion, velocity-time graph is a straight line.
- In case of non-uniformly accelerated motion, velocity-time graph can have any shape.

9. **Equations of Motion**

When an object moves along a straight with uniform acceleration, then its velocity, acceleration and distance covered in given time can be related by a set of equations, which are known as **equations of motion**.

If an object starts with velocity u and after time t its velocity becomes v and during time t the distance covered is s. The equations of motion are

(i) $v = u + at$ Ist equation of motion.

(ii) $s = ut + \dfrac{1}{2}at^2$ IInd equation of motion.

(iii) $v^2 = u^2 + 2as$ IIIrd equation of motion.

10. **Circular Motion** If an object moves around a fixed point in circular path, then its motion is called circular motion.

11. **Uniform Circular Motion** In an object moves in a circular path with uniform speed, its motion is called uniform circular motion.

(i) In circular motion, direction of motion changes continuously *i.e.*, velocity changes (due to change in direction), therefore the motion along a circular path is accelerated.

(ii) The force needed to make an object moving in a circular path is called **centripetal force**.

(iii) The acceleration present in circular motion is called **centripetal acceleration**.

(iv) If an object is moving in a circular path of radius r and it takes time t to complete one round, then velocity of the object.

$$v = \frac{2\pi r}{t}$$

Intext Questions

On Page 100

Question 1. An object has moved through a distance. Can it have zero displacement? If yes, support your answer with an example.

Answer An object can have zero displacement, yet it covers some distance, in the conditions if it comes back to its initial position.

If a boy starts from his home to market and comes back to home then its displacement is zero because its initial and final position are same.

Question 2. A farmer moves along the boundary of a square field of side 10 m in 40 s. What will be the magnitude of displacement of the farmer at the end of 2 minutes 20 seconds, from his initial position?

Answer Farmer takes 40 s to move along the boundary of the square field, *i.e.*, after 40 s farmer is again his initial position so his displacement is zero.

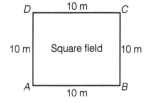

Time given = 2 min 20 s

= (2 × 60 + 20) s = 140 s

= (40 × 3 + 20) s

Displacement of farmer after 2 min 20 s *i.e.*, after 140 s

= Displacement after (3 × 40 + 20) s

= 0 + displacement after 20 s

(∵ after each 40 s displacement is zero)

Farmer completes one round in 40 s, so he will complete 1/2 round in 20 s, *i.e.*, after 20 s final position of farmer is C.

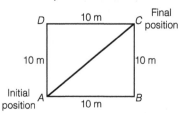

Displacement of farmer $= AC$
$$= \sqrt{AB^2 + BC^2}$$
$$= \sqrt{10^2 + 10^2}$$
$$= 10\sqrt{2}$$
$$= 10 \times 1.414$$
$$= 14.14\, m$$

Question 3. Which of the following is true for displacement?

(a) It cannot be zero.

(b) Its magnitude is greater than the distance travelled by the object.

Answer

(a) Statement (a) is false because displacement of a moving object can be zero.

(b) Statement (b) is false because magnitude of displacement can never be greater than the distance travelled by the object.

On Page 102

Question 1. Distinguish between speed and velocity.

Answer

S.N.	Speed	Velocity
1.	Speed is a scalar quantity.	Velocity is a vector quantity.
2.	Speed of a moving object can never be zero.	Velocity of a moving object can be zero.
3.	Speed of an object is always positive.	Velocity of an object can be positive or negative both.

Question 2. Under what condition(s) is the magnitude of average velocity of an object equal to its average speed?

Answer When an object moves in a straight line, then the magnitude of average velocity is equal to the average speed.

Question 3. What does the odometer of an automobile measure?

Answer Odometer of an automobile measures the distance travelled by it.

Question 4. What does the path of an object look like when it is in uniform motion?

Answer When the object is in uniform motion then its path is straight.

Question 5. During an experiment, a signal from a spaceship reached the ground station in five minutes. What was the distance of the spaceship from the ground station? The signal travels at the speed of light, that is, 3×10^8 ms^{-1}.

Answer Speed of signal $= 3 \times 10^8$ ms^{-1}

Time taken by the signal in reaching the earth

$$= 5 \text{ min}$$
$$= 5 \times 60 = 300 \text{ s}$$

Distance of spaceship from ground station

$$= \text{Distance travelled by the signal in 5 min.}$$
$$= \text{Speed} \times \text{Time}$$
$$= 3 \times 10^8 \times 300 = 9 \times 10^{10} \text{ m}$$

On Page 103

Question 1. When will you say a body is in

(i) uniform acceleration?

(ii) non-uniform acceleration?

Answer

(i) A body has uniform acceleration, if its velocity changes by equal amount in equal interval of time.

(ii) A body has non-uniform acceleration, if its velocity changes by unequal amount in equal interval of time.

Question 2. A bus decreases its speed from 80 kmh^{-1} to 60 kmh^{-1} in 5 s. Find the acceleration of the bus.

Answer   Initial speed $u = 80$ kmh^{-1}

$$= 80 \times \frac{5}{18} \text{ ms}^{-1}$$

$$= \frac{200}{9} \text{ ms}^{-1}$$

Final speed $v = 60$ kmh^{-1}

$$= 60 \times \frac{5}{18} = \frac{150}{9} \text{ ms}^{-1}$$

Acceleration $a = \dfrac{v-u}{t} = \dfrac{\dfrac{150}{9} - \dfrac{200}{9}}{5}$

$$= -\frac{50}{9 \times 5} = \frac{-10}{9} \text{ ms}^{-2}$$

Hence, acceleration is negative because speed decreases.

Question 3. A train starting from a railway station and moving with uniform acceleration attains a speed 40 kmh^{-1} in 10 minutes. Find its acceleration.

Answer Train starts from railway station, so initial speed, $u = 0$.

Final speed, $v = 40$ kmh^{-1}

$$= 40 \times \frac{5}{18} = \frac{100}{9} \text{ ms}^{-1}$$

Time $t = 10$ min

$$= 10 \times 60$$

$$= 600 \text{ s}$$

Acceleration, $a = \dfrac{v - u}{t} = \dfrac{\dfrac{100}{9} - 0}{600} = \dfrac{100}{9 \times 600} = \dfrac{1}{54} \text{ ms}^{-2}$

On Page 107

Question 1. What is the nature of the distance-time graphs for uniform and non-uniform motion of an object?

Answer
(i) For uniform motion of an object, its distance-time graph is a straight line with constant slope.
(ii) For non-uniform motion of an object, its distance-time graph is a curved line with increasing or decreasing slope.

Question 2. What can you say about the motion of an object whose distance-time graph is a straight line parallel to the time axis?

Answer Distance-time graph is parallel to time axis, it means that the distance of the object is not changing with time *i.e.,* the object is at rest.

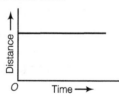

Question 3. What can you say about the motion of an object if its speed-time graph is a straight line parallel to the time axis?

Answer Speed-time graph is a straight line parallel to time axis, it means that the speed of the object is not changing with time, *i.e.,* the object is performing uniform motion.

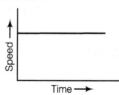

Question 4. What is the quantity which is measured by the area occupied below the velocity-time graph?

Answer Area under the velocity-time graph gives the magnitude of displacement.

On Page 109

Question 1. A bus starting from rest moves with a uniform acceleration of 0.1 ms^{-2} for 2 minutes. Find

(a) the speed acquired,
(b) the distance travelled.

Answer Here, acceleration $a = 0.1 \text{ms}^{-2}$
Time $t = 2 \text{ min} = 2 \times 60 = 120 \text{ s}$
Initial speed $u = 0$

(a) From Ist equation of motion, speed acquired, $v = u + at$
$$= 0 + 0.1 \times 120$$
$$= 12 \text{ ms}^{-1}$$

(b) From IInd equation of motion,
Distance travelled, $s = ut + \dfrac{1}{2} at^2 = 0 \times 120 + \dfrac{1}{2} \times 0.1 \times 120 \times 120$
$$= 0.1 \times 60 \times 120 = 720 \text{ m}$$

Question 2. A train is travelling at a speed of 90 kmh^{-1}. Brakes are applied so as to produce a uniform acceleration of -0.5 ms^{-2}. Find how far the train will go before it is brought to rest?

Answer Here, initial speed, $u = 90 \text{ kmh}^{-1} = 90 \times \dfrac{5}{18} = 25 \text{ ms}^{-1}$
Acceleration, $a = -0.5 \text{ ms}^{-2}$
Train brought to rest, so final speed, $v = 0$
From third equation of motion, $v^2 = u^2 + 2as$
$$0 = (25)^2 + 2 \times 0.5 \times s$$
$$0 = 625 - s$$
$$s = 625 \text{ m}$$

Question 3. A trolley, while going down an inclined plane, has an acceleration of 2 cm s^{-2}. What will be its velocity 3s after the start?

Answer Here, initial velocity, $u = 0$
Acceleration, $a = 2 \text{ cm s}^{-2}$
Time, $t = 3 \text{ s}$
From, Ist equation of motion, $v = u + at = 0 + 2 \times 3 = 6 \text{ ms}^{-1}$

Question 4. A racing car has a uniform acceleration of 4 ms^{-2}. What distance will it cover in 10 s after start?

Answer Here $u = 0$, $a = 4 \text{ ms}^{-2}$, $t = 10 \text{ s}$.

From 2nd equation of motion, distance travelled

$$s = ut + \frac{1}{2} at^2$$

$$= 0 + \frac{1}{2} \times 4 \times (10)^2$$

$$= \frac{1}{2} \times 4 \times 100 = 200 \text{ m}$$

Question 5. A stone is thrown in a vertically upward direction with a velocity of 5 ms^{-1}. If the acceleration of the stone during its motion is 10 ms^{-2} in the downward direction, what will be the height attained by the stone and how much time will it take to reach there?

Answer Here $u = 5 \text{ ms}^{-1}$

$\qquad a = -10 \text{ ms}^{-2}$ $\qquad$ (− ve sign is due to upward direction)

$\qquad v = 0$ $\qquad$ (at maximum height velocity is zero)

Height attained $s = ?$, time taken $t = ?$.

(i) $\qquad v^2 = u^2 + 2as$

$$0 = (5)^2 + 2 \times -10 \times s$$

$$s = \frac{25}{20} = 1.25 \text{ m}$$

(ii) $v = u + at$

$$0 = 5 + (-10) t$$

$$t = \frac{5}{10} = 0.5 \text{ s}$$

Exercises

Question 1. An athlete completes one round of a circular track of diameter 200 m in 40 s. What will be the distance covered and the displacement at the end of 2 minutes 20s?

Answer (i) Diameter of circular track = 200 m

∴ Radius of circular track $= \frac{200}{2} = 100 \text{ m}$

Circumference of circular track $= 2\pi r = 2 \times \frac{22}{7} \times 100 = \frac{4400}{7} \text{ m}$

Total time given = 2 min 20 s = 2 × 60 + 20 = 140 s

According to question, athlete takes 40 s to complete one round.

$\therefore$ Distance covered in 40 s $= \dfrac{4400}{7}$ m

($\because$ Distance covered in one round is equal to the circumference of the track.)

Distance covered in 1 s $= \dfrac{4400}{7 \times 40}$

or distance covered in 140 s $= \dfrac{4400}{7 \times 40} \times 140 = 2200$ m $= 2.2$ km

(ii) As per the question, athlete completes one round in 40 s *i.e.*, after 40 s. athlete comes back to its initial position or after 40 s his displacement is zero. Similarly after 120 s (40 × 3), his displacement is zero.

$\therefore$ Displacement after 2 min 20 s or 140 s = Displacement after 20 s.
($\because$ After 120 s displacement is zero.)

In 20 s athlete will cover half the circular track from A to B (in 40 s one complete round is taken, so in 20 s half round will be taken.)

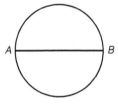

Displacement after 20 s = AB

(Initial position is A and after half round, final position is B)

= Diameter of circular track

= 200 m

Question 2. Joseph jogs from one end A to the other end B of a straight 300 m road in 2 minutes 30 seconds and then turns around and jogs 100 m back to point C in another 1 min. What are Joseph's average speeds and velocities in jogging (a) from A to B and (b) from A to C?

Answer Distance covered from A to B = 300 m

Displacement from A to B = 300 m

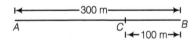

($\because$ If an object is moving along a straight line, then its distance and displacement are same.)

Time taken by Joseph to move from A to B

$$t = 2 \text{ min } 20 \text{ s}$$
$$= 2 \times 60 + 30$$
$$= 120 + 30$$
$$= 150 \text{ s} \qquad (\because 1 \text{ min} = 60 \text{ s})$$

(a) Average speed in jogging from A to B

$$= \dfrac{\text{Distance from } A \text{ to } B}{\text{Time taken from } A \text{ to } B} = \dfrac{300}{150} = 2 \text{ ms}^{-1}$$

Average velocity in jogging from A to B

$$= \frac{\text{Displacement from } A \text{ to } B}{\text{Time taken from } A \text{ to } B}$$

$$= \frac{300}{150} = 2 \, ms^{-1}$$

(b) Distance covered from A to $C = AB + BC$

$$= 300 + 100 = 400 \, m$$

Displacement from A to C = Minimum distance from A to C

$$= 300 - 100 = 200 \, m$$

Time taken in jogging from A to C = 2 min 30 s + 1min

$$= 2 \times 60 + 30 + 60 = 210 \, s$$

Average speed in jogging from A to C

$$= \frac{\text{Displacement from } A \text{ to } C}{\text{Time taken from } A \text{ to } C} = \frac{400}{210} = 1\frac{19}{21} \, ms^{-1}$$

Average velocity in jogging from A to C

$$= \frac{\text{Displacement from } A \text{ to } C}{\text{Time taken from } A \text{ to } C} = \frac{200}{210} = \frac{20}{21} \, ms^{-1}$$

Question 3. Abdul, while driving to school, computes the average speed for his trip to be 20 kmh^{-1}. On his return trip along the same route, there is less traffic and the average speed is 30 kmh^{-1}. What is the average speed for Abdul's trip?

Answer Let the distance of school from Abdul's home be x km.

Time taken by Abdul to reach the school

$$= \frac{\text{Distance}}{\text{Average speed}} = \frac{x}{20} \, h$$

Similarly, time taken by Abdul to reach the home from school

$$= \frac{\text{Distance}}{\text{Average speed}} = \frac{x}{40} \, h$$

Average speed for Abdul's trip $= \dfrac{\text{Total distance}}{\text{Total time}}$

$$= \frac{x + x}{\dfrac{x}{20} + \dfrac{x}{40}}$$

$$= \frac{2x}{\dfrac{4x + 2x}{80}}$$

$$= \frac{2x \times 80}{6x}$$

$$= \frac{80}{3} \, kmh^{-1}$$

Question 4. A motorboat starting from rest on a lake accelerates in a straight line at a constant rate of 3.0 ms^{-2} for 8.0 s. How far does the boat travel during this time?

Answer   The motorboat starts from rest, so initial velocity, $u = 0$

Time taken $t = 8$ s, acceleration, $a = 3$ ms^{-2}

Distance covered during the given time

$$s = ut + \frac{1}{2} at^2 \quad \text{(From second equation of motion)}$$

$$= 0 \times 8 + \frac{1}{2} \times 3 \times (8)^2$$

$$= \frac{1}{2} \times 3 \times 64$$

$$= 0.96 \, \text{m}$$

Question 5. A driver of a car travelling at 52 kmh^{-1} applies the brakes and accelerates uniformly in the opposite direction. The car stops in 5 s. Another driver going at 3 kmh^{-1} in another car applies his brakes slowly and stops in 10 s. On the same graph paper, plot the speed *versus* time graphs for the two cars. Which of the two cars travelled farther after the brakes were applied?

Answer   Initial speed of car $A = 52$ km h^{-1}

$$= 52 \times \frac{5}{18}$$

$$= 14.44 \, \text{ms}^{-1}$$

The car stops in 5 s *i.e.*, final speed of car $v = 0$, time $t = 5$ s.

For speed-time graph of car A.

s	14.44 ms^{-1}	0
t	0	5

Initial speed of car $B = 3$ kmh^{-1}

$$= 3 \times \frac{5}{18} = 0.83 \, \text{ms}^{-1}$$

The car stops in 10 s *i.e.*, final speed of car $v = 0$, time $t = 10$ s.

For speed-time graph of car B

s	0.83 ms^{-1}	0
t	0	10

The speed-time graph of both cars A and B is shown below.

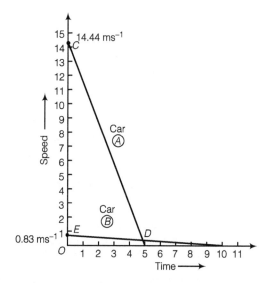

Question 6. Figure shows the distance-time graph of three objects A, B and C. Study the graph and answer the following questions

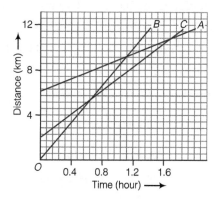

(a) Which of the three is travelling the fastest?
(b) Are all three ever at the same point on the road?
(c) How far has C travelled when B passes A?
(d) How far has B travelled by the time it passes C?

Answer

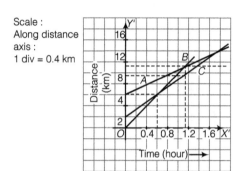

Scale :
Along distance
axis :
1 div = 0.4 km

(a) The object for which slope of speed-time graph is maximum will have maximum speed *i.e.*, will travel the fastest. Here for object *B*, slope is maximum so it is travelling the fastest.

(b) All the three objects will ever be at the same point on the road if the speed-time graph intersect each other at any point. Here all the three graphs do not intersect each other, so these three will never be at the same point on the road.

(c) When *B* passes *A*, distance travelled by *C* = 9.6 − 2 = 7.6 km.

(d) Distance travelled by *B* by the time it passes *C* = 6 km.

Question 7. A ball is gently dropped from a height of 20 m. If its velocity increases uniformly at the rate of 10 ms^{-2}, with what velocity will it strike the ground? After what time will it strike the ground?

Answer The ball is dropped from height *i.e.*, it starts from rest, so initial velocity $u = 0$.

Height $h = 10\,m$, acceleration $g = 10\,ms^{-2}$

(In the motion against gravity, acceleration is taken as g acceleration due to gravity.)

From equation of motion, $h = ut + \dfrac{1}{2}\,gt^2$

$$20 = 0 \times t + \dfrac{1}{2} \times 10 \times t^2$$

$$20 = 5t^2 \;\Rightarrow\; t^2 = 4 \;\Rightarrow\; t = \sqrt{4}$$

$$= 2\,s$$

i.e., the ball will take 2 s to strike the ground.

Again from equation of motion $v = u + gt$

$$v = 0 + 10 \times 2 = 20\,ms^{-1}$$

i.e., the ball will strike the ground with velocity of 20 ms^{-1}.

Question 8. The speed-time graph for a car is shown in figure.

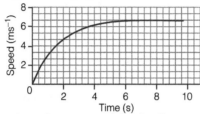

(a) Find how far does the car travel in the first 4 seconds. Shade the area on the graph that represents the distance travelled by the car during the period.

(b) Which part of the graph represents uniform motion of the car?

Answer

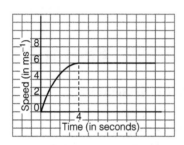

(a) Distance travelled in 4 s = Area under speed-time graph

$$= \text{Average speed} \times \text{Time}$$

$$= \left(\frac{6+0}{2}\right) \times 4 = 12\,\text{m}$$

(b) For uniform motion, the speed-time graph is a straight line parallel to time axis. So, the straight part of the curve parallel to time axis represents the uniform motion of the car.

Question 9. State which of the following situations are possible and give an example for each of these

(a) an object with a constant acceleration but with zero velocity.

(b) an object moving in a certain direction with an acceleration in the perpendicular direction.

Answer
(a) When an object is thrown vertically upward, then at highest point its velocity is zero but it has constant acceleration $9.8\,\text{ms}^{-2}$ (acceleration due to gravity).

(b) An aeroplane flies in horizontal direction but the acceleration due to gravity acts on it in vertically downward direction *i.e.*, along the direction perpendicular to the direction of motion.

Question 10. An artificial satellite is moving in a circular orbit of radius 42250 km. Calculate its speed if it takes 24 hours to revolve around the earth.

Answer Radius of the orbit, $r = 42250$ km

Distance covered in one revolution

$$d = 2\pi r \qquad \text{(Circumference of the orbit)}$$
$$= 2 \times \frac{22}{7} \times 42250 = 265571.43 \text{ km}$$

Time taken in one revolution $t = 24$ h

$$\therefore \qquad \text{Speed of satellite} = \frac{\text{Distance}}{\text{Time}}$$
$$= \frac{265571.43}{24}$$
$$= 11065.48 \text{ kmh}^{-1}$$

Selected NCERT Exemplar Problems

Multiple Choice Questions

Question 1. A particle is moving in a circular path of radius r. The displacement after half a circle would be

(a) zero   (b) πr (c) $2r$ (d) $2\pi r$

Answer   (c) After half the circle, the particle will reach the diametrically opposite point

   i.e., from point A to point B.
   $\therefore$ Displacement after half circle $= AB$

$$= r + r$$
$$= 2r$$

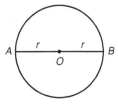

Question 2. A body is thrown vertically upward with velocity u, the greatest height h to which it will rise is

(a) u/g (b) $u^2/2g$ (c) u^2/g (d) $u/2g$

Answer   (b) Initial velocity $= u$, height $= h$

At the highest point, velocity becomes zero

i.e., final velocity $v = 0$

From equation of motion, $v^2 = u^2 - 2gh$

$$0 = u^2 - 2gh \implies h = \frac{u^2}{2g}$$

(Here, we have used negative sign because the body is moving against the gravity).

Question 3. The numerical ratio of displacement of distance for a moving object is

(a) always less than 1   (b) always equal to 1
(c) always more than 1   (d) equal or less than 1

Answer (d) Displacement of an object can be less than or equal to the distance covered by the object, so the ratio of displacement to distance is always equal to or less than 1.

Question 4. If the displacement of an object is proportional to square of time, then the object moves with

(a) uniform velocity   (b) uniform acceleration
(c) increasing acceleration   (d) decreasing acceleration

Answer (b) From equation of motion $s = ut + \dfrac{1}{2} at^2$

If object starts from rest *i.e.*, $u = 0$

Then $$s = \frac{1}{2} at^2$$

$s \propto t^2$, if a = constant

∴ The object moves with constant or uniform acceleration.

Question 5. From the given v-t graph (see figure), it can be inferred that the object is

(a) in uniform motion
(b) at rest
(c) in non-uniform motion
(d) moving with uniform acceleration

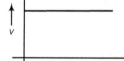

Answer (a) From the given v-t graph it is clear that the velocity of the object is not changing with time *i.e.*, the object is in uniform motion.

Question 6. Suppose a boy is enjoying a ride on a *merry-go-round* which is moving with a constant speed of 10 ms^{-1}. It implies that the boy is

(a) at rest   (b) moving with no acceleration
(c) in accelerated motion   (d) moving with uniform velocity

Answer (d) In *merry-go-round*, the speed is constant but velocity is not constant because its direction goes on changing *i.e.*, there is acceleration in the motion. So, we can say that the boy is in accelerated motion.

Question 7. Area under v-t *graph represents a physical quantity which has the unit*

(a) m^2 (b) m   (c) m^3 (d) ms^{-1}

Answer (b) Area under v-t graph represent displacement whose unit is metre or m.

Question 8. Four cars A, B, C and D are moving on a levelled road. Their distance *versus* time graphs are shown in figure. Choose the correct statement.

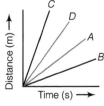

(a) Car A is faster than car D
(b) Car B is the slowest
(c) Car D is faster than car C
(d) Car C is the slowest

Answer   (b) The slope of distance-time graph represents the speed. From the graph, it is clear that the slope of distance-time graph for car B is minimum. So, car B is slowest.

Question 9. Which of the following figures represents uniform motion of a moving object correctly?

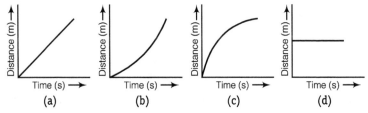

(a)   (b)   (c)   (d)

Answer   (a) For uniform motion, the distance-time graph is a straight line (because in uniform motion object covers equal distance in equal interval of time).

Question 10. Slope of a velocity-time graph gives

(a) the distance   (b) the displacement
(c) the acceleration   (d) the speed

Answer   (c) Slope of velocity-time graph gives acceleration.

Question 11. In which of the following cases of motions, the distance moved and the magnitude of displacement are equal?

(a) If the car is moving on straight road
(b) If the car is moving in circular path
(c) The pendulum is moving to and fro
(d) The Earth is revolving around the sun

Answer   (a) The distance moved and magnitude of displacement are equal only in the case of motion along a straight line.

So, for car moving on straight road, distance moved and magnitude of displacement are equal.

Short Answer Type Questions

Question 12. The displacement of a moving object in a given interval of a time is zero. Would the distance travelled by the object also be zero? Justify your answer?

Answer The displacement of a moving object in a given interval is zero *i.e.,* the object comes back to its initial position in the given time (displacement is the shortest distance between the initial and final position of an object). The distance in this case will not be zero because distance is the total lenght of the path travelled by the body. If the object comes back to its initial position then length of path travelled is not zero.

Question 13. How will the equations of motion for an object moving with a uniform velocity change?

Answer Equations of uniformly accelerated motion are
(i) $v = u + at$
(ii) $s = ut + \dfrac{1}{2} at^2$
(iii) $v^2 = u^2 + 2as$
    where, u = Initial velocity
        v = Final velocity
        a = Acceleration
        t = Time
    and s = Distance

For an object moving with uniform velocity (velocity which is not changing with time), acceleration $a = 0$.
So, equations of motions change to (putting $a = 0$)
(i) $v = u$
(ii) $s = ut$
(iii) $v^2 = u^2$

Question 14. A girl walks along a straight path to drop a letter in the letter box and comes back to her initial position. Her displacement-time graph is shown in figure. Plot a velocity-time graph for the same.

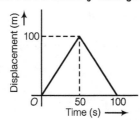

Answer   From the graph,

(i) Initial velocity $v = 0$

(ii) Velocity after 50 s, $v = \dfrac{\text{Displacement}}{\text{Time}}$

$\qquad\qquad\qquad\qquad = \dfrac{100}{50} = 2\,\text{m s}^{-1}$

(iii) Velocity after 100 s, $v = \dfrac{\text{Displacement}}{\text{Time}}$

$\qquad\qquad\qquad\qquad = \dfrac{0}{100} = 0$

Therefore,

v	0	2	0
t	0	50	100

Velocity-time graph plotted from the above data is shown below.

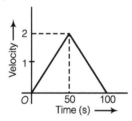

Question 15. A car starts from rest and moves along the x-axis with constant acceleration 5 m s^{-2} for 8 s. If it then continues with constant velocity. What distance will the car cover in 12 s since it started from rest?

Answer   The car starts from rest, so its initial velocity $u = 0$

Acceleration $a = 5\,\text{m s}^{-2}, t = 8\,\text{s}$

Velocity after 8 s, $v = u + at$

$\qquad\qquad\qquad = 0 + 5 \times 8$

$\qquad\qquad\qquad = 40\,\text{m s}^{-1}$

Distance covered in 8 s, $s = ut + \dfrac{1}{2}at^2$

$\qquad\qquad\qquad = 0 \times 8 + \dfrac{1}{2} \times 5\,(8)^2$

$\qquad\qquad\qquad = \dfrac{1}{2} \times 5 \times 64$

$\qquad\qquad\qquad = 160\,\text{m}$

Remaining time $t' = 12 - 8 = 4$ s
The distance covered in the last 4 s, s' = Velocity × Time
$$= 40 \times 4 = 160\,m$$
(We have used the direct formula because after 8 s, car is moving with constant velocity *i.e.*, zero acceleration).
∴ Total distance travelled in 12 s from the start
$$D = s + s' = 160 + 160 = 320\,m$$

Question 16. A motorcyclist drives from A to B with a uniform speed of 30 kmh^{-1} and returns back with a speed of 20 kmh^{-1}. Find its average speed.

Answer   Let the distance between A and B be x km.
Time taken in driving from A to B
$$t_1 = \frac{\text{Distance}}{\text{Speed}} = \frac{x}{30}\,h$$
Similarly, time taken in returning from B to A.
$$t_2 = \frac{\text{Distance}}{\text{Speed}} = \frac{x}{20}\,h$$
$$\text{Average speed} = \frac{\text{Total distance}}{\text{Total time}}$$
$$= \frac{x + x}{\dfrac{x}{30} + \dfrac{x}{20}} = \frac{2x}{\dfrac{2x + 3x}{60}} = \frac{2x \times 60}{5x} = 24\,kmh^{-1}$$

Question 17. The velocity-time graph (see figure) shows the motion of a cyclist. Find (i) its acceleration (ii) its velocity and (iii) the distance covered by the cyclist in 15 s.

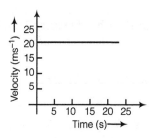

Answer
(i) From the graph, it is clear that velocity is not changing with time *i.e.*, acceleration is zero.
(ii) Again from the graph, we can see that there is no change in the velocity with time, so velocity is after 15 s will remain same as 20 ms^{-1}.
(iii) Distance covered in 15 s = Velocity × Time = 20 × 15 = 300 m

Question 18. Draw a velocity *versus* time graph of a stone thrown vertically upwards and then coming downwards after attaining the maximum height.

Answer When a stone is thrown vertically upwards, it has some initial velocity (let u). As the stone goes its velocity goes on decreasing (∵ it is moving against the gravity) and at the highest point *i.e.,* maximum height) its velocity become zero. Let the stone takes time 't' seconds to reach at the highest point. After that stone begins to fall (with zero initial velocity) and its velocity goes on increasing (∵ it is moving with the gravity) and it reaches its initial point of projection with the velocity v in the same time (with which it was thrown).

So,

Velocity	u	0	$-u$
Time	0	t	$2t$

Here, we have taken $-u$ because in the upward motion velocity of stone is in upward direction and in the downward motion, the velocity is in downward direction. The velocity-time graph for the whole journey is shown below.

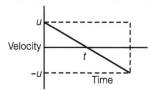

Long Answer Type Questions

Question 19. An object is dropped from rest at a height of 150 m and simultaneously another object is dropped from rest at height 100 m. What is the difference in their heights after 2 s if both the objects drop with same accelerations? How does the difference in heights vary with time?

Answer Distance covered by stone A in 2 s

$$h = ut + \frac{1}{2}gt^2$$

Here, $u = 0$ because stone is dropped from rest.

$$h = 0 \times 2 + \frac{1}{2} \times 10 \,(2)^2 = 20\,m$$

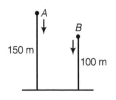

Height of stone A from the ground after 2 s

$$= 150 - 20 = 130\,m$$

Similarly, distance covered stone B in 2 s

$$h = ut + \frac{1}{2}gt^2 = 0 + \frac{1}{2} \times 10 \times (2)^2 = 20\,m$$

Motion

Height of stone B from the ground after 2 s = 100 – 20 = 80 m
Difference in the height after 2 s = 130 – 80 = 50 m
The difference in heights of the stones will remain same with time as both the stones have been dropped from rest and are falling with same acceleration (acceleration due to gravity).

Question 20. An object starting from rest travels 20 m in first 2s and 160 m in next 4 s. What will be the velocity after 7s from the start?

Answer   Object starts from rest, so, $u = 0$

From $\qquad s = ut + \dfrac{1}{2} at^2$

$$20 = 0 \times 2 + \dfrac{1}{2} \times a \, (2)^2$$

$$20 = 2a \implies a = 10 \, \text{m/s}^2$$

∴ Velocity after 7 s from the start

$$v = u + at$$
$$= 0 + 10 \times 7$$
$$= 70 \, \text{m/s}$$

Question 21. Using following data, draw time-displacement graph for a moving object

Time(s)	0	2	4	6	8	10	12	14	16
Displacement (m)	0	2	4	4	4	6	4	2	0

Use this graph to find average velocity for first 4 s, for next 4 s and for last 6 s.

Answer   Displacement-time graph is shown in figure.

Average velocity for first 4s = Slope of displacement – Time graph (*i.e.*, OA part)

$$= \dfrac{4 \, \text{m}}{4 \, \text{s}} = 1 \, \text{ms}^{-1}$$

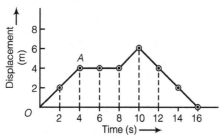

Average velocity for next 4 s (*i.e.*, in the interval of 4 s to 8 s) = zero

Average velocity for last 6 s = $\dfrac{(0 - 6) \, \text{m}}{(16 - 10) \, \text{s}} = -1 \, \text{ms}^{-1}$

Question 22. An electron moving with a velocity of $5 \times 10^4 \, ms^{-1}$ enters into a uniform electric field and acquires a uniform acceleration of $10^4 \, ms^{-2}$ in the direction of its initial motion.

(i) Calculate the time in which the electron would acquire a velocity double of its initial velocity.

(ii) How much distance the electron would cover in this time?

Answer   Initial velocity $u = 5 \times 10^4 \, ms^{-1}$

         Acceleration $a = 10^4 \, ms^{-2}$

(i) Final velocity $v = 2u, t = ?$

     From

$$v = u + at$$
$$2u = u + 10^4 \times t$$
$$10^4 \times t = u$$

$$\Rightarrow \qquad t = \frac{4}{10^4} = \frac{5 \times 10^4}{10^4} = 5 \, s$$

i.e., After 5 s electron will acquire a velocity double of its initial velocity.

(ii) Distance covered, $s = ut + \dfrac{1}{2}at^2$

$$= 5 \times 10^4 \times 5 + \frac{1}{2} \times 10^4 (5)^2$$
$$= 25 \times 10^4 + 12.5 \times 10^4$$
$$= 37.5 \times 10^4 \, m = 375 \times 10^3 \, m$$
$$= 375 \, km$$

Question 23. Obtain a relation for the distance travelled by an object moving with a uniform acceleration in the interval between 4th and 5th seconds.

Answer   Distance travelled in t s

$$S = ut + \frac{1}{2}at^2$$

Distance travelled in 4 s

$$S_4 = u \times 4 + \frac{1}{2}a(4)^2$$
$$= 4u + 8a$$

Distance travelled in 5 s

$$S_5 = ut + \frac{1}{2}at^2$$
$$= u \times 5 + \frac{1}{2}a(5)^2$$
$$= 5u + \frac{25}{2}a$$

∴ Distance travelled in the interval between 4th and 5th seconds.

$$S = S_5 - S_4$$

$$= \left(5u + \frac{25}{2}a\right) - (4u + 8a)$$

$$= u + \frac{9}{2}a$$

Question 24. Two stones are thrown vertically upwards simultaneously with their initial velocities u_1 and u_2 respectively. Prove that the height reached by them would be in the ratio of $u_1^2 : u_2^2$ (Assume upward acceleration is $-g$ and downward acceleration to be $+g$).

Answer **For Ist stone,** Initial velocity $u = u_1$

Let height attained by it be h_1

From equation of motion

$$v^2 = u^2 + 2gh$$

At the highest point the velocity becomes zero *i.e.*, $v = 0$

$$0 = u_1^2 + 2gh_1 \implies h_1 = \frac{-u_1^2}{2g}$$

For IInd stone, Initial velocity $u = u_2$

Let the height attained by it be h_2

Even equation of motion

$$v^2 = u^2 + 2gh$$
$$0 = u_2^2 + 2gh_2$$

(At the highest point velocity becomes zero)

∴
$$h_2 = \frac{-u_2^2}{2g}$$

Now, ratio of heights reached by the two stones

$$h_1 : h_2 = \frac{-u_1^2}{2g} : \frac{-u_2^2}{2g}$$

$$= u_1^2 : u_2^2$$

9

Force and Laws of Motion

Important Concepts

1. In our everyday life, we observe that some effort is required to put a stationary object into motion or to stop a moving object, this effort is called **force**. In this chapter, we will study about force, its effect, types and concerned laws etc.

2. **Force** Force is a push or pull which can change the state of rest/state of motion of an object.
   - Force cannot be seen but its effect on an object can be felt.
   - Force can bring the stationary object in motion.
   - Force can stop a moving object.
   - Force can change the direction of motion of an object.
   - Force can change the shape and size of object.
   - Force is a vector quantity and its SI unit is newton.

   $$1 \text{ newton} = 1 \text{ kg-ms}^{-2}$$

3. **Balanced and Unbalanced Forces**
   - **Balanced Forces** If the net effect of all the forces acting on an object is zero, then the forces are called balanced forces.
     - If balanced forces are acting on an object, then it appears as if no force is acting on it.
     - An object under the effect of balanced forces cannot change its state of motion or rest.
     - If balanced forces are acting on an object in uniform motion, then the object remains in state of uniform motion.

- **Unbalanced Forces** If the net effect of all the forces acting on an object is not zero, then these forces are called unbalanced forces.
  - Unbalanced forces can move a stationary object or can stop a moving object.

4. **Newton's Laws of Motion**

(a) **First Law of Motion** According to first law of motion, "If a body is in rest or in uniform motion along a straight line, then it will remain in same state until and unless an external force is applied on it".

  - **Inertia** The property of an object to resist any change in its state of motion or rest is called inertia. If an object is at rest, then it tends to remain at rest and if it is moving, it tends to keep moving.
    - The mass of an object is a measure of its inertia, heavier objects have higher inertia than lighter objects.
    - If an object resists the change in its state of rest, its inertia is called inertia of rest.
    - If an object resists the change in its state of motion, its inertia is called inertia of motion.
    - If an object resists the change in its direction of motion, its inertia is called inertia of direction.

  Some Daily Life Examples of Inertia
  - (i) When a bus suddenly starts, the passenger in the bus falls backward.
  - (ii) When a moving bus stops suddenly, the passenger is pushed forward.
  - (iii) When a bus turns to a corner sharply, passenger tends to fall sideways.
  - (iv) A bullet fired from a gun makes a small hole in the window pane while a stone striking a window pane breaks it into pieces.
  - (v) When a tree is vigoursly shaken, then some leaves fall from it.

- **Momentum** The amount of motion possessed by an object is called the momentum of the object.
  - Momentum of an object is equal to the product of its mass (m) and velocity (v).

$$\text{Momentum } p = m \times v$$

  - It is a vector quantity. Its SI unit is kg-ms^{-1}. In CGS system, its unit is g-cms^{-1}.

- Momentum of an object is directly proportional to
  (i) mass of the object.
  (ii) velocity of the object.
- Direction of momentum is same as that of velocity.

Example What is the momentum of a motorbike having mass 125 kg, moving with a velocity of 54 kmh^{-1}?

Sol. Mass, $m = 125$ kg

$$\text{Velocity, } v = 54 \, kmh^{-1} = 54 \times \frac{5}{18} = 15 \, ms^{-1}$$

Momentum of motorbike, $p = mv = 125 \times 15 = 1875$ kg $-ms^{-1}$

(b) **Second Law of Motion** According to second law of motion, "The rate of change of momentum of an object is directly proportional to the force applied on it". The change in momentum takes place in direction of force.

According to second law of motion,

$$F \propto \frac{\Delta p}{\Delta t} \qquad \qquad ...(i)$$

Here, $\Delta p =$ change in momentum

$\Delta t =$ time taken in change

If an object of mass m is moving with velocity u and after time t its velocity becomes v, then

$$\text{Initial momentum, } p_1 = mu$$

$$\text{Final momentum, } p_2 = mv$$

Change in momentum $\Delta p = p_2 - p_1 = mv - mu = m(v - u)$

Rate of change of momentum $= \dfrac{\Delta p}{\Delta t}$

$$= m\left(\frac{v - u}{t}\right)$$

From Eq. (i),

$$F \propto m\left(\frac{v - u}{t}\right)$$

We know that

$$\frac{v - u}{t} = a \text{ (acceleration of the object)}$$

$\therefore$ $\qquad\qquad\qquad F \propto ma$

or $\qquad\qquad\qquad F = kma$

where, k is a constant of proportionality.

If $F = 1$ unit, $m = 1$ unit and $a = 1$ unit, then

$$k = 1$$

$$\therefore \qquad F = ma$$

i.e., force applied on an object is equal to the product of mass of the body and acceleration produced in it.

If $m = 1$ kg, $a = 1$ ms^{-2}

$$\therefore \qquad F = 1 \times 1 = 1 \text{ kg-ms}^{-2} = 1 \text{ N}$$

"1 newton is defined as amount of force which, when applied, produces an acceleration of 1 ms^{-2} in an object of mass 1 kg."

Example *Velocity of a car increases from 10 ms^{-1} to 20 ms^{-1}. If the mass of the car is 1500 kg, calculate change in momentum of the car. If time taken in changing the velocity is 10 s, also find the force applied on the car.*

Sol. Mass, $m = 1500$ kg

$$\text{Initial velocity } u = 10 \text{ ms}^{-1}$$
$$\text{Final velocity } v = 20 \text{ ms}^{-1}$$
$$\text{Time taken } t = 10 \text{ s}$$

Change in momentum = Final momentum – Initial momentum

$$= mv - mu = m (v - u)$$
$$= 1500 (20 - 10) = 1500 \times 10 = 15000$$
$$= 1.5 \times 10^4 \text{ kg-ms}^{-1}$$

Force applied on the car

$$F = \text{Rate of change of momentum}$$
$$= \frac{\text{Change in momentum}}{\text{Time taken}}$$
$$= \frac{1.5 \times 10^4}{10} = 1.5 \times 10^3 \text{ N}$$

Some Daily Life Examples of Newton's Second Law

(i) A cricket fielder lowers his hands while catching a ball.

(ii) A high jumping athlete is provided either a cushion or heap of sand on the ground to fall upon.

(iii) Vehicles are provided with shockers.

(iv) If a moving train collides with a stationary train, then huge damage takes place.

(c) **Third Law of Motion** According to this law, "To every action there is equal and opposite reaction." It means if a body 'X' exerts force F on another body 'Y', then body 'Y' also exerts the same force F on body 'X'.

Action and reaction always act on different bodies.

Some Daily Life Examples of Newton's Third Law

(i) Recoiling of a gun on firing the bullet.

(ii) Flying of jet planes.

(iii) Rebounding of a ball after striking on the floor.

(iv) Motion of boat.

5. **Law of Conservation of Momentum** According to this law, "The total momentum of a system remains constant, till an external force is applied on it."

Momentum of the system, p = constant, if $F = 0$

We can say that total initial momentum of the system equal to the total final momentum of the system remains same, if there is no external force acting on the system.

If two objects collide with each other, then we can say

Total momentum before collision
= Total momentum after collision.

Intext Questions

On Page 118

Question 1. Which of the following has more inertia

(a) a rubber ball and a stone of the same size?

(b) a bicycle and a train?

(c) a five-rupees coin and a one-rupee coin?

Answer Inertia of an object is the measurement of its mass.

(a) A stone of same size as that of rubber ball will have greater mass, so stone will have more inertia.

(b) A train has much greater mass than that of a bicycle, so the train will have more inertia.

(c) A five-rupees coin has more mass than a one-rupee coin, so five-rupees coin will have greater inertia.

Question 2. In the following example, try to identify the number of times the velocity of the ball changes

"A football player kicks a football to another player of his team who kicks the football towards the goal. The goalkeeper of the opposite team collects the football and kicks it towards a player of his own team."

Also identify the agent supplying the force in each case.

Answer   Given below are the number of times at which the velocity of the ball changes.

Whenever a force will be applied on the ball then the velocity of the ball will change.

(i) When first player kicks the ball towards another player of his team then the velocity of ball will change because first player applies some force on the ball.

(ii) When another player kicks the ball towards the goal, then the velocity of ball will change, here again the force is applied on the ball.

(iii) When goalkeeper of the opposite team collects the ball, then the velocity of ball will change, it becomes zero. Here the goalkeeper applies some force on the ball to stop.

(iv) When the goalkeeper kicks the ball towards his own team, the velocity of the ball changes because goalkeeper applies some force on the ball.

Question 3. Explain why some of the leaves may get detached from a tree if we vigorously shake its branch?

Answer   When a tree is vigourerly shaken, the branches of the tree come in the state of motion but the leaves tend to maintain their state of rest, so leaves get detached from the tree and fall down.

Question 4. Why do you fall in the forward direction when a moving bus brakes to a stop and fall backwards when it accelerates from rest?

Answer   When a moving bus brakes suddenly to stop, the lower part of the body which is in contact with the bus comes in the state of rest, but the upper part of the body tends to maintain its state of motion due to which we fall in the forward direction.

On Page 126

Question 1. If action is always equal to the reaction, explain how a horse can pull a cart.

Answer   To pull the cart horse pushes the ground with its foot in the backward direction by pressing the ground. As a reaction of this force, the ground pushes the horse in forward direction. Due to which the horse pulls the cart.

Question 2. Explain, why is it difficult for a fireman to hold a hose, which ejects large amounts of water at a high velocity.

Answer   A fireman finds it difficult to hold a hose-pipe which is ejecting large amount of water at high velocity. Because the stream of water rushing out of the pipe in the forward direction exerts a large force on the pipe. Due to the reaction of the forward force, a force is applied on the pipe in backward direction. Therefore, the fireman struggles to keep the hose-pipe in rest.

Question 3. From a rifle of mass 4 kg, a bullet of mass 50 g is fired with an initial velocity of 35 ms^{-1}. Calculate the initial recoil velocity of the rifle.

Answer Mass of gun $M = 4$ kg

Mass of bullet $m = 50$ g

$$= 50 \times 10^{-3} \text{ kg}$$

Initial velocity of bullet, $v = 35$ ms^{-1}

Let recoil velocity of the gun be v ms^{-1}

Before firing the bullet both gun and bullet were in rest so total momentum of gun and bullet is zero. After firing

momentum of bullet $= mv$

momentum of gun $= Mv$

Total momentum of bullet and gun after firing $= mv + Mv$.

Since, there is no external force applied on the system.

So, total momentum after firing = total momentum before firing

$$mv + Mv = 0$$

$$Mv = -mv$$

$$\Rightarrow \qquad v = -\frac{mv}{M}$$

$$= \frac{50 \times 10^{-3} \times 35}{4} = -0.44 \text{ ms}^{-1}$$

Here negative sign shows that the recoil velocity of the gun is in the direction opposite to the velocity of the bullet.

Question 4. Two objects A and B of masses 100 g and 200 g are moving along the same line and direction with velocities of 2 ms^{-1} and 1 ms^{-1}, respectively. They collide and after the collision, the first object moves at a velocity of 1.67 ms^{-1}. Determine the velocity of the second object.

Answer Before collision,

$$m_1 = 100 \text{ g} = \frac{100}{1000} = 0.1 \text{ kg} \qquad (\because 1 \text{ kg} = 1000 \text{ g})$$

$$m_2 = 200 \text{ g} = \frac{200}{1000} = 0.2 \text{ kg}$$

$$v_1 = 2 \text{ ms}^{-1}$$

$$v_2 = 1 \text{ ms}^{-1}$$

After collision,

$$m_1 = 100 \text{ g} = 0.1 \text{ kg}$$

$$m_2 = 200 \text{ g} = 0.2 \text{ kg}$$

$$v_1' = 1.67 \text{ ms}^{-1}$$

Let velocity of second object after collision be v_2' ms^{-1}. Since, there is no external force on the system.

So, total momentum before collision = total momentum after collision

$$m_1 v_1 + m_2 v_2 = m_1 v_1' + m_2 v_2'$$

$$0.1 \times 2 + 0.2 \times 1 = 0.1 \times 1.67 + 0.2 \times v_2'$$

$$0.2 + 0.2 = 0.167 + 0.2 v_2'$$

$$0.2 v_2' = 0.4 - 0.167$$

$$= 0.333$$

$$v_2' = \frac{0.333}{0.2} = 1.65 \text{ ms}^{-1}$$

Exercises

Question 1. An object experiences a net zero external unbalanced force. Is it possible for the object to be travelling with a non-zero velocity? If yes, state the conditions that must be placed on the magnitude and direction of the velocity. If no, provide a reason.

Answer As per the Newton's Ist law of motion, no force is needed to move an object which is moving with a constant (non-zero) velocity. So, when an object experiences a net zero external unbalanced force, then it can move with a non-zero velocity. Also, an object may not move at all, if it experiences a net zero external unbalanced force, if the object is initially at rest.

Question 2. When a carpet is beaten with a stick, dust comes out of it. Explain.

Answer When a carpet is beaten with a stick, then the fibres of the carpet attain the state of motion while the dust particles remain in rest due to inertia of rest. Therefore, the dust particles fall down.

Question 3. Why is it advised to tie any luggage kept on the roof of a bus with a rope?

Answer It is advised to tie any luggage kept on the roof of a bus because when the bus stops suddenly then bus comes in the state of rest but the luggage remain in the state of motion. So, due to inertia of motion, the luggage move forward and fall down from the roof of the bus.

If the bus starts suddenly, then bus comes in the state of motion but luggage remain in the state of rest. Due to inertia of rest, the luggage move in the backward direction and fall down.

Question 4. A batsman hits a cricket ball which then rolls on a level ground. After covering a short distance, the ball comes to rest. The ball slows to a stop because

(a) the batsman did not hit the ball hard enough.

(b) velocity is proportional to the force exerted on the ball.

(c) there is a force on the ball opposing the motion.

(d) there is no unbalanced force on the ball, so the ball would want to come to rest.

Answer (c) The ball slows down to rest because the force of friction acting between the ground and the ball opposes the motion of the ball.

Question 5. A truck starts from rest and rolls down a hill with a constant acceleration. It travels a distance of 400 m in 20 s. Find its acceleration. Find the force acting on it if its mass is 7 tonnes. (Hint 1 tonne = 1000 kg).

Answer The truck starts from rest, so initial velocity $u = 0$, distance $s = 400$ m, $t = 20$ s, $m = 7$ tonnes $= 7 \times 1000 = 7000$ kg.

From 2nd equation of motion,

$$s = ut + \frac{1}{2} at^2$$

$$400 = 0 \times 20 + \frac{1}{2} \times a \times (20)^2$$

$$400 = 200\, a$$

$$\Rightarrow \qquad a = 2 \text{ ms}^{-2}$$

From Newton's 2nd law of motion, force acting on the truck

$$F = ma$$
$$= 7000 \times 2 = 14000 \text{ N}$$
$$= 1.4 \times 10^4 \text{ N}$$

Question 6. A stone of 1 kg is thrown with a velocity of 20 ms^{-1} across the frozen surface of a lake and comes to rest after travelling a distance of 50 m. What is the force of friction between the stone and the ice?

Answer Mass of stone $m = 1$ kg, initial velocity $u = 20$ ms^{-1}, final velocity $v = 0$ ($\because$ the stone comes to rest), distance covered $s = 50$ m.

From third equation of motion,

$$v^2 = u^2 + 2as$$
$$(0)^2 = (20)^2 + 2a\,(50)$$
$$100a = -400$$
$$\Rightarrow \qquad a = -4 \text{ ms}^{-2}$$

Here negative sign shows that there is retardation in the motion of stone.

Force of friction between stone and ice = Force required to stop the stone

$$= ma$$
$$= 1 \times -4 = -4 \text{ N} \text{ or } 4 \text{ N}$$

Question 7. A 8000 kg engine pulls a train of 5 wagons, each of 2000 kg, along a horizontal track. If the engine exerts a force of 40000 N and the track offers a friction force of 5000 N, then calculate

(a) the net acceleration force and

(b) the acceleration of the train.

Answer (a) Net accelerating force = Force exerted by engine – Friction force

(Here frictional force is subtracted because it opposes the motion)

$$= 40000 - 5000$$
$$= 35000\,N$$
$$= 3.5 \times 10^4\,N$$

(b) From Newton's second law of motion,

Accelerating force = Mass of the train $\times$ Acceleration of train

$$a = \frac{F}{m}$$

Mass of train = Mass of engine + Mass of all wagons

$$= 8000 + 5 \times 2000$$
$$= 8000 + 10000 = 18000\,kg$$

$\therefore$ Acceleration $= \dfrac{35000}{18000}$

$$= \frac{35}{18} = 1.95\,ms^{-2}$$

Question 8. An automobile vehicle has a mass of 1500 kg. What must be the force between the vehicle and road if the vehicle is to be stopped with a negative acceleration of 1.7 ms^{-2}?

Answer Mass, $m = 1500\,kg$, Acceleration, $a = -1.7\,ms^{-2}$

From Newton's second law of motion,

$$F = ma$$
$$= 1500 \times (-1.7)$$
$$= -2550\,N$$

Question 9. What is the momentum of an object of mass m, moving with a velocity v ?

(a) $(mv)^2$ (b) mv^2 (c) $\dfrac{1}{2}mv^2$ (d) mv

Answer (d) The momentum of an object of mass m moving with a velocity v.

$$p = mv$$

Question 10. Using a horizontal force of 200 N, we intend to move a wooden cabinet across a floor at a constant velocity. What is the friction force that will be exerted on the cabinet?

Answer The cabinet will move across the floor with constant velocity, if there is no net external force is applied on it.

Here a horizontal force of 200 N is applied on the cabinet, so for the net force to be zero, an external force of 200 N should be applied on the cabinet in opposite direction.

Thus, the frictional force = 200 N

(Frictional force always acts in the direction opposite to direction of motion.)

Question 11. Two objects, each of mass 1.5 kg, are moving in the same straight line but in opposite directions. The velocity of each object is 2.5 ms^{-1} before the collision during which they stick together. What will be the velocity of the combined object after collision?

Answer Mass of first object, $m_1 = 1.5$ kg

Mass of second object, $m_2 = 1.5$ kg

Velocity of first object before collision, $u_1 = 2.5$ ms^{-1}

Velocity of second object before collision, $u_2 = -2.5$ ms^{-1}

(Here negative sign is taken because second object is moving in the direction opposite to the direction of motion of first object).

Mass of combined object after collision

$$M = m_1 + m_2 \qquad (\because \text{they stick together})$$
$$= 1.5 + 1.5 = 3 \text{ kg}$$

Let velocity of combined object after collision be v ms^{-1}.

Here there is no external force, so from law of conservation of momentum.

Momentum after collision = Momentum before collision

$$mv = m_1 u_1 + m_2 u_2$$
$$3 \times v = 1.5 \times 2.5 + 1.5 \, (-2.5) = 0$$
$$v = 0$$

Question 12. According to the third law of motion, when we push on an object, the object pushes back on us with an equal and opposite force. If the object is a massive truck parked along the roadside, it will probably not move. A student justifies this by answering that the two opposite and equal forces cancel each other. Comment on this logic and explain why the truck does not move.

Answer The logic given by the student is not correct because two equal and opposite forces cancel each other only in the case if they act on the same body. According to Newton's third law, action and reaction force always act on two different bodies, so they cannot cancel each other.

When a massive truck is pushed, then the truck may not move because the force applied is not sufficient to move the truck.

Question 13. A hockey ball of mass 200 g travelling at 10 ms^{-1} is struck by a hockey stick so as to return it along its original path with a velocity at 5 ms^{-1}. Calculate the change of momentum occurred in the motion of the hockey ball by the force applied by the hockey stick.

Answer   Mass of hockey ball
$$m = 200\,g = 0.2\,kg$$
Initial velocity, $u = 10\,ms^{-1}$
Final velocity, $v = -5\,ms^{-1}$
($\because$ Final velocity of the ball is in the direction opposite to the direction of initial velocity.)
Change in momentum of the ball = Final momentum – Initial momentum
$$= mv - mu$$
$$= m\,(v - u)$$
$$= 0.2\,(-5 - 10)$$
$$= 0.2 \times -15 = -3\,kg\text{-}ms^{-1}$$

Question 14. A bullet of mass 10 g travelling horizontally with a velocity of 150 ms^{-1} strikes a stationary wooden block and comes to rest in 0.03 s. Calculate the distance of penetration of the bullet into the block. Also calculate the magnitude of the force exerted by the wooden block on the bullet.

Answer   Mass of bullet, $m = 10\,g = \dfrac{10}{1000}\,kg = 0.01\,kg$

Initial velocity, $u = 150\,ms^{-1}$
Final velocity, $v = 0$ ($\because$ the bullet comes to rest)
Time, $t = 0.03\,s$
From equation of motion
$$v = u + at$$
$$0 = 150 + a \times 0.03$$
$$a = \frac{-150}{0.03}$$
$$= -5000\,ms^{-2}$$
Distance covered by the bullet before coming to rest is given by
$$v^2 = u^2 + 2as$$
$$0 = (150)^2 + 2\,(-5000)\,s$$
$$s = \frac{(150)^2}{10000}$$
$$= 2.25\,m$$

Magnitude of the force applied by the bullet on the block

$$F = ma$$
$$= 0.01 \times -5000 = -50\,N$$

Question 15. An object of mass 1 kg travelling in a straight line with a velocity of 10 ms^{-1} collides with and sticks to, a stationary wooden block of mass 5 kg. Then they both move off together in the same straight line. Calculate the total momentum just before the impact and just after the impact. Also, calculate the velocity of the combined object.

Answer   Mass of object, $m_1 = 1\,kg$,

Velocity, $u = 10\,ms^{-1}$

Mass of wooden block, $m_2 = 5\,kg$

Velocity, $u_2 = 0$ ($\because$ Wooden block is at rest)

Total momentum just before the impact

$$= \text{Momentuam of object} + \text{Momentum of block}$$
$$= 1 \times 10 + 5 \times 0 = 10\,kg\text{-}ms^{-1}$$

According to law of conservation of momentum

Momentum after impact = Momentum before impact

$$(m_1 + m_2)\,v = 10$$

where, v = velocity of combined object

$$(1 + 5)\,v = 10$$

$\Rightarrow$ $v = \dfrac{10}{6} = 1.67\,ms^{-1}$

Question 16. An object of mass 100 kg is accelerated uniformly from a velocity of 5 ms^{-1} to 8 ms^{-1} in 6 s. Calculate the initial and final momentum of the object. Also, find the magnitude of the force exerted on the object.

Answer   Mass of the object, $m = 100\,kg$,

Initial velocity, $u = 5\,ms^{-1}$

Final velocity, $v = 8\,ms^{-1}$

(i) Initial momentum $= mu = 100 \times 5 = 500\,kg\text{-}ms^{-1}$

Final momentum $= mv = 100 \times 8 = 800\,kg\text{-}ms^{-1}$

(ii) From Newton's second law, force exerted on the object = Rate of change of momentum

$$= \frac{\text{Change in momentum}}{\text{Time}}$$
$$= \frac{\text{Final momentum} - \text{Initial momentum}}{\text{Time}}$$
$$= \frac{800 - 50}{6} = \frac{300}{6} = 50\,N$$

Question 17. Akhtar, Kiran and Rahul were riding in a motorcar that was moving with a high velocity on an expressway when an insect hit the windshield and got stuck on the windscreen. Akhtar and Kiran started pondering over the situation. Kiran suggested that the insect suffered a greater change in momentum as compared to the change in momentum of the motorcar (because the change in the velocity of the insect was much more than that of the motorcar). Akhtar said that since the motorcar moving with a larger velocity, it exerted a larger force on the insect. And as a result the insect died. Rahul while putting an entirely new explanation said that both the motorcar and the insect experienced the same force and a change in their momentum. Comment of these suggestions.

Answer Rahul is correct, because there is no external force on the system, so both the insect and motorcar experienced the same force and a change in momentum.

Question 18. How much momentum will a dumb-bell of mass 10 kg transfer to the floor if it falls from a height of 80 cm? Take its downward acceleration to be 10 ms^{-2}?

Answer $m = 10$ kg, $u = 0$ (because it falls from rest)
Distance covered, $s = 80$ cm $= 0.8$ m
$$a = 10\,\text{ms}^{-2}$$
From equation of motion, $v^2 = u^2 + 2as$
$$v^2 = 0 + 2 \times 10 \times 0.8 = 16$$
$$v = \sqrt{16} = 4\,\text{ms}^{-1}$$
Momentum of dumb-bell just before it touches the floor
$$p = mv$$
$$= 10 \times 4$$
$$= 40\,\text{kg-ms}^{-1}$$
When the dumb-bell touches the floor, its velocity becomes zero and hence the momentum. Thus, the total momentum of the dumb-bell is transfered to the floor.
$\therefore$ The momentum transferred to floor $= 40$ kg-ms^{-1}

Additional Exercises

Question 1. The following is the distance-time table of an object in motion.

Time (in seconds)	Distance (in metres)
0	0
1	1
2	8
3	27
4	64
5	125
6	216
7	343

(a) What conclusion can you draw about the acceleration? Is it constant, increasing, decreasing or zero?

(b) What do you infer about the force acting on the object?

Answer (a) Here $u = 0$

Using
$$s = ut + \frac{1}{2}at^2 = \frac{1}{2}at^2 \qquad\qquad (\because u = 0)$$

We get
$$a = \frac{2s}{t^2}$$

Time (in seconds)	Distance (in metres)	$a = 2s/t^2$
0	0	0
1	1	2
2	8	4
3	27	6
4	64	8
5	125	10
6	216	12
7	343	14

Thus, acceleration is increasing.

(b) Since, acceleration is increasing, so net unbalanced force is acting on the object.

Question 2. Two persons manage to push a motorcar of mass 1200 kg at a uniform velocity along a level road. The same motorcar can be pushed by three persons to produce an acceleration of 0.2 ms^{-2}. With what force does each person push the motorcar? (Assume that all persons push the motorcar with the same muscular effort.)

Answer Mass of motorcar, $m = 1200\,kg$

Acceleration produced, $a = 0.2\,ms^{-2}$

$\therefore$ Force applied on the car by three persons

$$F = ma$$
$$= 1200 \times 0.2$$
$$= 240\,N$$

Force applied on the car by one person

$$= \frac{240}{3} = 80\,N$$

Question 3. A hammer of mass 500 g, moving at 50 ms^{-1}, strikes a nail. The nail stops the hammer in a very short time of 0.01 s. What is the force of the nail on the hammer?

Answer Mass of the hammer $= 500\,g = 0.05\,kg$

Initial velocity of hammer, $u = 50\,ms^{-1}$

Final velocity of hammer, $v = 0$ (because the hammer stops)

Time $t = 0.01\,s$

Force of the nail on the hammer

$$= \text{Rate of change of momentum of hammer}$$
$$= \frac{mv - mu}{t}$$
$$= \frac{0.5 \times 0 - 0.5 \times 50}{0.01}$$
$$= -\frac{25}{0.01} = -2500\,N$$

Question 4. A motorcar of mass 1200 kg is moving along a straight line with a uniform velocity of 90 kmh^{-1}. Its velocity is slowed down to 18 kmh^{-1} in 4 s by an unbalanced external force. Calculate the acceleration and change in momentum. Also calculate the magnitude of the force required.

Answer Mass $m = 1200\,kg$

Initial velocity, $u = 90\,km\text{-}h^{-1}$

$$= 90 \times \frac{5}{18} = 25\,ms^{-1}$$

Final velocity, $v = 18\,kmh^{-1} = 18 \times \frac{5}{10} = 5\,ms^{-1}$

Time $t = 4\,s$

(i) Acceleration $= \dfrac{v - u}{t} = \dfrac{5 - 25}{t} = -\dfrac{20}{4} = -5\,ms^{-2}$

(Here negative sign indicates that the velocity decreases)

(ii) Change in momentum = Final momentum − Initial momentum

$$= mv - mu = m(v - u) = 1200(5 - 25)$$
$$= 1200 \times -20 = -24000 \text{ kg-ms}^{-1}$$

(iii) Magnitude of the force required = Rate of change of momentum

$$= \frac{\text{Change in momentum}}{\text{Time}}$$

$$= \frac{-24000}{4} = -6000 \text{ N}$$

Selected NCERT Exemplar Problems

Multiple Choice Questions

Question 1. Which of the following statement is not correct for an object moving along a straight path in accelerated motion?

    (a) Its speed keeps changing
    (b) Its velocity always changes
    (c) It always goes away from the earth
    (d) A force is always acting on it

Answer (c) For an object moving along a straight path in an accelerated motion, it is not necessary that it always goes away from the earth.

Question 2. According to the third law of motion, action and reaction

    (a) always act on the same body
    (b) always act on different bodies in opposite directions
    (c) have same magnitude and direction
    (d) act on either body at normal to each other

Answer (b) According to third law of motion, action and reaction always act on different bodies in opposite directions.

Question 3. A goalkeeper in a game of football pulls his hands backwards after holding the ball shot at the goal. This enables the goalkeeper to

    (a) exert larger force on the ball
    (b) reduce the force exerted by the ball on hands
    (c) increase the rate of change of momentum
    (d) decrease the rate of change of momentum

Answer (d) The goalkeeper pulls his hands backwards after holding the ball to decrease the rate of change of momentum by increasing the time. By doing this, less force is exerted on his hands (∵ Force is directly proportional to the rate of change of momentum).

Question 4. The inertia of an object tends to cause the object
(a) to increase its speed
(b) to decrease its speed
(c) to resist any change in its state of motion
(d) to decelerate due to friction

Answer (c) The inertia of an object tends to cause the object to resist any change in its state of rest or motion.

Question 5. A passenger in a moving train tosses a coin which falls behind him. It means that motion of the train is
(a) accelerated   (b) uniform
(c) retarded   (d) along circular tracks

Answer (a) If the coin falls behind the passenger that means the train is accelerated. When the coin is tossed it has same velocity as that of train but during the time it is in air its velocity becomes less than that of train (because the train is accelerated), so it falls behind the passanger.

Question 6. An object of mass 2 kg is sliding with a constant velocity of 4 ms^{-1} on a frictionless horizontal table. The force required to keep the object moving with the same velocity is
(a) 32 N   (b) 0 N
(c) 2 N   (d) 8 N

Answer (b) Mass $m = 2$ kg, velocity $v = 4$ ms^{-1}
As the object is moving with a constant velocity and there is no opposing force ($\because$ table is frictionless). So, there is no force *i.e.*, 0 N is required to keep the object moving with same velocity.

Question 7. Rocket works on the principle of conservation of
(a) mass   (b) energy
(c) momentum   (d) velocity

Answer (c) Rocket works on the conservation of momentum.

Question 8. A water tanker filled upto $\frac{2}{3}$ of its height is moving with a uniform speed. On sudden application of the brake, the water in the tank would
(a) move backward   (b) move forward
(c) be unaffected   (d) rise upwards

Answer (b) On the sudden application of brake, the tanker will come in the state of rest but the water remains in the state of motion, so the water will move forward.

Short Answer Type Questions

Question 9. Two balls of the same size but of different materials, rubber and iron, are kept on the smooth floor of a moving train. The brakes are applied suddenly to stop the train. Will the balls start rolling? If so, in which direction? Will they move with the same speed? Give reasons for your answer.

Answer When the train is stopped suddenly, then it comes in the state of rest but the balls remain in the state of motion. So, due to inertia of motion, the balls move in the forward direction.

As the balls are of same size but of differnt materials that means their mass will be different. So, both the balls will move with different speeds.

Question 10. Two identical bullets are fired one by one by a light rifle and another by a heavy rifle with the same force, which rifle will hurt the shoulder more and why?

Answer As both the bullets are identical and are fixed with the same force. So, according to Newton's third law of motion, same froce will be applied on both the rifles. With the application of same force, the light rifle will move more quickly in the forward direction, so it will hurt more to the shoulder.

Question 11. A horse continues to apply a force in order to move the cart with a constant speed. Explain why?

Answer The cart will move with a constant speed if there is no external force applied on it. When a horse applies a force on the cart, frictional force acting between the wheels of the cart and the road opposes the motion of the cart. The cart will move with the constant speed only when the force applied by horse is equal to the force of friction.

Question 12. Suppose a ball of mass m is thrown vertically upward with an initial speed v, its speed decreases continuously till it becomes zero. Thereafter, the ball begins to fall downward and attain the speed v again before striking the ground. It implies that the magnitude of initial and final momentums of the ball are same. Yet, it is not an example of conservation of momentum. Explain why?

Answer Momentum of a system remains conserved if no external force acts on the system. In the given example, there is gravitational force acting on the ball, so it is not an example of conservation of momentum.

Question 13. Velocity *versus* time graph of a ball of mass 50 g rolling on a concrete floor is shown in figure. Calculate the acceleration and frictional force of the floor on the ball.

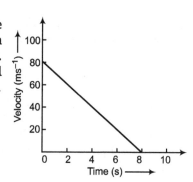

Answer Mass,

$$m = 50\,g = \frac{50}{1000} = 0.05\,kg$$

Initial velocity, $u = 80\,ms^{-1}$
Final velocity, $v = 0\,ms^{-1}$
  Time taken, $t = 8$ s
Acceleration, $a = \dfrac{v - u}{t} = \dfrac{0 - 80}{8} = \dfrac{-80}{8} = -10\,ms^{-2}$

Frictional force of the floor on the ball
$$F = ma = 0.05 \times -10 = 0.5\,N$$

Question 14. A truck of mass m is moved under a force F. If the truck is then loaded with an object equal to the mass of the truck and the driving force is halved, then how does the acceleration change.

Answer Initial mass, $m_1 = M$
  Initial force, $F_1 = F$
New mass, $m_2 = M + M = 2M$
  New force, $F_2 = \dfrac{F}{2}$

From Newton's second law, $F = ma \Rightarrow a = \dfrac{F}{m}$

Change in acceleration
$$\frac{a_1}{a_2} = \frac{F_1}{F_2} \times \frac{m_2}{m_1} = \frac{F}{F/2} \times \frac{2M}{M} = 4$$

$$\Rightarrow \qquad a_2 = \frac{1}{4}$$

i.e., acceleration becomes one-fourth.

Question 15. Two friends on roller skates are standing 5 m apart facing each other. One of them throws a ball of 2 kg towards the other, who catches it. How will this activity affect the position of the two? Explain your answer.

Answer When first boy throws the ball then he will move in backward direction due to reaction force of the ball. On the other hand, the second boy will move away from the first ball due to force applied by the ball. So, the distance between the two boys will increase.

Question 16. Water sprinkler used for grass lawn begins to rotate as soon as the water is supplied. Explain the priniciple on which it works.

Answer Water sprinkler works on Newton's third law of motion. When the water supplied, then force applies on the sprinkler due to which it rotates.

Long Answer Type Questions

Question 17. Derive the unit of force using the second law of motion. A force of 5 N produces an acceleration of 8 ms^{-2} on a mass m_1 and an acceleration of 24 ms^{-2} on a mass m_2. What acceleration would the same provide if both the masses are tied together?

Answer From Newton's second law, $F = ma$

SI unit of mass, $m = 1 \text{kg}$

SI unit of acceleration, $a = 1 \text{ms}^{-2}$

SI unit of force, $F = 1 \text{kg} \times 1 \text{ms}^{-2}$

$$= 1 \text{kg-ms}^{-2}$$

1 kg-ms^{-2} is known as 1 newton (N)

$\therefore$ $1 \text{ newton (N)} = 1 \text{kg-ms}^{-2}$

$\therefore$ 1 newton can be defined as, "The force is said to be 1 newton if it produces 1 ms^{-2} acceleration in a body of 1 kg mass".

$$F_1 = 5 \text{ N}, a_1 = 8 \text{ ms}^{-2}, m_1 = m_1$$
$$F_2 = 5 \text{ N}, a_2 = 24 \text{ ms}^{-2}, m_2 = m_2$$

From $F = ma$ or $5 = m_1 \times 8$

$\Rightarrow$ $m_1 = \dfrac{5}{8} \text{ kg}$

Similarly, $5 = m_2 \times 24$

$\Rightarrow$ $m_2 = \dfrac{5}{24} \text{ kg}$

$\therefore$ $m_1 + m_2 = \dfrac{5}{8} + \dfrac{5}{24}$

$$= \dfrac{15 + 5}{24} = \dfrac{20}{24} = \dfrac{10}{12} = \dfrac{5}{6}$$

Acceleration produced by the same force provided if both the masses are tied together.

$$a = \dfrac{F}{(m_1 + m_2)}$$

$$= \dfrac{5}{5/6} = 6 \text{ms}^{-2}$$

Question 18. What is momentum? Write its SI unit. Interpret force in terms of momentum. Represent the following graphically

(a) momentum *versus* velocity when mass is fixed.

(b) momentum *versus* mass when velocity is constant.

Answer **Momentum** The quantity of motion possessed by a moving body is known as momentum of the body.

Momentum of an object of mass m moving with a velocity v.

Momentum, $p = mv$

Its SI unit is kg-ms^{-1}

Force applied on an object of mass m moving with acceleration a.

$$F = ma$$
$$= m \frac{\Delta v}{\Delta t}$$

$$\left(\because \text{Acceleration} = \text{Rate of change of velocity} = \frac{\Delta v}{\Delta t}\right)$$

$$= \frac{\Delta p}{\Delta t}$$

$\therefore$ Force applied on an object is equal to the rate of change of momentum of the object.

(a) Momentum *versus* velocity when mass is fixed.

$$p = mv$$

If m is fixed, then $p \propto v$

$\therefore$ Momentum *versus* velocity graph will be a straight line passing through the origin (If $v = 0$, then $p = 0$).

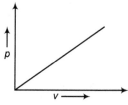

(b) Momentum *versus* mass graph when velocity is constant.

$$p = mv$$

If velocity is constant, then

$$p \propto m$$

So, the momentum *versus* mass graph will be a straight line passing through the origin (if $m = 0$, then $p = 0$).

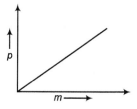

10

Gravitation

Important Concepts

1. **Gravitation** The force with which earth pulls everything towards itself is called gravitational force or gravity. Due to gravitational force

    (i) all objects falls down when released from a height.

    (ii) we can stand.

    (iii) moon goes around the earth, etc.

2. **Newton's Universal Law of Gravitation** "Every object in the universe attracts every other object with a force which is directly proportional to the product of their masses and inversely proportional to the square of distance between them."

    This force acts along the line joining the centres of two objects.

    According to Newton's law of gravitation, force of attraction (F) between two objects of mass m_1 and m_2 having a distance r between their centres is

    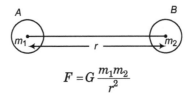

    $$F = G \frac{m_1 m_2}{r^2}$$

    where G is called universal gravitational constant and its value is 6.67×10^{-11} N-m^{-2}-kg^{-2}.

- Newton's gravitational law is said to be universal law because it is applicable to all bodies, whether the bodies are big or small, whether they are celestial or terestrial.
- Though different object on earth attract one another but they do not cause any motion because the gravitational force acting between them is very small.
- Due to gravitation, earth keeps moving around the sun in uniform circular motion.
- Gravitational force holds the solar system together.
- Gravitational force applied by earth on a body of mass m placed on its surface

$$F = G \frac{m_e m}{R_e^2}$$

where, m_e = mass of earth,
R_e = radius of earth.

3. **Characteristics of Gravitational Force**
   (i) Gravitational force is action at a distance i.e., it does not need any contact between the two bodies.
   (ii) Gravitational force is an **inverse square force** because it is inversely proportional to the square of the distance between the two bodies.
   (iii) Gravitational force between two bodies form **action-reaction** pair.
   (iv) Gravitational force between two small bodies is very small. On the other hand, gravitational force between two large bodies (say the sun and the earth) is large.

4. **Importance of Universal Law of Gravitation**
   - Universal law of gravitation successfully explained several phenomena like
   (i) The force that binds us to the earth.
   (ii) The motion of the moon around the earth.
   (iii) The motion of planets around the sun.
   (iv) The tides due to the moon and the sun.

5. **Kepler's Laws of Planetary Motion** Kepler derived three laws which govern the motion of planets around the sun. These are
   (i) The orbit of a planet is an ellipse with the sun at one of the foci.
   (ii) The line joining the planet and the sun sweep equal area in equal intervals of time.

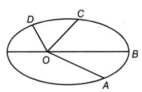

(iii) The cube of the mean distance of a planet from the sun is proportional to the square of its orbital period.

$$\frac{r^3}{T^2} = \text{constant}$$

6. **Free Fall : Acceleration due to Gravity** Whenever objects fall towards the earth under the earth's gravitational force alone, such object are called freely falling objects and such fall is called **Free Fall**.

Whenever an object falls towards the earth, an acceleration is involved, this acceleration is due to the earth's gravitational pull and is called acceleration due to gravity.

The acceleration with which an object falls towards the earth due to earth's gravitational pull is called acceleration due to gravity.

Acceleration due to gravity is represented by g and its value at earth's surface is 9.8 ms^{-2}.

$$g = \frac{GM}{R^2}$$

Its SI unit is ms^{-2}. Here G = Universal gravitational constant. M = Mass of earth, R = Radius of earth.

- The value of g decreases with the height from the surface of earth.
- The value of g decreases with the depth into the crust of the earth.
- The value of g does not depend on the mass of the object.

7. **Equations of motion for an object under the influence of gravitational force of the earth.**

Equations of motion for the object moving under the influence of gravitational force of the earth are

(i) $v = u + gt$

(ii) $h = ut + \frac{1}{2}gt^2$

(iii) $v^2 = u^2 + 2gh$

Note *The only difference between the equations of motion for object moving in straight line is that in place of acceleration a, we take acceleration due to gravity g.*

- If an object falls vertically downward then acceleration due to gravity is taken as positive ($\because$ its velocity increases while falling.)
- If an object is thrown vertically upward then acceleration due to gravity is taken as negative ($\because$ its velocity decreases as it moves upward.)
- If an object is dropped freely from a height, its initial velocity u is zero.
- If an object is thrown vertically upwards, its final velocity v becomes zero.
- Time taken by an object to fall from a height is same as that taken by it to rise the same height.

8. **Mass** The total amount of matter contained in an object is called its mass.
   - SI unit of mass is kilogram (kg).
   - Mass of a body does not change from time to time, it remains constant.
   - The mass of a body cannot be zero.

9. **Weight** The weight of an object is the force with which it is attracted towards the earth.
   Weight of an object $w = mg$
   where, m = mass, g = acceleration due to gravity
   or
   $$w = \frac{GMm}{R^2}$$
   Here, M = mass of the earth, R = radius of the earth.

Note *From the above formula it is clear that weight of object will change at same planet other than earth.*

10. Weight of an object on the moon is 1/6th of the weight on the earth (because on the moon, the acceleration due to gravity is 1/6th that of earth's).

11. Weight is a vector quantity, it acts in vertically downward direction and its SI unit is newton (N). Weight of 1 kg mass is 9.8 newton.

12. Weight of an object is not constant, it changes from place to place.

13. In the space where $g = 0$, weight of an object is zero. At the centre of earth, weight of an object is zero.

14. **Thrust and Pressure**
    - **Thrust** The force acting on an object perpendicular to its surface is called thrust.

- **Pressure** It is defined as the 'Normal force acting per unit surface area'.

or

The thrust on unit area is called pressure.

$$\text{Pressure} = \frac{\text{Thrust}}{\text{Surface area}} \quad \text{or} \quad p = \frac{F}{A}$$

- Pressure is a scalar quantity, its SI unit is N-m^{-2} or pascal (Pa).
- One pascal is defined as the pressure exerted on a unit surface area by a thrust of one newton.

15. **Some Daily Life Applications of Pressure**
    - The handles of bags and suitcase etc, are made broad so that the small pressure is exerted on the hand.
    - Building are provided **broad foundations** so that the pressure exerted on the ground becomes less.
    - Railway tracks are laid on cement or iron sleepers so that the pressure exerted by train is spread over the larger area and thus becomes less.
    - Pins, needles and nails are provided sharp pointed ends.
    - Cutting tools have sharp edges.

16. **Pressure in Fluids** The substances which can flow are called fluids. Fluids have weight, so they exert pressure on the base and walls of the container in which they are enclosed.

    Pressure exerted in any confined mass of fluid is transmitted undiminished in all directions.

17. **Buoyancy** When an object is immersed in a liquid, then liquid exerts an upward force on the object, this phenomena is called buoyancy.

    The upward force exerted by the liquid on the objects immersed in it, is called upthrust or buoyant force. The magnitude of buoyant force depend on the density of the fluid.
    - If the buoyant force applied by a liquid on an object is greater than the weight of the object then the object will float in that liquid.
    - If buoyant force is less than the weight of the object then the object will sink in that liquid.
    - The magnitude of buoyant force depends on the density.

18. **Floating or Sinking of Objects in Liquid** Objects having density less than that of the liquid in which they are immersed, float on the surface of the liquid. If the density of

the object is more than the density of the object in which it is immersed then it sinks in the liquid.

19. **Archimedes' Principle** When a body is immersed fully or partially in a fluid, it experiences an upward force that is equal to the weight of the fluid displaced by it.
Archimedes' principle is used in

   (i) designing ships and submarines.

   (ii) lactometer (used to determine density of liquid) is based on Archimedes' principle.

   (iii) hydrometer (used for determining density of liquid) is based on Archimedes' principle.

20. **Relative Density** The relative density of a substance is the ratio of its density to that of water.

$$\text{Relative density} = \frac{\text{Density of a substance}}{\text{Density of water}}$$

Relative density is a ratio, so it has no unit.

Intext Questions

On Page 134

Question 1. State the universal law of gravitation.

Answer According to universal law of gravitation, the force of attraction between two objects is directly proportional to the product of their masses and inversely proportional to the square of the distance between them.

Force of attraction between two objects of mass m_1 and m_2 placed at d distance apart is given by

$$F = G\frac{m_1 m_2}{d^2}$$

where, G = universal gravitational constant.

Question 2. Write the formula to find the magnitude of the gravitational force between the earth and an object on the surface of the earth.

Answer The force of attraction between the earth and an object on its surface is given by

$$F = \frac{GMm}{R^2}$$

where G = Universal gravitational constant, M = Mass of earth,

m = Mass of object, R = Radius of earth.

(Here we have considered that the whole mass of earth is concentrated at its centre.)

On Page 136

Question 1. What do you mean by free fall?

Answer When an object falls towards the earth under the effect of earth's gravitational pull alone, then the object is said to be in free fall.

Question 2. What do you mean by acceleration due to gravity?

Answer The acceleration that an object has in its free fall towards earth is called acceleration due to gravity. For earth, the value of acceleration due to gravity is $9.8\,\text{m-s}^{-2}$.

On Page 138

Question 1. What are the differences between the mass of an object and its weight?

Answer The difference between mass and weight of an object are given below.

S.No.	Mass	Weight
1.	The quantity of matter contained in a body is called the mass of the body.	The force with which the earth attracts a body towards its centre is called the weight of the body.
2.	Mass of a body remains constant.	Weight of a body changes from place to place
3.	Mass of a body is never zero.	Weight of a body at the centre of the earth is zero.
4.	Mass is a scalar quantity.	Weight is a vector quantity.
5.	Mass is measured in kg.	Weight is measured in kg-wt or N.
6.	Mass is measured by a beam balance.	Weight is measured by a weighing machine or a spring balance.

Question 2. Why is the weight of an object on the moon $\frac{1}{6}$th its weight on the earth?

Answer Weight of an object $w = mg$

where, m = mass of the object, g = acceleration due to gravity.

The mass of an object m remains constant at all the places. Acceleration due to gravity changes from place to place. So, we can say that the weight of an object depends on the acceleration due to gravity.

At moon, the acceleration due to gravity is $\frac{1}{6}$th that of the earth, this is the reason why the weight of an object on the moon is $\frac{1}{6}$th of its weight on the earth?

On Page 141

Question 1. Why is it difficult to hold a school bag having a strap made of a thin and strong string?

Answer It is difficult to hold a school bag having a strap made of a thin and strong string because the area under the strap is small. Hence large pressure is exerted by the strap on the fingers or shoulders.

Due to the large pressure, the strap tends to cut the skin and hence pain is caused.

Question 2. What do you mean by buoyancy?

Answer The tendency of an object to float in a liquid or the ability of liquid to make an object float in it is called buoyancy.

Question 3. Why does an object float or sink when placed on the surface of water?

Answer When an object is placed on the surface of water, two forces acts on the object.

  (i) The weight of the object, acting vertically downward.

  (ii) The upthrust of the water, acting vertically upward.

The object will float on the surface of water if the upthrust is greater than the weight of the object.

The object will sink if the weight of the object is more than the upthrust of the water.

On Page 142

Question 1. You find your mass to be 42 kg on a weighing machine. Is your mass more or less than 42 kg?

Answer The weight of an object $w = mg$

where, m = mass of the object

g = acceleration due to gravity = $9.8 \, ms^{-2}$

So, mass of the object, $m = \dfrac{w}{g}$

From the above expression, it is clear that mass is less than the weight of the object.

Question 2. You have a bag of cotton and an iron bar, each indicating a mass of 100 kg when measured on a weighing machine. In reality, one is heavier than other. Can you say which one is heavier and why?

Answer Iron bar is heavier than the cotton bag because for the mass the iron bar will have lesser surface area and hence will apply more pressure on holding.

Exercises

Question 1. How does the force of gravitation between two objects change when the distance between them is reduced to half?

Answer Force of gravitation between two objects

$$F = G\frac{m_1 m_2}{r^2}$$

If distance is reduced to half *i.e.*, $r' = r/2$

Then new force of gravitation $F' = \dfrac{Gm_1 m_2}{r'^2}$

$$= \frac{Gm_1 m_2}{(r/2)^2} = 4\frac{Gm_1 m_2}{r^2}$$

$$= 4F$$

i.e., the force of gravitation becomes 4 times than the original value.

Question 2. Gravitational force acts on all objects in proportion to their masses. Why then, a heavy object does not fall faster than a light object?

Answer Each object falls towards the earth with the acceleration, equal to acceleration due to gravity, which is constant (9.8 ms^{-2}) and does not depend on the mass of the object. So, heavy object does not fall faster than the light object.

Question 3. What is the magnitude of the gravitational force between the earth and a 1 kg object on its surface? (Mass of the earth is 6×10^{24} kg and radius of the earth is 6.4×10^6 m.)

Answer Gravitational force between the earth and an object

$$F = \frac{GMm}{R^2}$$

where, G = Gravitational constant $= 6.67 \times 10^{-11} \text{ Nm}^{-2}\text{-kg}^{-2}$

M = Mass of earth = 6×10^{24} kg

R = Radius of earth = 6.4×10^6 m

m = Mass of object = 1 kg

$\therefore \qquad F = \dfrac{6.67 \times 10^{-11} \times 6 \times 10^{24} \times 1}{(6.4 \times 10^6)^2} = 9.8 \text{ N}$

Question 4. The earth and the moon are attracted to each other by gravitational force. Does the earth attract the moon with a force that is greater or smaller or the same as the force with which the moon attracts the earth? Why?

Answer When two objects attract each other then gravitational force of attraction applied by first object on the second object is same as the force applied by the second object on the first object. So, both earth and moon attract each other by the same gravitational force of attraction.

Question 5. If the moon attracts the earth, why does the earth not move towards the moon?

Answer The earth does not move towards the moon in spite of the attraction by moon because the force with which moon attracts the earth is same by which earth attracts the moon. So, net force on the system becomes zero.

Question 6. What happens to the force between two objects, if
   (i) the mass of one object is doubled?
   (ii) the distance between the objects is doubled and tripled?
   (iii) the masses of both objects are doubled?

Answer Force of attraction between two objects

$$F = \frac{Gm_1 m_2}{r^2}$$

where, m_1, m_2 = Masses of the objects,
            r = Distance between the objects,
            G = Gravitational constant.

(i) If mass of one object is doubled, then the new force

$$F' = \frac{G(2m_1)\, m_2}{r^2} = 2\,\frac{Gm_1 m_2}{r^2} = 2F$$

i.e., force becomes-double.

(ii) If the distance between the objects is doubled, then the new force

$$F' = \frac{Gm_1 m_2}{(2r)^2} = \frac{Gm_1 m_2}{4r^2}$$

$$= \frac{1}{4}\frac{Gm_1 m_2}{r^2} = \frac{1}{4}(F) = \frac{F}{4}$$

i.e., force becomes one-fourth.
If the distance between the objects is tripled, then

new force $F' = \dfrac{Gm_1 m_2}{(3r)^2} = \dfrac{Gm_1 m_2}{9r^2}$

$$= \frac{1}{9}\left(\frac{Gm_1 m_2}{r^2}\right) = \frac{1}{9}F = \frac{F}{9}$$

i.e., force becomes one-ninth.

(iii) If masses of both objects are doubled, then

new force $F' = \dfrac{G(2m_1)\,(2m_2)}{r^2} = 4\,\dfrac{Gm_1 m_2}{r^2} = 4F$

i.e., force becomes four times.

Question 7. What is the importance of universal law of gravitation?

Answer The importance of universal law of gravitation can be understood from the following points:

1. All the planets revolve around the sun due to gravitational force between the sun and planets. Hence gravitational force is responsible for the existence of solar system.
2. Tides in oceans are formed due to the gravitational force between the moon and water in oceans.
3. Artificial satellites revolve around the earth due to gravitational force of earth.
4. The atmosphere of the earth is attached with it due to gravitational force of earth.
5. We can stand on the surface of earth due to gravitational force of earth.

Question 8. What is the acceleration of free fall?

Answer The acceleration of free fall is the acceleration produced in the motion of an object when it falls freely towards the earth. It is also called acceleration due to gravity. Its value on earth surface is $9.8 \, \text{ms}^{-2}$.

Question 9. What do we call the gravitational force between the earth and an object?

Answer The gravitational force between the earth and an object is called force of gravity.

Question 10. Amit buys few grams of gold at the poles as per the instruction of one of his friends. He hands over the same when he meets him at the equator. Will the friend agree with the weight of the gold bought. If not, why?
[**Hint** The value of g is greater at the poles than at the equator.]

Answer Weight of an object, $w = mg$

where, g = acceleration due to gravity
The value of g is greater at the poles than at the equator. So, the weight of the gold at the equator will be less than the weight of the gold at poles. So, Amit's friend will find the weight of the gold less than the weight told by Amit.

Question 11. Why will a sheet of paper fall slower than one that is crumpled into a ball?

Answer The sheet of paper falls slower than one that is crumpled into a ball because in first case the area of the sheet is more so it experiences large opposing force due to air. While the sheet crumpled into a ball experience less opposing force due to small area.

Question 12. Gravitational force on the surface of the moon is only $\frac{1}{6}$ as strong as gravitational force on the earth. What is the weight in newtons of a 10 kg object on the moon and on the earth?

Answer Mass of the object $m = 10\,\text{kg}$

Weight on the earth $w = mg$

$$= 10 \times 9.8 = 98\,\text{N}$$

Weight on the moon $= \frac{1}{6}$ of the weight on the earth

$$= \frac{1}{6} \times 98 = 16.33\,\text{N}$$

Question 13. A ball is thrown vertically upwards with a velocity of $49\,\text{ms}^{-1}$. Calculate

(i) the maximum height to which it rises,

(ii) the total time it takes to return to the surface of the earth.

Answer Initial velocity, $u = 49\,\text{ms}^{-1}$

(i) At the maximum height velocity becomes zero,

∴ Final velocity $v = 0$

From equation of upward motion

$$v^2 = u^2 - 2gh$$
$$0 = (49)^2 - 2 \times 9.8 \times h$$

∴ $$h = \frac{(49)^2}{2 \times 9.8} = 122.5\,\text{m}$$

Maximum height attained $= 122.5\,\text{m}$

(ii) Time taken by the ball to reach the maximum height.

From equation of upward motion $v = u - gt$

$$0 = 49 - 9.8 \times t$$
$$t = \frac{49}{9.8} = 5\,\text{s}$$

In the motion against gravity, the time of descent is same as the time of ascent.

So, time taken by the ball to fall from maximum height $= 5$ s

∴ Total time taken by the ball to return to surface of the earth $= 5 + 5 = 10\,\text{s}$

Question 14. A stone is released from the top of a tower of height 19.6 m. Calculate its final velocity just before touching the ground.

Answer Given, $h = 19.6\,\text{m}$

Initial velocity $u = 0$ \hfill (∵ It starts from rest)

From equation of motion, $v^2 = u^2 + 2gh$

$$v^2 = 0 + 2 \times 9.8 \times 19.6$$
$$= 19.6 \times 19.6$$
$$\therefore \qquad v = \sqrt{19.6 \times 19.6}$$
$$= 19.6\,ms^{-1}$$

Final velocity of stone just before touching the ground $= 19.6\,ms^{-1}$

Question 15. A stone is thrown vertically upward with an initial velocity of 40 ms^{-1}. Taking $g = 10$ ms^{-2}, find the maximum height reached by the stone. What is the net displacement and the total distance covered by the stone?

Answer   Initial velocity $u = 40\,ms^{-1}$

At maximum height, final velocity becomes zero *i.e.*, $v = 0$

From equation of motion $v^2 = u^2 - 2gh$
$$(0)^2 = (40)^2 - 2 \times 10 \times h$$
$$0 = 1600 - 20h$$
$$h = \frac{1600}{20} = 80\,m$$

$\therefore$ Maximum height reached by the stone $= 80\,m$

After reaching the maximum height, the stone will fall towards the earth and will reach the earth surface covering the same distance.

So, distance covered by the stone $= 80 + 80 = 160\,m$

Displacement of the stone $= 0$

(because the stone starts from the earth surface and finally reaches the earth surface again, *i.e.*, the initial and final position of the stone are same)

Question 16. Calculate the force of gravitation between the earth and the Sun, given that the mass of the earth $= 6 \times 10^{24}$ kg and of the sun $= 2 \times 10^{30}$ kg. The average distance between the two is 1.5×10^{11} m.

Answer   The force of attraction between the earth and the sun
$$F = \frac{GM_s M_e}{r^2}$$

where, $G = 6.67 \times 10^{-11}$ Nm^2-kg^{-2}

Given, mass of the sun, $M_s = 2 \times 10^{30}$ kg

Mass of the earth, $M_e = 6 \times 10^{24}$ kg

Average distance between the earth and the sun $= 1.5 \times 10^{11}$

$$\therefore \qquad F = \frac{6.67 \times 10^{-11} \times 2 \times 10^{30} \times 6 \times 10^{24}}{(1.5 \times 10^{11})^2}$$

$$= 3.6 \times 10^{22}\,N$$

Question 17. A stone is allowed to fall from the top of a tower 100 m high and at the same time another stone is projected vertically upwards from the ground with a velocity of 25 ms^{-1}. Calculate when and where the two stones will meet.

Answer Let after time t both stone meet and s be the distance travelled by the stone dropped from the top of tower at which the stones will meet.

Distance travelled by the stone dropped $= s$

$\therefore$ Distance travelled by the stone projected upwards

$$= (100 - s)\,m$$

For the stone dropped from the tower

$$s = ut + \frac{1}{2}gt^2$$

$$= 0 + \frac{1}{2}(10)t^2$$

($u = 0$ because stone is dropped i.e., it starts from rest)

$$s = 5t^2 \qquad \qquad ...(i)$$

For the stone projected upward

$$s' = ut - \frac{1}{2}gt^2$$

(Due to upward motion negative sign is taken)

$$(100 - s) = 25t - \frac{1}{2} \times 10t^2$$

$$100 - s = 25t - 5t^2$$

From Eq. (i)

$$100 - 5t^2 = 25\,t - 5t^2$$

$$25t = 100 \quad \Rightarrow \quad t = 4\,s$$

$\therefore$ The stones will meet after 4 s

$$s = 5t^2 = 5 \times (4)^2 = 80\,m$$

$\therefore$ The stones will be at a distance of 80 m from the top of tower or 20 m (100 m – 80 m) from the base of the tower.

Question 18. A ball thrown up vertically returns to the thrower after 6 s. Find

   (a) the velocity with which it was thrown up,

   (b) the maximum height it reaches, and

   (c) its position after 4 s.

Answer Total time taken $= 6\,s$

$\therefore$ Time taken to reach the maximum height $= \dfrac{6}{2} = 3\,s$

($\therefore$ Time of ascent = Time of descent)

(a) From equation of motion, $v = u - gt$

(Negative sign is taken due to upward motion)

$0 = u - 9.8 \times 3$ ($\because$ At maximum height $v = 0$)

$u = 29.4 \text{ ms}^{-1}$

(b) From equation of motion

$$v^2 = u^2 - 2gh$$

$$0 = (29.4)^2 - 2 \times 9.8 \times h$$

$$h = \frac{(29.4)^2}{2 \times 9.8} = 44.1 \text{m}$$

Maximum height attained by the ball is 44.1 m.

(c) In initial 3 s, the ball will rise then in next 3 s it falls toward the earth.

$\therefore$ The position after 4 s (3 + 1)

= Distance covered in 1 s in the downward motion

From equation of motion, $h = ut + \dfrac{1}{2} gt^2$

$$= 0 + \frac{1}{2} \times 9.8 \times (1)^2$$

$$= 4.9 \text{m}$$

i.e., the ball will be at 4.9 m from the top of the tower.

Question 19. In what direction does the buoyant force on an object immersed in a liquid act?

Answer The buoyant force on an object immersed in a liquid always act in upward direction.

Question 20. Why does a block of plastic released under water come up to the surface of water?

Answer The upthrust or buoyant force acting on the block of plastic by the water is greater then the weight of the plastic block. So, plastic block come up to the surface of water.

Question 21. The volume of 50g of a substance is 20 cm^3. If the density of water is 1 g cm^{-3}, will the substance float or sink.

Answer Mass of substance = 50g

Volume of substance = 20 cm^3

$\therefore$ Density of substance, $d = \dfrac{\text{Mass}}{\text{Volume}}$

$$= \frac{50}{20} = 1.25 \text{ g cm}^{-3}$$

i.e., the density of the substance is greater than the density of water, so it will sink in water.

Question 22. The volume of a 500 g sealed packet is 350 cm^3. Will the packet float or sink in water if the density of water is 1 gcm^{-3}? What will be the mass of the water displaced by this packet?

Answer   Mass of packet = 500 g

Volume of packet = 350 cm^3

∴ Density of packet, $d = \dfrac{\text{Mass}}{\text{Volume}}$

$= \dfrac{500}{350} = 1.43$ gcm^{-3}

i.e., the density of packet is greater than density of water, so it will sink in water.

Mass of water displaced by the packet

= Volume of packet × Density of water

= 350 × 1 = 350 g

Selected NCERT Exemplar Problems

Multiple Choice Questions

Question 1. Two objects of different masses falling freely near the surface of moon would

(a) have same velocities at any instant
(b) have different accelerations
(c) experience forces of same magnitude
(d) undergo a change in their inertia

Answer   (a) Objects of different masses falling freely near the surface of the moon would have the same velocities at any instant because they will have same acceleration due to gravity.

Question 2. The value of acceleration due to gravity

(a) is same on equator and poles   (b) is least on poles
(c) is least on equator   (d) increases from pole to equator

Answer   (c) At poles, the acceleration due to gravity is maximum and at equator it is minimum.

Question 3. The gravitational force between two objects is F. If masses of both objects are halved without changing distance between them, then the gravitational force would become

(a) $F/4$ (b) $F/2$ (c) F (d) $2F$

Answer   (a) Force of gravitation, $F = \dfrac{Gm_1 m_2}{r^2}$

If masses of both objects are halved then,

$$\text{New force } F' = \dfrac{G\left(\dfrac{m_1}{2}\right)\left(\dfrac{m_2}{2}\right)}{r^2}$$

$$= \dfrac{1}{4}\dfrac{Gm_1 m_2}{r^2} = \dfrac{F}{4}$$

Question 4. A boy is whirling a stone tied with a string in an horizontal circular path. If the string breaks, the stone
(a) will continue to move in the circular path
(b) will move along a straight line towards the centre of the circular path
(c) will move along a straight line tangential to the circular path
(d) will move along a straight line perpendicular to the circular path away from the boy

Answer   (c) In circular motion, the direction of velocity at a point is always along the tangent at that point. If string breaks then the centripetal force acting on the stone becomes zero and it will move along a straight line tangential to the circular path.

Question 5. An object is put the one by one in three liquids having different densities. The object floats with $\dfrac{1}{9}, \dfrac{2}{11}$ and $\dfrac{3}{7}$ parts of their volumes outside the liquid surface in liquids of densities d_1, d_2 and d_3 respectively. Which of the following statement is correct?
(a) $d_1 > d_2 > d_3$ (b) $d_1 > d_2 < d_3$
(c) $d_1 < d_2 > d_3$ (d) $d_1 < d_2 < d_3$

Answer   (d) In a liquid of higher density more part of the object remains outside the liquid. Since the order of part of their volume outside the liquid is

$$\dfrac{1}{9} < \dfrac{2}{11} < \dfrac{3}{7}$$

Thus, the order of densities is

$$d_1 < d_2 < d_3$$

Question 6. In the relation $F = GMm/d^2$, the quantity G
(a) depends on the value of g at the place of observation
(b) is used only when the earth is one of the two masses
(c) is greatest at the surface of the earth
(d) is universal constant of nature

Answer (d) The quantity G is universal constant of nature. The accepted value of G is $6.67 \times 10^{-11}\,Nm^{-2}\,kg^{-2}$.

Question 7. Law of gravitation gives the gravitational force between
(a) the earth and a point mass only
(b) the earth and Sun only
(c) any two bodies having some mass
(d) two charged bodies only

Answer (c) Law of gravitation is applicable to all bodies having same mass.

Question 8. The value of quantity G in the law of gravitation
(a) depends on mass of earth only
(b) depends on radius of earth only
(c) depends on both mass and radius of earth
(d) is independent of mass and radius of the earth

Answer (d) G is the constant of proportionality and is called the universal gravitational constant. It is independent of mass and radius of the earth.

Question 9. Two particles are placed at some distance. If the mass of each of the two particle is doubled, keeping the distance between them unchanged, the value of gravitational force between them will be
(a) $\frac{1}{4}$ times (b) 4 times (c) $\frac{1}{2}$ times (d) unchanged

Answer (b) Gravitational force $F = G\dfrac{Mm}{r^2}$

If mass of each particle is doubled

$\therefore$
$$F' = G\frac{(2M)\,(2m)}{r^2}$$
$$F' = 4G\frac{Mm}{r}$$
$$F' = 4F$$

Question 10. The atmosphere is held to the earth by
(a) gravity (b) wind
(c) clouds (d) earth's magnetic field

Answer (a) The atmosphere is held to the earth by gravity.

Question 11. The force of attraction between two unit point masses separated by a unit distance is called
(a) gravitational potential (b) acceleration due to gravity
(c) gravitational field (d) universal gravitational constant

Answer (*d*) We have

$$F = G\frac{Mm}{r^2}$$

$$F = G\frac{1 \times 1}{(1)^2}$$

$$\Rightarrow \qquad F = G$$

Therefore, the force of attraction between two unit point masses separated by a unit distance is called universal gravitational constant.

Question 12. The weight of an object at the centre of the earth of radius R is

(a) zero
(b) infinite
(c) R times the weight at the surface of the earth
(d) $1/R^2$ times the weight at surface of the earth

Answer (a) Weight $w = mg$

At the centre of earth, acceleration due to gravity g is zero.

$$\therefore \qquad w = m \times 0 = 0$$

Question 13. An object weighs 10 N in air. When immersed fully in water, it weighs only 8 N. The weight of the liquid displaced by the object will be

(a) 2 N   (b) 8 N   (c) 10 N   (d) 12 N

Answer (a) Weight of liquid displaced, $F = 10 - 8 = 2$ N

Question 14. A girl stands on a box having 60 cm length, 40 cm breadth and 20 cm width in three ways. In which of the following cases, pressure exerted by the brick will be

(a) maximum when length and breadth form the base
(b) maximum when breadth and width form the base
(c) maximum when width and length form the base
(d) the same in all the above three cases

Answer (b) Pressure $= \dfrac{\text{Thrust}}{\text{Area}}$

Pressure exerted by the brick will be maximum when area is small.

$\therefore$ Area will be minimum, then breadth and width are formed the base.

Question 15. An apple falls from a tree because of gravitational attraction between the earth and apple. If F_1 is the magnitude of force exerted by the earth on the apple and F_2 is the magnitude of force exerted by apple on earth, then

(a) F_1 is very much greater than F_2
(b) F_2 is very much greater than F_1
(c) F_1 is only a little greater than F_2
(d) F_1 and F_2 are equal

Answer (d) From third law of motion, to every action, there is an equal and opposite reaction and they act on two different bodies, so F_1 and F_2 are equal.

Short Answer Type Questions

Question 16. What is the source of centripetal force that a planet requires to revolve around the Sun? On what factors does that force depend?

Answer The motion of the planet around the earth is due to the centripetal force. This centripetal force is provided by the gravitational force between the planet and the Sun.

Question 17. On the earth, a stone is thrown from a height in a direction parallel to the earth's surface while another stone is simultaneously dropped from the same height. Which stone would reach the ground first and why?

Answer Time taken by both stone

$$t = \sqrt{\frac{2h}{g}}$$

Therefore, if we drop down a stone from a height and at same time throw another stone in horizontal direction, then both the stone strike the earth simultaneously at different places.

Question 18. Suppose gravity of earth suddenly becomes zero, then in which direction will the moon begin to move if no other celestial body affects it?

Answer In the absence of gravity of earth, the moon flies off along a straight line. This straight line will be a tangent to the circular path.

Question 19. Identical packets are dropped from two aeroplanes, one above the equator and the other above the north pole, both at height h. Assuming all conditions are identical, will those packets take same time to reach the surface of earth. Justify your answer.

Answer No, those packets do not take same time to reach the surface of earth.

The earth is not a perfect sphere. As the radius of the earth increases from the poles to the equator, the value of g becomes greater at the poles than at the equator.

Time taken by packets

$$t = \sqrt{\frac{2h}{g}}$$

Since g is greatest at the poles than at the equator. So, packet dropped above the north pole will reach first at the surface of earth.

Question 20. The weight of any person on the moon is about 1/6 times that on the earth. He can lift a mass of 15 kg on the earth. What will be the maximum mass, which can be lifted by the same force applied by the person on the moon?

Answer Mass does not change at every place. So, 15 kg will be maximum mass which can be lifted by the same force applied by the person on the moon.

Question 21. Calculate the average density of the earth in terms of g, G and R.

Answer Mass of earth, $M = \dfrac{gR^2}{G}$

If the earth is considered as a sphere of radius R and of material of density ρ then

$$M = \frac{4}{3}\pi R^3 \rho$$

$$\therefore \qquad \frac{4}{3}\pi R^3 \rho = \frac{gR^2}{G}$$

$$\rho = \frac{3g}{4\pi GR}$$

Question 22. The earth is acted upon by gravitation of Sun, even though it does not fall into the Sun. Why?

Answer The earth revolves around the Sun. The centripetal force is needed by the earth to revolve around the Sun. This centripetal force is provided by the gravitational force between the sun and the earth.

Long Answer Type Questions

Question 23. How does the weight of an object vary with respect to mass and radius of the earth. In a hypothetical case, if the diameter of the earth becomes half of its present value and its mass becomes four times its present value, then how would the weight of any object on the surface of the earth be affected?

Answer Weight of the object,

$$w = mg = \frac{GMm}{R^2}$$

If
$$D' = \frac{D}{2}$$

i.e.,
$$R' = \frac{R}{2}$$

and
$$M' = 4M$$

Now, weight of the object
$$w' = \frac{G\,Mm}{R'}$$

$$w' = \frac{G4Mm}{(R/2)^2} = \frac{16\,GMm}{R^2}$$

$$w' = 16w$$

Thus, weight of the object will become 16 times of its original weight.

Question 24. How does the force of attraction between the two bodies depend upon their masses and distance between them? A student thought that two bricks tied together would fall faster than a single one under the action of gravity. Do you agree with his hypothesis or not? Comment.

Answer The force of attraction between two bodies of masses m_1 and m_2 and separated by distance r is given by
$$F = \frac{Gm_1m_2}{r^2}$$

where, G is the universal constant in nature.

This force is known as gravitational force. The gravitational force is directly proportional to the product of the masses of two bodies and inversely proportional to the square of the distance between them.

All bodies fall with the same acceleration due to gravity whatever their masses have.

So, two bricks tied together will not fall faster than a single bricks under the action of gravity. Hence the hypothesis is not correct.

Question 25. Two objects of masses m_1 and m_2 having the same size are dropped simultaneously from heights h_1 and h_2 respectively. Find out the ratio of time they would take in reaching the ground. Will this ratio remain the same if (i) one of the objects is hollow and the other one is solid and (ii) both of them are hollow, size remaining the same in each case. Give reason.

Answer From equation of motion
$$h = \frac{1}{2}gt^2$$

i.e.,
$$t = \sqrt{\frac{2h}{g}}$$

∴ Time taken by object of mass m_1

$$t_1 = \sqrt{\frac{2h_1}{g}}$$

Time taken by object of mass m_2

$$t_2 = \sqrt{\frac{2h_2}{g}}$$

∴

$$\frac{t_1}{t_2} = \sqrt{\frac{h_1}{h_2}}$$

Yes, in case (i) and case (ii), this ratio remains same because time taken by objects does not depend upon their masses.

Question 26.

(a) A cube of side 5 cm is immersed in water and then in saturated salt solution. In which case will it experience a greater buoyant force. If each side of the cube is reduced to 4 cm and then immersed in water, what will be the effect on the buoyant force experienced by the cube as compared to the first case for water. Give reason for each case.

(b) A ball weighing 4 kg of density 4000 kgm^{-3} is completely immersed in water of density 10^3 kgm^{-3} Find the force of buoyancy on it. (Given $g = 10$ ms^{-2}.)

Answer

(a) Buoyant force, $F = V\rho g$

Buoyant force depends upon volume and density since saturated salt solution have higher density than the water. So, in saturated solution, cube will experience a greater buoyant force.

If each side of the cube is reduced to 4 cm, the volume of cube become less. So, buoyant force will be less than as compared to the first case for water.

(b) The magnitude of the buoyant force depends on the density of the fluid

$$\text{Volume of solid} = \frac{\text{Mass}}{\text{Density}} = \frac{4}{4000} = \frac{1}{1000} \text{ m}^3$$

$$\text{Buoyancy, } F = V\rho g$$
$$= \frac{1}{1000} \times 1000 \times 10$$
$$= 10 \text{ N}$$

11

Work and Energy

Important Concepts

1. **Work** Work is said to be done if on applying a force on an object, it is displaced.

   If a constant force F acts on an object and object is displaced

   through a distance and in the direction of force.

   Then   Work, $W = Fs$

   * Work is scalar quantity, its unit is Joule.
   * If there is angle θ between the direction of force and direction of displacement, then

      Work, $W = Fs \cos \theta$

2. **Energy** The ability of a body to do some work is called energy. It is a scalar quantity and its unit is Joule.
   Larger unit of energy is kilojoule (kJ).

      $1 \text{ kJ} = 1000 \text{ J}$

   There are many forms of energies like mechanical energy (kinetic energy + potential energy), heat energy, chemical energy, light energy etc.

3. **Kinetic energy** The ability of a body to do some work due to virtue of its motion, is called kinetic energy.

If an object of mass m is placed at height h above the earth surface, then the work done in lifting the object is stored in the form of gravitational potential energy.

Gravitational potential energy = mgh

The potential energy of an object at a height depends on the ground level or the zero level. An object in a given position can have a certain potential energy with respect to another level.

4. **Law of conservation of energy** According to law of conservation of energy, energy can only be converted from one form to another, it can neither be created nor be destroyed.

The total energy before and after the transformation remains same.

This law is valid in all situations and for all kinds of transformations.

5. **Power : Rate of doing work** Power is defined as the rate of doing work or the rate of transfer of energy. If an object does a work W in time t, then power is given by

$$\text{Power} = \frac{\text{Work}}{\text{Time}} = \frac{W}{t}$$

Its unit is watt having the symbol W.

6. **Average power** Average power is obtained by dividing the total energy consumed by the total time taken.

7. **Commercial unit of energy** The unit joule is too small so it is inconvenient to express large quantity of energy in joule. A bigger unit called kWh is used to express large quantity of energies. It is called commercial unit of energy.

$$1 \text{ kWh} = 3.6 \times 10^6 \text{ J}$$

The energy used in house holds, industries and commercial establishment are usually expressed in kilowatt hour. 1 kWh is also called 1 unit.

Intext Questions

On Page 148

Question 1. A force of 7 N acts on an object. The displacement is, say 8 m, in the direction of the force as shown in figure. Let us take it that the force acts on the object through the displacement. What is the work in this case?

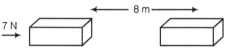

Answer Given, Force $F = 7$ N

Displacement, $s = 8$ m

$\therefore$ Work done, $W = F \cdot s$

$= 7 \times 8 = 56$ N-m or 56 J

On Page 149

Question 1. When do we say that work is done?

Answer Work is said to be done when force acts on an object and displaces it from its initial position.

Question 2. Write an expression for the work done when a force is acting on an object in the direction of its displacement.

Answer Expression for the work done when the displacement in the position of the object is along the direction of the force, is

$W = Fs$

where F = force applied,

s = displacement.

Question 3. Define 1 J of work.

Answer Work is said to be 1 J, if 1N force displaces an object through 1 metre in its own direction.

Question 4. A pair of bullocks exerts a force of 140 N on a plough. The field being ploughed is 15 m long. How much work is done in ploughing the length of the field?

Answer Given, Applied force, $F = 140$ N

Displacement, $s = 15$ m

Work done in ploughing the field, $W = F \cdot s$

$= 140 \times 15 = 2100$ J

$= 2.1 \times 10^3$ J

On Page 152

Question 1. What is the kinetic energy of an object?

Answer The energy possessed by an object due to the virtue of its motion is known as the kinetic energy of the object.

Question 2. Write the expression for the kinetic energy of an object.

Answer The expression for the kinetic energy of an object,

$$KE = \frac{1}{2}mv^2$$

where m = mass of the object,
               v = speed of the object.

Question 3. The kinetic energy of an object of mass m moving with a velocity of 5 ms^{-1} is 25 J. What will be its kinetic energy when its velocity is increased three times?

Answer Kinetic energy $K = \frac{1}{2}mv^2$

where, m = mass of object,
                v = velocity of the object.
Here, mass (m) is same in both cases ($\because$ object is same).

$\therefore$ $$\frac{K_1}{K_2} = \left(\frac{v_1}{v_2}\right)^2$$

Initial kinetic energy K_1 = 25 J.
Initial velocity $v_1 = 5$ ms^{-1}.
New kinetic energy $K_2 = ?$
New velocity $v_2 = 3v_1 = 3 \times 5 = 15$ ms^{-1}

$\therefore$ $$\frac{25}{K_2} = \left(\frac{5}{15}\right)^2$$

$$\frac{25}{K_2} = \frac{1}{9}$$

$\Rightarrow$ $$K_2 = 225 \text{ J}$$

On Page 156

Question 1. What is power?

Answer Power is defined as the rate of doing work. If the work done by an object in time t is W. Then,

$$\text{Power } P = \frac{W}{t}$$

Its unit is Joule/second or watt.

Question 2. Define 1 watt of power?

Answer Power, $P = \dfrac{W}{t}$

If $W = 1\,J, t = 1\,s$

then $P = \dfrac{1}{1} = 1\,W$

Power of an object is said to be 1 watt if it does 1 Joule of work in 1 second.

Question 3. A lamp consumes 1000 J of electrical energy in 10 s. What is its power?

Answer Energy = 1000 J, *i.e.*, work W = 1000 J

Time $t = 10\,s$

Power of lamp $P = \dfrac{W}{t} = \dfrac{1000}{10} = 100\,W.$

Question 4. Define average power.

Answer Average power is defined as the ratio of total work done by an agent to the total time taken.

Exercises

Question 1. Look at the activities listed below. Reason out whether or not work is done in the light of your understanding of the term 'work'.

(a) Suma is swimming in a pond.

(b) A donkey is carrying a load on its back.

(c) A wind mill is lifting water from a well.

(d) A green plant is carrying out photosynthesis.

(e) An engine is pulling a train.

(f) Food grains are getting dried in the sun.

(g) A sail boat is moving due to wind energy.

Answer

(a) What is being done by Suma because she displaces the water by applying the force.

(b) No work is being done by the donkey because the direction of force *i.e.*, load is vertically downward and displacement is along horizontal. If displacement and force are perpendicular then no work is done.

(c) Work is done, because wind mill is lifting the water *i.e.*, it is changing the position of water.

(d) No work is done, because there is no force and displacement.

(e) Work is done, because engine is changing the position of train.

(f) No work is done because there is no force and no displacement.

(g) Work is done because the force acting on the boat is moving it.

Question 2. An object thrown at a certain angle to the ground moves in a curved path and falls back to the ground. The initial and the final points of the path of the object lie on the same horizontal line? What is the work done by the force of gravity on the object?

Answer Work done by the force of gravity, $W = mgh$.

where h = difference in height of initial and final positions of the object.

According to question, the initial and final positions of the object lie in same horizontal line, so $h = 0$.

$\therefore$ $\quad\quad$ Work done, $W = mg \times 0 = 0$

Question 3. A battery lights a bulb. Describe the energy changes involved in the process.

Answer In the case given in the question, the battery has chemical energy which is converted energy. Electrical energy provided to the bulb further converted into light energy.

Question 4. Certain force acting on a mass 20 kg mass changes its velocity from 5 ms^{-1} to 2 ms^{-1}. Calculate the work done by the force?

Answer Given, $\quad$ mass, $m = 20$ kg

$\quad\quad$ Initial velocity, $u = 5$ ms^{-1}

$\quad\quad$ final velocity, $\quad v = 2$ ms^{-1}

$\quad$ Work done by the force = Change in kinetic energy

$\quad\quad$ = Final kinetic energy − Initial kinetic energy

$$= \frac{1}{2}mv^2 - \frac{1}{2}mu^2$$

$$= \frac{1}{2}m\,(v^2 - u^2) = \frac{1}{2} \times 20\,[(2)^2 - (5)^2]$$

$$= 10\,(4 - 25) = 10 \times -21 = -210\,J$$

Question 5. A mass of 10 kg is at a point A on a table. It is moved to a point B. If the line joining A and B is horizontal, what is the work done on the object by the gravitational force? Explain your answer.

Answer Work done by gravitational force $W = mgh$

where h = difference in the heights of initial and final positions of the object.

Here, both the initial and final positions are on the same horizontal line. So, there is no difference in height *i.e.*, $h = 0$

$\therefore$ $\quad\quad$ Work done, $W = mg \times 0 = 0$

Question 6. The potential energy of a freely falling object decreases progressively. Does this violate law of conservation of energy? Why?

Answer It is true that the potential energy of freely falling object decreases progressively.

But as the object falls down, its speed increases progressively *i.e.,* the kinetic energy of the object increases progressively (kinetic energy will increase with the increase in speed).

Now we can say that the law of conservation of energy is not violated, because the decrease in potential energy results in the increase of kinetic energy.

Question 7. What are the various energy tansformations that occur when you are riding on a bicycle?

Answer In case of bicycle, the muscular energy is converted into the kinetic energy of the bicycle.

Question 8. Does the transfer of energy take place when you push a huge rock with all your might and fail to move it? Where is the energy you spend going?

Answer When we push a huge rock, then the rock also exerts a huge force on us (according to Newton's third law of motion). The muscular energy spent by us in the process is used to oppose the huge force acting on us due to the rock.

Question 9. A certain household has consumed 250 units of energy during a month. How much energy is this in Joules?

Answer Energy consumed = 250 units

$$= 250 \text{ kWh}$$
$$= 250 \times 1000 \text{ W} \times 3600 \text{ s}$$
$$= 250 \times 1000 \text{ J / s} \times 3600 \text{ s}$$
$$= 9 \times 10^8 \text{ J}$$

Question 10. An object of mass 40 kg is raised to a height of 5 m above the ground. What is its potential energy? If the object is allowed to fall, find its kinetic energy when it is half-way down.

Answer Given, mass $m = 40$ kg, height $h = 5$ m

Potential energy $PE = mgh = 40 \times 9.8 \times 5 = 1960$ J

KE at half-way down = PE at half-way down

$$= mg\frac{h}{2}$$

$$= 40 \times 9.8 \times \frac{5}{2} = 980 \text{ J}$$

Question 11. What is the work done by the force of gravity on a satellite moving round the earth? Justify your answer.

Answer The satellite round the earth moves in a circular orbit.

Here, the force of gravity acts towards the centre of the earth and displacement of the satellite is along the tangent of circular path. That means the force and displacement are perpendicular to each other.

So,   Work done, $W = F \cdot s \cos \theta$

$$= F \cdot s \cos 90°$$

$$= F \cdot s \times 0 = 0$$

i.e., no work is done by the force of gravity.

Question 12. Can there be displacement of an object in the absence of any force acting on it? Think, discuss this question with your friends and teacher.

Answer If an object moves with a constant velocity, (*i.e.,* there is no acceleration) then no force acts on it. As the object is moving (*i.e.,* it is displaced from one position to another position.

Question 13. A person holds a bundle of hay over his head for 30 minutes and gets tried. Has he done some work or not? Justify your answer.

Answer The person has no movement *i.e.,* his displacement is zero, so the person has done no work ($\because$ work is done only when the object is displaced).

Question 14. An electric heater is rated 1500 W. How much energy does it use in 10 hours?

Answer   Power $= 1500\,W$

$$Time = 10\,h = 10 \times 60\,min$$

$$= 10 \times 60 \times 60\,s$$

$$Power = \frac{Energy \text{ or work}}{Time}$$

$\therefore$ $$Energy = Power \times Time$$

$$= 1500 \times 10 \times 60 \times 60$$

$$= 5.4 \times 10^7 \text{ J}$$

Question 15. Illustrate the law of conservation of energy by discussing the energy changes which occur when we draw a pendulum bob to one side and allow it to oscillate. Why does the bob eventually come to rest? What happens to its energy eventually? Is it a violation of the law of conservation of energy?

Answer

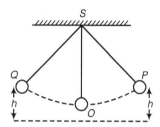

Let a simple pendulum be suspended from a rigid support S. Let OS be the equilibrium position of the pendulum. Let the pendulum be displaced to a position P, where it is at rest. At position P, the pendulum has potential energy (*mgh*). When the pendulum is released from position P, it begins to move towards position O. The speed of the pendulum increases and its height decreases that means the potential energy is converting into kinetic energy.

At position O, whole of the potential energy of the pendulum is converted into its kinetic energy. Then the pendulum swings to other side due to inertia of motion. As the pendulum begins to move towards position Q, the speed of pendulum decreases and height increases that means kinetic energy is converting into potential energy. At point Q, whole of the kinetic energy is converted into potential energy. Thus we find that the potential energy is converted into kinetic energy and *vice-versa* during the motion of the pendulum. But the total energy remains constant.

When the pendulum oscillates in air, the air friction opposes its motion. So, some part of kinetic energy of pendulum is used to overcome this friction. With the passage of time, kinetic energy of the pendulum goes on decreasing and finally becomes zero. The kinetic energy of the pendulum is transferred to the atmosphere. So, energy is being transferred *i.e.,* is converted into one from to another. So, here is no violation of law of conservation of energy.

Question 16. An object of mass *m* is moving with a constant velocity *v*. How much work should be done on the object in order to bring the object to rest?

Answer The work done on the object to bring the object to rest

= Change in kinetic energy

= Final kinetic energy − Initial kinetic energy

Here, final kinetic energy is zero because the object is brought to rest.

$$= 0 - \frac{1}{2} mv^2 = - \frac{1}{2} mv^2$$

Question 17. Calculate the work required to be done to stop a car of 1500 kg moving at a velocity of 60 kmh^{-1}.

Answer   Given, $m = 1500$ kg, Initial velocity $u = 60$ kmh^{-1}

$$= 60 \times \frac{5}{18} = 16.67 \text{ ms}^{-1}$$

Final velocity $v = 0$ ($\because$ the car comes to rest)

$\therefore$ Work done to stop the car

$$= \text{Change in kinetic energy}$$
$$= \text{Final kinetic energy} - \text{Initial kinetic energy}$$
$$= \frac{1}{2} mv^2 - \frac{1}{2} mu^2$$
$$= \frac{1}{2} \times 1500 \times (0)^2 - \frac{1}{2} \times 1500 \times (16.67)^2$$
$$= -\frac{1}{2} \times 1500 \times (16.67)^2 = -208333.33 \text{ J}$$

Question 18. In each of the following, a force F is acting on an object of mass m. The direction of displacement is from west to east shown by the longer arrow. Observe the diagrams carefully and state whether the work done by the force is negative, positive or zero.

Answer   **Case I** The force and displacement are perpendicular to each other, so $\theta = 90°$.

$$\text{Work done} = Fs \cos \theta$$
$$= Fs \cos 90°$$
$$= Fs \times 0 = 0 \qquad (\because \cos 90° = 0)$$

i.e., the work done is zero.

Case II The force and displacement are in the same direction, so $\theta = 0°$

$\therefore$ $\qquad$ Work done $W = Fs \cos \theta$
$$= Fs \cos 0°$$
$$= Fs \times 1 = Fs \qquad (\because \cos 0° = 1)$$

i.e., the work done is positive.

Case III The force and displacement in opposite directions,

so $\qquad\qquad\qquad \theta = 180°$

$\therefore$ $\qquad$ Work done $W = Fs \cos \theta$
$$= Fs \cos 180°$$
$$= Fs \times -1 \qquad (\because \cos 180° = -1)$$
$$= -Fs$$

i.e., the work done is negative.

Question 19. Soni says that the acceleration in an object could be zero even when several forces are acting on it. Do you agree with her? Why?

Answer Yes, I am agree with soni, the acceleration in an object can be zero even when several forces are acting on it, if the resultant of all the forces acting is zero.

Question 20. Find the energy in kWh consumed in 10 h by four devices of power 500 W each.

Answer Total power, $P = 500\,W \times 4 = 2000\,W$

$$\text{Time } t = 10\,h$$
$$\text{Energy consumed} = \text{Power} \times \text{Time}$$
$$= 2000\,W \times 10\,h$$
$$= 2\,kW \times 10\,h = 20\,kWh$$

Question 21. A freely falling object eventually stops on reaching the ground. What happens to its kinetic energy?

Answer When freely falling object strikes the earth then some sound and heat is produced. So, the kinetic energy of the object converts into sound energy and heat energy.

Selected NCERT Exemplar Problems
Multiple Choice Questions

Question 1. When a body falls freely towards the earth, then its total energy
- (a) increases
- (b) decreases
- (c) remains constant
- (d) first increases and then decreases

Answer (c) When a body falls freely towards the earth, then its total energy remains constant *i.e.*, the sum of the potential energy and kinetic energy of body would be same at all points.

Question 2. A car is accelerated on a lavelled road and attains a velocity 4 times of its initial velocity. In this process, the potential energy of the car
- (a) does not change
- (b) becomes twice to that of initial
- (c) becomes 4 times that of initial
- (d) becomes 16 times that of initial

Answer (d)   Initial velocity $= u$

$\therefore$ Energy $K_1 = \dfrac{1}{2} mu^2$

After some time velocity become 4 times of its initial velocity

Final velocity $= 4u$

$\therefore$ Energy $= \dfrac{1}{2} m (4u)^2$

$= \dfrac{1}{2} m\, 16u^2$

$K_2 = 16 \dfrac{1}{2} mu^2$

$K_2 = 16 K_1$

So, in this process the potential energy of car becomes 16 times that of initial.

Question 3. In case of negative work, the angle between the force and displacement is

(a) $0°$ (b) $45°$ (c) $90°$ (d) $180°$

Answer (d) Work done $W = F \cdot d \cos \theta$

$\cos 180° = -1$

$W = -F \cdot d$

For negative work, the angle between the force and displacement should be $180°$.

Question 4. An iron sphere of mass 10 kg has the same diameter as an aluminum sphere of mass 3.5 kg. Both spheres are dropped simultaneoulsy from a tower. When they are 10 m above the ground, they have the same

(a) acceleration   (b) momenta
(c) potential energy   (d) kinetic energy

Answer (d) When both spheres are dropped simultaneously from a tower, they have same acceleration.

Question 5. A girl is carrying a school bag of 3 kg mass on her back and moves 200 m on a lavelled road. The work done against the gravitational force will be ($g = 10$ ms^{-2})

(a) 6×10^3 J   (b) 6 J   (c) 0.6 J   (d) zero

Answer (d)   Work done $= F \cdot d \cos \theta$

School bag makes angle $90°$ from the road.

$W = F \cdot d \cos 90°$

$W = 0$

Question 6. Which one of the following is not the unit of energy?

(a) Joule (b) Newton metre
(c) Kilowatt (d) Kilowatt hour

Answer (c) Kilowatt is the unit of power.

Question 7. The work done on an object does not depend upon the

(a) displacement
(b) force applied
(c) angle between force and displacement
(d) initial velocity of the object

Answer (d) Work done = Displacement × Force × cos θ.

Question 8. Water stored in a dam possesses

(a) no energy (b) electrical energy
(c) kinetic energy (d) potential energy

Answer (d) Water stored in a dam possesses potential energy.

Question 9. A body is falling from a height h. After it has fallen a height $\dfrac{h}{2}$, it will possess

(a) only potential energy
(b) only kinetic energy
(c) half potential and half kinetic energy
(d) more kinetic and less potential energy

Answer (a) Mechanical energy of a freely-falling body remains constant at all positions which is equal to mgh i.e., potential energy.

Short Answer Type Questions

Question 10. A rocket is moving up with a velocity v. If the velocity of this rocket is suddenly tripled, which will be the ratio of two kinetic energies?

Answer Given, $v_1 = v$ and $v_2 = 3v$

The ratio of two kinetic energies

$$\frac{K_1}{K_2} = \frac{\dfrac{1}{2}mv_1^2}{\dfrac{1}{2}mv_2^2}$$

$$\frac{K_1}{K_2} = \frac{v_1^2}{v_2^2} = \frac{v}{(3v)^2}$$

$$\frac{K_1}{K_2} = \frac{1}{9}$$

Question 11. Avinash can run with a speed of 8 ms^{-1} against the frictional force of 10 N, and Kapil can move with a speed of 3 ms^{-1} against the frictional force of 25 N. Who is more powerful and why?

Answer   Force applied by Avinash = 10 N

Speed of Avinash = 8 ms^{-1}

Power of Avinash = $F \cdot v$

$= 10 \times 8 = 80$ W

Force applied by Kapil = 25 N

Speed of Kapil = 3 m s^{-1}

Power of Kapil = $F \cdot v$

$= 25 \times 3 = 75$ W

Since Avinash has more power $(80 - 75) = 5$ W than Kapil. So, Avinash is more powerful.

Question 12. A boy is moving on a straight road against a frictional force of 5 N. After travelling a distance of 1.5 km he forgot the correct path at a round about of radius 100 m as shown in figure. However, he moves on the circular path for one and half cycle and then he moves forward upto 2.0 km. Calculate the work done by him.

Answer   Force applied on road by boy = 5 N

Displacement on the circular path

$=$ One cycle + Half cycle

$= 0 +$ Half cycle

$= 0 +$ Diameter of circular path

$= 0 + 200 = 200$ m

∴   Total displacement $= 1.5 \times 1000 + 200 + 2 \times 1000$

$= 3700$ m

Work done by boy = $F \cdot s \cos \theta$

$= 5 \times 3700 \times \cos \theta = 18500$ J

Question 13. Can any object have mechanical energy even if its momentum is zero?

Answer   The energy in a body due to its position or state of strain is called potential energy (*mgh*).

Momentum, $p = mv$

If v is zero, then momentum will be zero. Since, potential energy (*i.e.*,mechanical energy) does not depend upon the velocity. So, object can have mechanical energy if its momentum is zero.

Question 14. Can any object have momentum even if its mechanical energy is zero? Explain.

Answer Potential energy, $p = mgh$

If h is zero, then potential energy will become zero.

Since momentum does not depend upon the height. So, momentum will not be zero.

Therefore, object can have momentum if its mechanical energy is zero.

Question 15. The power of a motor pump is 2 kW. How much water per minute the pump can raise to a height of 10 m? (Given $g = 10 \text{ ms}^{-2}$).

Answer Given, power of a motor = 2 kW = 2 × 1000 W = 2000 W

$$\text{Power, } P = \frac{\text{Energy}}{\text{Time}}$$

$$P = \frac{mgh}{t}$$

$$2000 = \frac{m \times 10 \times 10}{60}$$

or

$$m = \frac{2000 \times 60}{10 \times 10}$$

$$m = 1200 \text{ kg}$$

Question 16. The weight of a person on a planet A is about half that on the earth. He can jump upto 0.4 m height on the surface of the earth. How high he can jump on the planet A?

Answer The weight of person on the earth = W

$\therefore$ weight of planet = $\dfrac{W}{2}$

So, the person can jump 2 times higher on the planet. Hence height of jump on the planet

$$= 2 \times 0.4 = 0.8 \text{ m}$$

Question 17. The velocity of a body moving in a straight line is increased by applying a constant force F, for some distance in the direction of the motion. Prove that the increase in the kinetic energy of the body is equal to the work done by the force on the body.

Answer Consider an object of mass m moving with a uniform velocity u.

Let it now be displaced through a distance s when a constant force F acts on it in the direction of its displacement.

From the equation of motion

$$v^2 - u^2 = 2as$$

$$s = \frac{v^2 - u^2}{2a}$$

Work done by F,

$$W = F \cdot s$$
$$= ma \cdot s$$
$$= ma \times \left(\frac{v^2 - u^2}{2a}\right)$$
$$W = \frac{1}{2} m (v^2 - u^2)$$

If the object is starting from its stationary position i.e., $u = 0$

$$W = \frac{1}{2} mv^2$$

It is clear that the work done is equal to the change in the kinetic energy of an object.

Question 18. Is it possible that an object is in the state of accelerated motion due to external force acting on it, but no work is being done by the force. Explain it with an example.

Answer Yes, when force acts in a direction perpendicular to the direction of motion. For example, earth revolves around the sun under gravitational force of sun on earth, but no work is done by the sun, though earth has centripetal acceleration.

Question 19. A ball is dropped from a height of 10 m. If the energy of the ball reduces by 40% after striking the round, how much high can the ball bounce back? ($g = 10 \text{ ms}^{-2}$).

Answer If the energy of the ball reduces by 40% after striking the ground, then remaining energy of the ball will be 60% of initial energy

$\therefore$

$$mgh' = 60\% \text{ of } mgh$$
$$h' = \frac{60}{100} \times 10$$
$$h' = 6 \text{ m}$$

Question 20. If an electric iron of 1200 W is used for 30 minutes everyday, find electric energy consumed in the month of April.

Answer Given, Power of electric iron = 1200 W

$$\text{Power} = \frac{\text{Energy}}{\text{Time}}$$
$$1200 = \frac{E}{30 \times 60}$$
$$E = 1200 \times 20 \times 60$$
$$= 21.6 \times 10^5 \text{ J}$$

Energy used in one day $= 21.6 \times 10^5$ J
Energy used in 30 days $= 21.6 \times 10^5 \times 30$
$$= 6.4 \times 10^7 \text{ J}$$

Long Answer Type Questions

Question 21. A light and a heavy object have the same momentum. Find out the ratio of their kinetic energies. Which one has a larger kinetic energy?

Answer Suppose m_1 and m_2 are masses of a light and a heavy objects respectively.

We have, kinetic energy, $K = \dfrac{p^2}{2m}$

$\because$ Momentum is same

$\therefore$ Kinetic energy, $K \propto \dfrac{1}{m}$

Since, kinetic energy is inversely proportional to the mass.

So, lighter body has larger kinetic energy.

Question 22. An automobile engine propels a 1000 kg car (A) along a lavelled road at a speed of 36 kmh^{-1}. Find the power if the opposing frictional force is 100 N. Now, suppose after travelling a distance of 200 m, this car collides with another stationary car (B) of same mass and comes to rest. Let its engine also stop at the same time. Now car (B) starts moving on the same level road without getting its engine started. Find the speed of the car (B) just after the collision.

Answer Mass of car (A) = 1000 kg

Mass of car (B) = 1000 kg

Force applied by car (A) = 100 N

Speed of car (A) $= 36 \text{ kmh}^{-1} = 36 \times \dfrac{5}{18} = 10 \text{ ms}^{-1}$

Power of car (A), $P = F \cdot v$
$$= 100 \times 10$$
$$= 1000 \text{ N}$$

Again $F = ma$
$$100 = 1000 \times a$$
$$a = \dfrac{1}{10} \text{ ms}^{-2}$$

From equation of motion
$$v^2 = u^2 + 2as$$

$$v^2 = (10)^2 + 2 \times \frac{1}{10} \times 200$$
$$v^2 = 100 + 40$$
$$v = \sqrt{140} = 11.8 \, m \, s^{-1}$$

From conservation of linear momentum

$$m_1 u_1 + m_2 u_2 = m_1 v_1 + m_2 v_2$$
$$m_1 \times 11.8 + m_2 \times 0 = m_1 \times 0 + m_2 \times v_2$$
$$11.8 \, m_1 = m_2 v_2$$
$$v_2 = 11.8 \, m \, s^{-1} \qquad\qquad (\because m_1 = m_2)$$

Question 23. A girl having mass of 35 kg sits on a trolley of mass 5 kg. The trolley is given an initial velocity of 4 ms^{-1} by appling a force. The trolley comes to rest after traversing a distance of 16 m. (a) How much work is done on the trolley? (b) How much work is done by the girl?

Answer $u = 4 \, m/s$, $v = 0$ and $s = 16 \, m$

From the equation of motion

$$v^2 = u^2 - 2as$$
$$(0)^2 = (4)^2 - 2a \times 16$$
$$a = \frac{16}{32} = 0.5 \, m \, s^{-2}$$

(a) Total mass $= 35 + 5 = 40 \, kg$
Work is done on the trolley
$$W = F \cdot d = m \cdot a \cdot d$$
$$= 40 \times 0.5 \times 16 = 320 \, N$$
(b) Mass of girl $m_1 = 35$ kg
Work done by the girl
$$W = F \cdot d = m \cdot a \cdot d$$
$$= 35 \times 0.5 \times 16 = 280 \, N$$

Question 24. Four men lift a 250 kg box to a height of 1 m and hold it without raising or lowering it. (a) How much work is done by the men in lifting the box? (b) How much work do they do in just holding it? (c) Why do they get tired while holding it? ($g = 10$ ms^{-2}).

Answer   Given, $m = 250 \, kg$, $h = 1 \, m$ and $g = 10 \, m \, s^{-2}$
(a) Work done by the man in lifting the box
$$= \text{Potential energy of box}$$
$$W = 250 \times 1 \times 90$$
$$W = 2500 \, J$$
(b) Work done is zero in holding a box, because displacement is zero.
(c) In holding the box, the energy of man loses. Due to loss of energy he felt tired.

Question 25. What is power? How do you differentiate kilowatt from kilowatt hour? The Jog Falls in Karnataka state are nearly 20 m high. 2000 tonnes of water falls from it in a minute. Calculate the equivalent power if all this energy can be utilized? ($g = 10$ ms^{-2}).

Answer

(i) Power is defined as the rate of doing work or the rate of transfer of energy. The unit of power is watt or kilowatt.

(ii) Kilowatt is the unit of power while kilowatt hour is bigger unit of energy

$$1 \text{ kilowatt hour} = 3.6 \times 10^6 \text{ J}$$

(iii) Mass of water = 2000 tonnes

$$\because \qquad 1 \text{ tonne} = 1000 \text{ kg}$$
$$\therefore \qquad \text{Mass of water} = 2000 \times 1000$$
$$= 2 \times 10^6 \text{ kg}$$
$$\text{Power} = \frac{\text{Energy}}{\text{Time}}$$
$$P = \frac{mgh}{t}$$
$$P = \frac{2 \times 10^6 \times 10 \times 20}{60}$$
$$P = 6.67 \times 10^6 \text{ W}$$

This power can be utilized.

Question 26. How is the power related to the speed at which a body can be lifted? How many kilograms will a man working at the power of 100 W, be able to lift at constant speed of 1 ms^{-1} vertically? ($g = 10$ ms^{-2})

Answer

(i) The power delivered to a body can also expressed in term of the force F applied to the body and the velocity v of the body

$$P = \frac{W}{t}$$
$$P = \frac{F \cdot s}{t} \qquad (\because W = F \cdot s)$$
$$P = F \cdot v \qquad \left(\because v = \frac{s}{t}\right)$$

(ii) Power $P = F \cdot v$

$$100 = mg \cdot v$$
$$100 = m \times 10 \times 1$$
or $$m = 10 \text{ kg}$$

Therefore, man working at the power of 100 W can lift 10 kg.

Question 27. Define watt. Express kilowatt in terms of joule per second. A 150 kg car engine develops 500 W for each kg. What force does it exert in moving the car at speed of 20 ms^{-1}?

Answer

(i) One watt is the power of a body which does work at the rate of 1 joule per second.

$$1 \text{ watt} = 1 \frac{\text{joule}}{\text{second}}$$

(ii) 1 kilowatt = 1000 watt

$$= 1000 \text{ joule/second}$$

(iii) A car engine 150 kg develops 500 watt for each kg. So,

$$\text{total power} = 150 \times 500 = 75000 \text{ W}$$

We have   Power = Force × speed

$$75000 = \text{Force} \times 20$$

$$\text{Force } F = \frac{75000}{20} = 3750 \text{ N}$$

Question 28. Compare the power at which each of the following is moving upwards against the force of gravity? (given $g = 10$ ms^{-2})

(i) a butterfly of mass 1.0 g that flies upward at a rate of 0.5 ms^{-1}.

(ii) a 250 g squirrel climbing up on a tree at a rate of 0.5 ms^{-1}.

Answer   (i) Given,

$$\text{Mass of butterfly} = 1.09 = \frac{1}{1000} \text{ kg}$$

and   Speed = 0.5 m s^{-1}

∴   Power = Force × speed

$$P = mgv$$

$$P = \frac{1}{1000} \times 10 \times 0.5$$

$$P = \frac{1}{200} \text{ watt}$$

(ii) Given,

$$\text{Mass of squirrel} = 250 \text{ g} = \frac{250}{1000} \text{ kg}$$

and   speed = 0.5 m s^{-1}

∴   Power = Force × speed

$$P = mg \times v$$

$$P = \frac{250}{1000} \times 10 \times 0.5 = \frac{250}{200} \text{ W}$$

Therefore, squirrel has more power than butterfly.

12

Sound

Important Concepts

1. Sound is a form of energy which produces the sensation of hearing in our ears.

2. **Propagation of Sound** Sound is produced by vibrating objects. When an object vibrates, it sets the particles of the medium around it vibrating. The particles do not travel all the way from the vibrating object to the ear. A particle of the medium in contact with the vibrating object is first displaced from its equilibrium position. It then exerts a force on the adjacent particle. As a result of which the adjacent particle get displaced from its position at rest.

   After displacing, the particle comes back to its original position. This process continues in the medium till the sound reaches our ear.

   - Sound waves need a material medium like air, water 2or metal etc; for their propagation. Speed of sound in different media is different. The speed of sound in a medium depends primarily on the nature and temperature of the medium.
   - Sound waves are longitudinal waves, *i.e.*, the individual particles of the medium oscillate in a direction parallel to the direction of propagation of the wave (disturbance).
   - In transverse wave, the individual particles of the medium oscillate in a direction perpendicular to the direction of propagation of the wave (disturbance).

3. **Characteristics of a Sound Wave** The sound wave can be characterised by
   (i) Frequency
   (ii) Amplitude
   (iii) Speed

4. A sound wave in graphic form is shown below, it represents how density and pressure change when the sound wave moves in a medium. The density as well as pressure of the medium at a given time vary with distance.

   - **Compressions** are the regions where the particles are crowded together are represented by the upper portion of the curve. The peak represents the region of maximum compression.
   - At compressions, the density as well as pressure is high.
   - **Rarefactions** are the regions of low pressure where particles are spread apart and are represented by the valley, *i.e.,* the lower portion of the curve.
   - A peak is called the crest and a valley is called the trough of a wave.

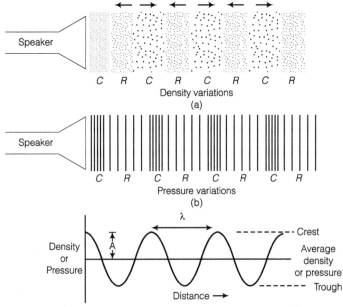

Sound propagates as density or pressure variations as shown in (a) and (b), (c) represents graphically the density and pressure variations.

5. **Wavelength** The distance between two consecutive compressions or rarefactions is called the wavelength. It is represented by λ (lambda). Its SI unit is metre (m).

6. **Frequency** The number of oscillations per unit time is called frequency of the sound wave. The number of compressions or rarefactions occuring per unit time is equal to the frequency of sound wave. It is represented by ν (nu). Its SI unit is hertz (Hz).

7. **Time Period** The time taken in one complete oscillation is called the time period of the wave. It is represented by T. Its SI unit is second (s).
$$\text{Time period } (T) = \frac{1}{\text{Frequency}(\nu)}$$

8. **Amplitude** The magnitude of the maximum disturbance in the medium on either side of the mean value is called the amplitude of the wave. It is represented by A. Its SI unit is metre (m).

9. **Pitch** Pitch is the characteristic of a sound that depends on the frequency received by a human ear.

   A sound wave of high frequency has high pitch and a sound wave of low frequency has low pitch.

10. **Loudness** Loudness of a sound depends on the amplitude of the vibrating body producing sound. It depends on the sensitivity of human ear.

11. **Timber a quality of sound** The characteristic of sound due to which one sound can be distinguished from the other.
    - A sound of single frequency is called a tone.
    - The sound produced due to a mixture of several frequencies is called a note, it is pleasant to hear.
    - Noise is unpleasant to hear, music is pleasant to hear.

12. **Relation between speed, frequency and wavelength of sound**

    The relation between speed (v), frequency (ν) and wavelength (λ) of a sound in a medium is
    $$\text{Speed} = \text{Frequency} \times \text{wavelength}$$
    i.e., $\qquad v = \nu\,\lambda$

13. **Reflection of sound** The bouncing back of sound wave travelling in a medium after striking the second medium is called reflection of sound.

14. **Echo** Echo is a repetition of sound due to the reflection of original sound by a large and hand obstacle.

15. Different conditions required for the production of echo are
    (i) The echo will be heard if the original sound reflected by an obstacle reaches our ear after 0.1 s.
    (ii) The echo will be heard only if the minimum distance between the source of sound and obstacle is 17 m.
    (iii) The echo can be produced if the size of the obstacle reflecting sound is quite large.

16. **Reverberation** In big rooms or halls, echoes follow so closely behind the original sound that the original sound appears to be prolonged even when the source of sound stops producing sound. This effect is called reverberation. It occurs due to multiple reflection of sound.

17. Different practical uses of multiple reflection of sound are; megaphone, hearing aid, sound boards, strethoscope, etc.

18. **Range of Hearing** The audible range of sound to human beings is 20 Hz to 20000 Hz.
    • The sound having frequency lesser than 20 Hz is called infrasound.
    • The sound having frequency higher than 20000 Hz are called ultrasound.
    • Some animals can hear the sound above and less than the above frequency range.

19. **Applications of Ultrasound** Ultrasounds are high frequency waves. These are able to travel along well defined paths even in the presence of obstacles. These are used for
    (i) cleaning the parts located in hard-to-reach places, *e.g.,* spiral tube, odd shaped parts, etc.
    (ii) these are used to detects cracks and flaws in metal blocks.
    (iii) these are used in echocardiography.
    (iv) ultrasound scanner is an application of ultrasound waves.
    (v) bats reach out prey and fly in dark night by emitting an detecting reflections of ultrasonic waves.

20. SONAR stands for Sound Navigation And Ranging. It is a device using ultrasonic waves to measure the distance, direction and speed of under water objects.

21. **Human ear** Ear is an extremely sensitive organ which makes us able to hear. It allows us to convert pressure vibrations in air with audible frequencies into electric signals that travel to the brain *via* auditory nerve.

The internal structure of ear is shown below.

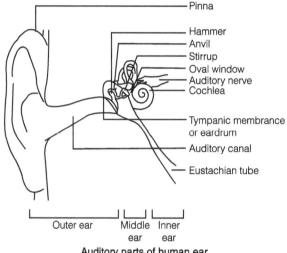

Auditory parts of human ear

Intext Questions

On Page 162

Question 1. How does the sound produced by a vibrating object in a medium reach your ear?

Answer **Propagation of Sound** Sound is produced by vibrating objects. When an object vibrates, it sets the particles of the medium around it vibrating. The particles do not travel all the way from the vibrating object to the ear. A particle of the medium in contact with the vibrating object is first displaced from its equilibrium position. It then exerts a force on the adjacent particle. As a result of which the adjacent particle get displaced from its position (a) rest. After displacing, the particle comes back to its original position. This process continues in the medium till the sound reaches our ear.

On Page 163

Question 1. Explain how sound is produced by your school bell?

Answer The bell produces the sound when it is struck by air hammer. When the bell is struck by hammer, it starts vibrating. Since, the vibrating objects produce sound, so the bell produces sound.

Question 2. Why are sound waves called mechanical waves?

Answer Sound waves are called mechanical waves because they produced by the motion of particles of a medium. Hence, sound waves are called mechanical waves.

Question 3. Suppose you and your friend are on the moon. Will you be able to hear any sound produced by your friend?

Answer I will not be able to hear any sound produced by my friend because the sound waves require some material medium like air to travel. There is no atmosphere or air on the moon, so the sound produced by my friend will not reach me and i will not be able to hear.

On Page 166
Question 1. Which wave property determines (a) loudness, (b) pitch?

Answer (a) Loudness of wave is determined by its amplitude.
  (b) Pitch of the wave is determined by its frequency.

Question 2. Guess which sound has a higher pitch : guitar or car horn?

Answer Pitch of guitar sound is higher because the frequency of sound produced by guitar is higher than that of car horn.

Question 3. What are wavelength, frequency, time period and amplitude of a sound wave?

Answer
1. **Wavelength** The distance travelled by the wave during its one complete oscillation is called wavelength of the wave.

    The distance between two consecutive regions of high pressure or high density (compression) or the distance between two consecutive regions of low pressure or low density (rarefaction) is equal to the wavelength. It is represented by λ. Its SI unit is metre (m).
2. **Frequency** The number of oscillations made by the wave in one second is called frequency of the wave. It is represented by v. Its SI unit is s^{-1} or hertz.
3. **Time period** The time taken by the wave to complete one oscillation is called the time period of the wave. It is represented by T. Its SI unit is second.
4. **Amplitude** The maximum displacement of the wave from its mean or equilibrium position is called the amplitude of the wave. It is represented by A or a. Its SI unit is metre (m).

Question 4. How are the wavelength and frequency of a sound wave related to its speed?

Answer The relation between wavelength (λ), frequency (v) and speed of wave (v) is

$$v = v\lambda$$

Question 5. Calculate the wavelength of a sound wave whose frequency is 220 Hz and speed is 440 ms^{-1} in a given medium.

Answer Frequency $v = 220\,Hz$, speed $v = 440\,ms^{-1}$, wavelength $\lambda = ?$

From the relation, $v = v\lambda$

$$440 = 220\lambda$$

$$\lambda = \frac{440}{220} = 2\,m$$

Question 6. A person is listening to a tone of 500 Hz sitting at a distance of 450 m from the source of the sound. What is the time interval between successive compressions from the source.

Answer The time interval between two successive compressions or rarefactions is equal to the time period of the wave.

$$\therefore \text{ Required time interval} = \text{Time period} = \frac{1}{\text{Frequency}}$$

$$= \frac{1}{500} = 0.002\,s$$

$$= 2 \times 10^{-3}\,s = 2\,ms$$

Question 7. Distinguish between loudness and intensity of sound.

Answer Distinguish between loudness and intensity is given below

S.N.	Loudness	Intensity
1.	It is a subjective quantity. A sound may be loud for one person but may be feeble for another person.	It is an objective physical quantity which does not change for person to person.
2.	It cannot be measured as it is just a sensation which can be felt only.	It can be measured as a physical quantity.

On Page 167

Question 1. In which of the three media, air, water or iron, does sound travel the fastest at a particular temperature?

Answer Sound waves travel fastest in solid medium i.e., out of the given media. Sound wave will travel fastest in iron.

On Page 168

Question 1. An echo is heard in 3 s. What is the distance of the reflecting surface from the source, given that the speed of sound is 342 ms^{-1}?

Answer Echo returns in 3 s. Therefore, time taken by sound to travel from the source to the reflecting surface $t = \frac{3}{2} = 1.5\,s$.

$$\text{Speed } v = 342 \text{ ms}^{-1}$$

∴ Distance of reflecting surface from the source

$$= \text{Speed} \times \text{Time}$$
$$= 342 \times 1.5 = 513 \text{ m}$$

On Page 169

Question 1. Why are the ceilings of concert halls curved?

Answer The ceilings of the concert halls in made curved so that the sound reflected from the ceilings reaches to all the corners of the hall.

On Page 170

Question 1. What is the audible range of the average human ear?

Answer The audible frequency range for the average human ear is
20 Hz - 20000 Hz.

Question 2. What is the range of frequencies associated with

(a) infrasound   (b) ultrasound?

Answer
(a) Sound waves having frequencies less than 20 Hz and greater than zero are called infrasound.
(b) Sound waves having frequencies more than 20000 Hz are called ultrasound.

On Page 172

Question 1. A submarine emits a sonar pulse, which returns from an under water cliff in 1.02 s. If the speed of sound in salt water is 1531 ms^{-1}, how far away is the cliff?

Answer Total time taken = 1.02 s

∴ Time taken by the pulse to go from submarine to the cliff

$$t = \frac{1.02}{2} = 0.51 \text{ s}$$

Speed of sound $v = 1531 \text{ ms}^{-1}$

∴ Distance of cliff from the submarine

$$= \text{Speed} \times \text{Time}$$
$$= 1531 \times 0.51$$
$$= 780.81 \text{ m}$$

Exercises

Question 1. What is sound and how is it produced?

Answer Sound is a form of energy. It produces when an object is set to vibrate or we can say that vibrating objects produce sound.

Question 2. Describe with the help of a diagram, how compressions and rarefactions are produced in air near a source of sound.

Answer The production of compression and rarefactions in air can be explained as:

When a vibrating object moves forward it pushes the air in front of it creating a region of high pressure. This region is called compression. This compression starts to move away from the vibrating object.

When the vibrating object moves backwards, it creates a region of low pressure called rarefaction. As the object moves back and forth rapidly, a series of compressions and rarefactions is created. These make the sound wave that propagates through the medium.

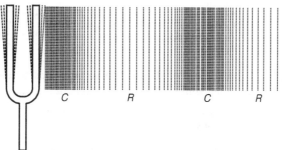

A vibrating object creating a series of compressions (C)
and rarefactions (R) in the medium.

Question 3. Cite an experiment to show that sound needs a material medium for its propagation.

Answer Experiment to show that sound, needs a material medium for its propagation is given below.

Take an electric bell and an airtight glass bell jar. The electric bell is suspended inside the airtight bell jar. The bell jar is connected to a vacuum pump, as shown in figure. If you press the switch you will be able to hear the bell. Now start the vacuum pump. When the air in the jar is pumped out gradually, the sound becomes fainter, although the same current is passing through the bell.

After some time when less air is left inside the bell jar you will hear a very feeble sound. On removal of complete air, no sound is heard.

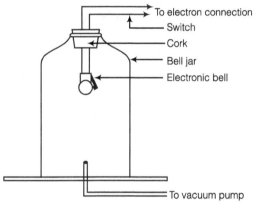

To electron connection
Switch
Cork
Bell jar
Electronic bell

To vacuum pump

Bell jar experiment showing sound cannot
travel in vacuum.

Question 4. Why is sound wave called a longitudinal wave?

Answer The sound wave is called longitudinal wave because on propagation of sound wave in a medium, the particles of the medium vibrate to and fro about their equilibrium positions parallel to the direction of propagation of the wave.

Question 5. Which characteristic of the sound helps you to identify your friend by his voice while sitting with others in a dark room?

Answer Timber a quality of sound is the characteristic by which we can identify the person by their voice.

Question 6. Flash and thunder are produced simultaneously. But thunder is heard a few seconds after the flash is seen, why?

Answer Thunder is heard few seconds later after the flash because speed of light in atmosphere (or air) is 3×10^8 ms^{-1} which is very high as compared to the speed of sound which is only 330 ms^{-1}. So sound of thunder reaches us later than the flash.

Question 7. A person has a hearing range from 20 Hz to 20 kHz. What are the typical wavelengths of sound waves in air corresponding to these two frequencies? Take the speed of sound in air as 344 ms^{-1}.

Answer Even the relation between speed (v) wavelength (λ) and frequency (v) of a wave, we have
$$v = v\lambda$$
$$\lambda = \frac{v}{v}$$

(i) Here, $v = 344$ ms^{-1}, $v = 20$ Hz

$\therefore$ Corresponding wavelength $\lambda = \dfrac{v}{\nu} = \dfrac{344}{20} = 17.2$ m

(ii) Here, $v = 344$ ms^{-1}, $\nu = 20$ kHz $= 20 \times 10^3$ Hz

$\therefore$ Corresponding wavelength $\lambda = \dfrac{v}{\nu} = \dfrac{344}{20 \times 10^3} = 1.72 \times 10^{-2}$ m

Question 8. Two children are at opposite ends of an aluminium rod. One strikes the end of the rod with a stone. Find the ratio of times taken by the sound wave in air and in the aluminium to reach the second child.

Answer Let l = length of the rod

Time taken by the sound to travel through the aluminium rod

$$t_1 = \frac{\text{Distasnce}}{\text{Speed}} = \frac{l}{v_{Al}}$$

Similarily, time taken by the sound to travel through the air

$$t_2 = \frac{\text{Distance}}{\text{Speed}} = \frac{l}{v_{air}}$$

$\therefore$ Required ratio, $\quad t_1 : t_2 = \dfrac{v_{air}}{v_{Al}}$

Question 9. The frequency of a source of sound is 100 Hz. How many times does it vibrate in a minute?

Answer Frequency = 100 Hz

From the definition of frequency, we can say that

Number of oscillations in 1 s = 100

$\therefore$ Number of oscillations in 1 min or 60 s = 100 × 60

$$= 6000 = 6 \times 10^3$$

Question 10. Does sound follow the same laws of reflection as light does? Explain.

Answer Yes, sound waves follow the same laws of reflection as light does.

Question 11. When a sound is reflected from a distant object, an echo is produced. Let the distance between the reflecting surface and the source of sound production remains the same. Do you hear echo sound on a hotter day?

Answer The time taken by echo to be heard

$$t = \frac{2d}{v}$$

where, d = distance between the reflecting surface and source of sound and v = speed of sound in air.

As we know that speed of sound increases with increase in temperature, so on a hotter day speed of sound will be higher, so the time after which echo is heard will decrease.

If time taken by the reflected sound is less than 0.1 s after the production of original sound, then echo is not heard.

Question 12. Give two practical applications of reflection of sound waves.

Answer   The two practical application of reflection of sound are
    (i) Megaphone   (ii) Hearing aid

Question 13. A stone is dropped from the top of a tower 500 m high into a pond of water at the base of the tower. When is the splash heard at the top? Given, $g = 10$ ms^{-2} and speed of sound $= 340$ ms^{-1}.

Answer   Time after which the splash is heard
$$= \text{Time taken by the stone to reach the pond}$$
$$+ \text{ time taken by splash sound to reach the top of tower}$$
(i) For the time taken by the stone to reach the pond.
    Here, $u = 0$ ($\because$ Stone is dropped from rest)
    From equation of motion against gravity
$$h = ut + \frac{1}{2}gt^2$$
$$500 = 0 \times t + \frac{1}{2} \times 10 \ (t)^2$$
$$500 = 5t^2$$
$$\Rightarrow \quad\quad t^2 = 100$$
$$\Rightarrow \quad\quad t = \sqrt{100} = 10 \text{ s}$$
(ii) Time taken by splash sound to reach the top of the tower
$$t' = \frac{\text{Distance}}{\text{Speed}} = \frac{500}{340} = 1.47 \text{ s}$$
$\therefore$ Time after which splash is heard $= 10 + 1.47 = 11.47$ s

Question 14. A sound wave travels at a speed of 339 ms^{-1}. If its wavelength is 1.5 cm, what is the frequency of the wave? Will it be audible?

Answer   Given, speed $v = 339$ ms^{-1}
    Wavelength, $\lambda = 1.5$ cm $= 1.5 \times 10^{-2}$ m
$$\therefore \quad \text{Frequency, } v = \frac{v}{\lambda} = \frac{339}{1.5 \times 10^{-2}} = 226 \times 10^2 = 26600 \text{ Hz}$$

This frequency is greater than 20000 Hz, so it will not be audible. For audible range for human ear is 20 Hz to 20000 Hz.

Sound

Question 15. What is reverberation? How can it be reduced?

Answer The phenomenon of prolongation of original sound due to the multiple reflection of sound waves even after the source of sound and stops producing sound is called reverberation. Reverberation can be reduced by covering the roofs and walls of the hall by absorbing materials.

Question 16. What is loudness of sound? What factors does it depend on?

Answer Loudness of a sound is a subjective quantity, it causes an unpleasant effect on air. Loudness depends on (i) the amplitude of the vibrating body and (ii) the sensitivity of human ear.

Question 17. Explain how bats use ultrasound to catch a prey?

Answer Bats can produce ultrasonic waves by flapping their wings, they can also detect these waves. The ultrasonic waves produced by a bat spread out. These waves after reflecting from a prey like an insert reach the bat. So, the bat can locate its prey.

Question 18. How is ultrasound used for cleaning?

Answer Ultrasound is generally used to clean parts located in hard-to-reach places, for example, spiral tube, odd shaped parts, electronic components etc. Objects to be cleaned are placed in a cleaning solution and ultrasonic waves are sent into the solution. Due to the high frequency, the particles of dust, grease and dirt get detached and drop out. The objects thus get thoroughly cleaned.

Question 19. Explain the working and application of a sonar.

Answer Sonar consists of a transmitter and a detector and is installed in a boat or a ship, as shown in figure.

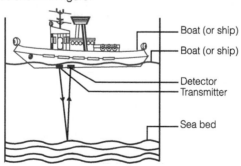

Ultrasound sent by the transmitter and
received by the detector.

The transmitter produces and transmits ultrasonic waves. These waves travel through water and after striking the object on the seabed, get reflected back and are sensed by the detector. The detector converts the ultrasonic waves into electrical signals which are appropriately interpreted. The distance of the object that reflected the sound wave can be calculated by knowing the speed of sound in water and the time interval between transmission and reception of the ultrasound. Let the time interval between transmission and reception of ultrasound signal be t and the speed of sound through seawater be v. The total distance, $2d$ travelled by the ultrasound is then, $2d = v \times t$.

The above method is called echo-ranging. The sonar technique is used to determine the depth of the sea and to locate underwater hills, valleys, submarine, icebergs, sunken ship etc.

Question 20. A sonar device on a submarine sends out a signal and receives an echo 5 s later. Calculate the speed of sound in water if the distance of the object from the submarine is 3625 m.

Answer   Time taken by the signal to go from submarine to object

$$t = \frac{5}{2} = 2.5 \text{ s}$$

Distance between submarine and object $s = 3625$ m

∴ Speed of sound in water

$$v = \frac{\text{Distance}}{\text{Speed}} = \frac{3625}{2.5} = 1450 \text{ ms}^{-1}$$

Question 21. Explain how defects in a metal block can be detected using ultrasound?

Answer   Ultrasounds can be used to detect cracks and flaws in metal blocks. Metallic components are generally used in construction of big structures like buildings, bridges, machines and also scientific equipment. The cracks or holes inside the metal blocks, which are invisible from outside reduces the strength of the structure. Ultrasonic waves are allowed to pass through the metal block and detectors are used to detect the transmitted waves. If there is even a small defect, the ultrasound gets reflected back indicating the presence of the flaw or defect, as shown in figure.

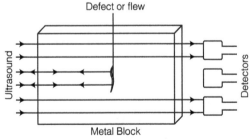

Ultrasound is reflected back from the
defective locations inside a metal block

Question 22. Explain how the human ear works?

Answer **Working of Human Ear** Ears make us able to hear. It is an extremely sensitive device. It allows us to convert pressure variations in air with audible frequencies into electric signals that travel to the brain *via* the auditory nerve. The auditory aspect of human ear is discussed below.

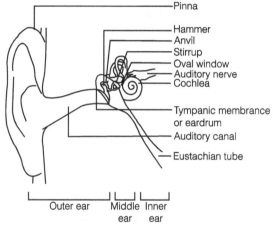

Auditory parts of human ear

The outer ear is called 'pinna'. It collects the sound from the surroundings. The collected sound passes through the auditory canal. At the end of the auditory canal there is a thin membrane called the ear drum or tympanic membrane. When a compression of the medium reaches the eardrum the pressure on the outside of the membrane increases and forces the eardrum inward. Similarly, the eardrum moves outward when a rarefaction reaches it. In this way the eardrum vibrates. The vibrations are amplified several times by three bones (the hammer, anvil and stirrup) in the middle ear. The middle ear transmits the amplified pressure variations received from the sound wave to the inner ear. In the inner ear, the pressure variations are turned into electrical signals by the cochlea. These electrical signals are sent to the brain *via* the auditory nerve, and the brain interprets them as sound.

Selected NCERT Exemplar Problems
Multiple Choice Questions

Question 1. Note is a sound
  (a) of mixture of several frequencies
  (b) of mixture of two frequencies only
  (c) of a single frequency
  (d) always unpleasant to listen

Answer (a) The sound which is produced due to a mixture of several frequencies is called a note and it is pleasant to listen too.

Question 2. A key of a mechanical piano struck gently and then struck again but much harder this time. In the second case
- (a) sound will be louder but pitch will not be different
- (b) sound will be louder and pitch will also be higher
- (c) sound will be louder but pitch will be lower
- (d) both loudness and pitch will remain unaffected

Answer (c) In the second case, sound will be louder but pitch will be lower.

Question 3. In SONAR, we use
- (a) ultrasonic waves
- (b) infrasonic waves
- (c) radio waves
- (d) audible sound waves

Answer (a) SONAR is a device that uses ultrasonic waves to measure the distance, direction and speed of under water objects.

Question 4. Sound travels in air if
- (a) particles of medium travel from one place to another
- (b) there is no moisture in the atmosphere
- (c) disturbance moves
- (d) both particles as well as disturbance travel from one place to another

Answer (a) Sound travels in air if disturbance moves.

Question 5. When we change feeble sound to loud sound we increase its
- (a) frequency
- (b) amplitude
- (c) velocity
- (d) wavelength

Answer (b) The loudness or softness of a sound is determined basically by its amplitude.

Question 6. In the given curve, half the wavelength is

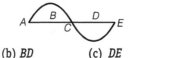

- (a) *AB*
- (b) *BD*
- (c) *DE*
- (d) *AE*

Answer (b) In this curve, half the wavelength is *BD*.

Question 7. Earthquake produces which kind of sound before the main shock wave begins
- (a) ultrasound
- (b) infrasound
- (c) audible sound
- (d) None of these

Answer (b) Earthquakes produces iron frequency infrasound before the main shock waves begin which possibly alert the animals.

Question 8. Infrasound can be heard by
    (a) dog   (b) bat
    (c) rhinoceros   (d) human beings

Answer   (a) Rhinoceroses communicate using infrasound of frequency as low as 5 Hz.

Question 9. Before playing the orchestra in a musical concert, a sitarist tries to adjust the tension and pluck the string suitably. By doing so, he is adjusting
    (a) intensity of sound only
    (b) amplitude of sound only
    (c) frequency of the sitar string with the frequency of other musical instruments
    (d) loudness of sounds

Answer   (c) Sitarist is adjusting frequency of the sitar string with the frequency of other musical instruments.

Short Answer Type Questions

Question 10. The given graph shows the displacement *versus* time relation for a disturbance travelling with velocity of 1500 ms^{-1}. Calculate the wavelength of the disturbance.

Answer   Given, velocity $v = 1500\,\text{ms}^{-1}$
$$\text{Time}, t = 2\,\mu s = 2 \times 10^{-6}$$
$$\text{Wavelength}, \lambda = vt$$
$$\lambda = 1500 \times 2 \times 10^{-6} = 3 \times 10^{-3}\text{m}$$

Question 11. Which of the two graphs (a) and (b) representing the human voice is likely to be the male voice? Give reason for your answer.

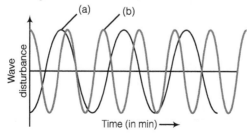

Answer   Graph (a) represents the male voice. Since the pitch and frequency of male voice is lower than the pitch of female voice and vibration of graph (a) represents lower frequency and lower pitch.

Question 12. A girl is sitting in the middle of a park of dimension 12 m × 12 m. On the left side of it there is a building adjoining the park and on right side of the park, there is a road adjoining the park. A sound is produced on the road by a cracker. Is it possible for the girl to hear the echo of this sound? Explain your answer.

Answer   No.

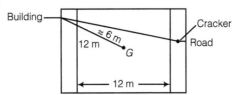

For hearing distinct echoes, the minimum distance of obstacle from the source of sound must be 17.2 m.

Since, distance of girls from sound source is less than 17.2 m. So, it is not possible for the girl to hear the echo of this sound.

Question 13. Why do we hear the sound produced by the humming bees while the sound of vibrations of pendulum is not heard?

Answer   The frequency of vibrations of pendulum is below of 20 Hz (infrasound). We cannot hear infrasound but humming produce audible sound which can be heard by human beings.

Question 14. If any explosion takes place ast the bottom of a lake, what type of shock waves in water will take place?

Answer   If any explosion takes place at the bottom of a lake. Infrasound type of shock waves in water will take place.

Question 15. Sound produced by a thunderstorm is heard 10 s after the lightning is seen. Calculate the approximate distance of the thunder cloud. (Given speed of sound = 340 ms^{-1}).

Answer   Distance = Velocity × Time
$$= 340 \times 10 = 340 \times 10 = 3400 \, m = 3.4 \, km$$

Question 16. For hearing the loudest ticking sound heard by the ear, find the angle x in the given figure.

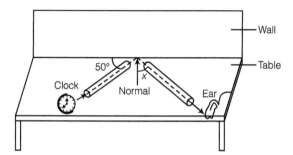

Answer For reflection, angle of incidence (x) is equal to angle of reflection (x).

$$50° + x + x + 50° = 180°$$
$$2x + 100° = 180°$$
$$2x = 180° - 100°$$
$$2x = 80°$$
$$x = \frac{80°}{2}$$
$$x = 40°$$

Question 17. Why is the ceiling and wall behind the stage of good conference halls or concert halls made curved?

Answer The ceiling of concert halls, conference halls and cinema halls are curved so that sound after reflection reaches all corners of the hall.

Long Answer Type Questions

Question 18. Represent graphically by two separate diagrams in each case

- (i) Two sound waves having the same amplitude but different frequencies.
- (ii) Two sound waves having the same frequency but different amplitudes.
- (iii) Two sound waves having different amplitudes and also different wavelengths.

Answer

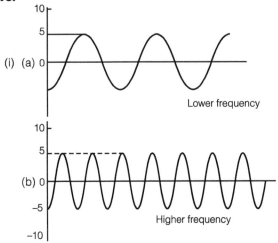

Lower frequency

Higher frequency

In both cases (a) and (b), amplitude is same.

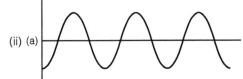

In both cases (a) and (b), frequency is same.

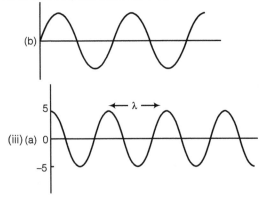

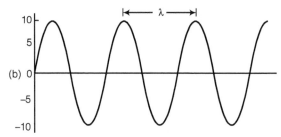

In both cases (a) and (b), amplitude and wavelength are different.

Question 19. Establish the relationship between speed of sound, its wavelength and frequency. If velocity of sound in air is 340 ms^{-1}. Calculate (i) wavelength when frequency is 256 Hz.

(ii) frequency when wavelength is 0.85 m.

Answer The speed of sound is defined as the distance which a point on a wave, such as a compression or a rarefaction, travels per unit time.

We know $\qquad$ Speed $v = \dfrac{\text{Distance}}{\text{Time}} = \dfrac{\lambda}{T}$

Here, λ is the wavelength of the sound wave. It is the distance travelled by the sound wave in one time period (T) of the wave.

$$v = \frac{\lambda}{T}$$

$$v = \lambda v \qquad \left(\because \frac{1}{T} = v \right)$$

i.e., $\qquad$ Speed = Wavelength × Frequency

(i) $\qquad$ Speed = Wavelength × Frequency

$$340 = \lambda \times 256$$

$$\lambda = \frac{340}{256} = 1.36 \, \text{m}$$

(ii) Speed = Wavelength × Frequency

$$340 = 0.85 \times v$$

$$v = \frac{340}{0.85} = 400 \, \text{Hz}$$

Question 20. Draw a curve showing density or pressure variations with respect to distance for a disturbance produced by sound. Mark the position of compression and rarefaction on this curve. Also define wavelengths and time period using this curve.

Answer

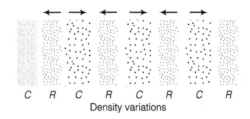

Density variations

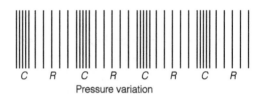

Pressure variation

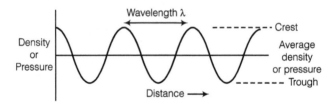

13

Why Do We Fall Ill?

Important Concepts

1. Health can be defined as a state of being good enough to function well physically, mentally and socially.
2. Various factors affect our health. Some of these are
   (i) social environment.
   (ii) public cleanliness.
   (iii) good economic conditions and earnings.
   (iv) social equality and harmony.
3. The word 'disease' means 'disturbed ease'. It means being uncomfortable.
4. In case of disease, either the functioning or the appearance of one or more systems of the body will change for the worse. These changes give rise to symptoms and signs of disease.
5. Symptoms of disease are the things we feel as being 'wrong'. Signs of disease are what physicians will look for on the basis of the symptoms.

   Signs will have a little more definite indication of the presence of a particular disease.
6. The diseases which last for only very short periods of time, are called acute diseases. For example, common cold.
7. The ailments which last for a long time sometimes take entire lifetime are called chronic diseases. For example, elephantiasis, which is an infection caused by filarial worm. It is very common in some parts of India.

8. Acute and chronic diseases have different effects on our health. Any disease that causes poor functioning of some parts of the body will affect our general health as well. Because, all functions of the body are necessary for general health.

9. An acute disease, which gets over very soon will not have time to cause major effects on general health, while a chronic disease will do so. For example, due to cold and cough, we do not lose weight, do not become short of breath and feel tired all the time because of its few days duration. But, in case of tuberculosis, patient loses weight and feels tired all the time.

10. Chronic diseases, therefore, have very drastic long-term effects on people's health as compared to acute disease.

11. Causes of diseases may be immediate and contributory.

12. The immediate cause of diseases may be infection caused by bacteria, virus, worm or protzoans.

13. The contributory causes are
    (i) lack of good nutrition.
    (ii) genetic factors or defects.
    (iii) poverty or lack of public services.

14. Infectious diseases are caused immediately because of microbes. These disease are named so, because the microbes can spread in the community and spread the diseases they can cause.

15. Non-infectious diseases are not caused by the infectious agents like microbes. So, they do not spread in the community. The causes of these diseases are mostly internal which are non-infectious.

16. Two Australians **Robin Warren** and **Barry Morhall** discovered that a bacterium *Helicobacter pylori* was responsible for peptic ulcers. Previously, it was thought that peptic ulcers were because of stressful life. Due to this discovery, peptic ulcer is no longer remain a chronic disease as it can be treated by a short period of treatment with antibiotics.

17. Infectious agents which spread disease are of various types. These are viruses, bacteria, fungi and protozoans. Some multicellular infectious agents are worms of different kinds.

18. Infectious diseases caused by viruses are common cold, influenza, dengue fever, AIDS, etc. Bacteria are responsible for typhoid, cholera, tuberculosis and anthrax, etc. Fungi cause many common skin infections. Protozoan microbes cause diseases like malaria and kala-azar and elephantiasis is caused by different species of worms.

19. Antibiotics commonly block biochemical pathways important for bacteria. Many antibiotics work against many species of bacteria rather than simple working against one, *i.e.*, broad spectrum.

20. Viral diseases cannot be treated by antibiotic treatment. Because, the viruses do not use these pathways at all, so antibiotics do not work against viral infections.

21. Communicable diseases are the diseases which can be 'communicated' by microbial agents from an affected person to some other healthy person in various ways.

22. The various means of spreading diseases are
   (i) Air—Common cold, pneumonia and tuberculosis.
   (ii) Water—Cholera and hepatitis.
   (iii) Sexual contact—Syphilis and AIDS.

23. The animals which transmit diseases from sick person to another potential host act as intermediaries and are called vectors. For example, mosquito transmits malaria from sick person to a healthy person.

24. The infectious agents or disease causing microbes which enter the body through various routes and affect that particular tissue/organ. For example
   (i) Air enters through the nose and enters in lungs (it may carry bacteria causing tuberculosis).
   (ii) Agents enter through the mouth and stay in alimentary tract (*e.g.*, typhoid causing bacteria) or they may go to the liver (viruses causing hepatitis or jaundice).
   (iii) Through sexual contact, they spread to lymph nodes all over the body (*e.g.*, HIV virus).
   (iv) Through mosquito bites, they may enter liver and then to the red blood cells (malaria causing microbes). They may also enter brain through blood (virus causing japanese encephalitis or brain fever).

25. The signs and symptoms of a disease, thus depend on the tissue or organ which the microbe targets. For example:
   (i) If the lungs are target, then symptoms will be cough and breathlessness.
   (ii) If liver is the target, jaundice may occur.
   (iii) In case of brain as target, headache, vomiting, fits or unconsciousness may occur.

26. An active immune system recruits many cells to the affected area to kill off the disease causing microbes. This is called

inflammation. Due to this, there may be local effects like swelling, pain and fever.

27. The severity of disease manifestations depend on the number of microbes in the body. If the number of microbes is small, the disease manifestation may be minor or unnoticed. If the number is large, the disease can be severe enough to be life-threatening. Thus, the immune system is a major factor that determines the number of microbes surviving in the body.

28. The principles of treatment of diseases are mainly two:
   (i) To reduce the effects of disease by providing treatment that will reduce sympotms. But, this way will not kill off the microbes.
   (ii) To kill the microbes or the cause of disease by taking antibiotics.

29. The antibiotics block the pathways used by bacteria. There are some drugs which kill Protozoa such as malarial parasite.

30. Viruses have few biochemical mechanisms of their own. They enter the body and use our machinery for the life processes. Due to this, making antiviral medicines is a tough task. Despite this, there are now some effective antiviral drugs, such as to keep HIV infection under control.

31. Principles of prevention of an infectious disease are
   (i) To prevent the exposure of infectious diseases
      (a) to avoid overcrowding conditions for living.
      (b) by using safe and clean drinking water.
      (c) by providing clean environment.
   (ii) To provide proper sufficient and hygenice nourishment to everyone.
   (iii) To have strong immune system to fight off microbes.

32. Specific ways to prevent infections is adopting the principle of immunisation. Immunisation process is based on developing a memory for a particular infection by putting something, that mimics the microbe we want to vaccinate against into the body. This prevents the exposure to the infecting microbe from turning into actual disease.

33. Vaccines are available under child immunisation programme against diseases like tetanus, diphtheria, whooping cough, measles, polio, and many others. A vaccine against hepatitis-A is also available in the market.

Intext Questions

Question 1. State any two conditions essential for good health.

Answer Good health of a person depends on
  (i) social environment.
  (ii) public cleanliness.
  (iii) good economic conditions and earnings.
  (iv) social equality and harmony.

Question 2. State any two conditions essential for being free of disease.

Answer The conditions essential for being free of diseases
  (i) Taking good food (balanced diet)
  (ii) Maintaining personal and public hygiene.

Question 3. Are the answers to the above questions necessarily the same or different? Why?

Answer The answers are not same all the time. Because the meaning of health varies from person to person. For example, good health for a dancer may be being able to stretch his body into difficult but graceful positions. On the other hand, good health for a musician may mean having enough breathing capacity in his/her lungs to control his/her voice.

There is one similarity in both the cases. If the conditions essential for good health are maintained, then there are no chances of getting a disease.

On Page 180

Question 1. List any three reasons why you would think that you are sick and ought to see a doctor. If only one of these symptoms were present, would you still go to the doctor? Why or why not?

Answer When there is a disease, its symptoms and signs appear. These symptoms may be headache, cough, loose-motions, wound with pus, etc. These symptoms indicate disease but do not tell what the disease is. So, it is advisable to go to the doctor to diagnose any signs of a disease on the basis of these symptoms. The doctor will get laboratory tests done, if required for the confirmation of a particular disease.

Question 2. In which of the following case do you think the long-term effects on your health are likely to be most unpleasant?
  • If you get jaundice,
  • If you get lice,
  • If you get acne.
    Why?

Answer Lice and acne will not cause long lasting effects on our body. But in case of jaundice, there will be severe long lasting effects. For example:
  (i) High temperature, headache and joint pains.
  (ii) Feeling of nausea and vomiting.
  (iii) Initiating rashes.
The patient will suffer from poor health and will recover by taking complete bed rest for sometime.

On Page 186

Question 1. Why are we normally advised to take bland and nourishing food when we are sick?

Answer In case of illness, the normal functions of the body get disturbed. So, a nourishing food is required which is easily digestable and contains all the nutrients. Therefore, bland and nourishing food is advised to take during sickness.

Question 2. What are the different means by which infectious diseases are spread?

Answer Infectious diseases spread by different means. These are:
  (i) **Through air** An infected person when sneezes or coughs releases droplets containing germs. These droplets infect another healthy person through air and microbes enter a new body. Examples of such diseases are common cold, pneumonia and tuberculosis.
  (ii) **Through water** If the water source is polluted by the excreta of infectious persons having gut diseases and this water is used by other people they will be infected by diseases. For example, cholera, amoebiasis, hepatitis spread through water.
  (iii) **Through sexual contact** Some diseases like AIDS and syphilis, etc., are transmitted by sexual contact. Other than this, AIDS virus also spread through blood, infected syringes, infected mother to her baby during pregnancy and through breast feeding.
  (iv) **Through vectors** There are some animals which act as intermediaries or vectors for a particular diseases. The vectors carry diseases from infected person to the healthy person. For example, mosquito spread malaria causing organism in humans, while sucking their blood.

Question 3. What precautions can you take in your school to reduce the incidence of infectious diseases?

Answer To prevent the incidence of infectious diseases in school following precautions can be taken:
  (i) Avoid contact of students suffering from air borne diseases like common cold, cough, eye, flu, etc.
  (ii) By checking the availability of clean drinking water in school.

(iii) Clean surroundings in school will not allow the growth and multiplication of vectors.

(iv) Starting childhood immunisation programme in schools.

Question 4. What is immunisation?

Answer Immunisation is a process of administration (injecting) of vaccine into a healthy person in order to develop immunity against a disease. Immunity means the ability of a body to recognise, destroy and eliminate external disease causing agents. This immunisation through administering vaccine is called vaccination. Vaccine contains disease-causing organisms in a diluted or weakened form or in living or dead form. It prevents further infection by microbes from causing the disease. The diseases like small pox, rabies, diphtheria chicken pox, polio, hepatitis are controlled by vaccination. Small pox is eliminated from the world through a world wide vaccination programme.

Question 5. What are the immunisation programmes available at the nearest health centre in your locality? Which of these diseases are the major health problems in your area?

Answer The following immunisation programme is available at the nearest health centre in our locality

(i) Immunisation for infants—DPT, BCG, polio, measles and MMR.

(ii) For children—Typhoid, TT, DT, small pox and TAB.

(iii) For pregnant woman— TT and hepatitis-B.

The diseases like typhoid, polio, measles, tetanus are the major health problems in our locality. To prevent these diseases, our government have initiated expanded immunisation programme all over the country.

Exercises

Question 1. How many times did you fall ill in the last one years? What were the illnesses?

(a) Think of one change you could make in your habits in order to avoid any of/most of the above illnesses.

(b) Think of one change you would wish for in your surroundings in order to avoid any of/most of the above illnesses.

Answer I fell ill twice in the last one year. The disease, I first suffered from was diarrhoea and secondary the dengue fever.

(a) The changes I brought in my habits after suffering from these disease to protect myself in near future are

(i) I will always drink clean, pure water and wash hands before eating anything.

(ii) I will live in clean surroundings where disease spreading vectors could not mulitply. For example, mosquitoes.

(b) Pure drinking water should be available always. The intake of impure water is the main cause of many infectious diseases.

Question 2. A doctor/nurse/health-worker is exposed to more sick people than others in the community. Find out how she/he avoids getting sick herself/himself.

Answer A doctor/nurse/health-worker take following precautions to avoid become sick themselves

(i) Wear masks while diagnosing mouth or chest infections.

(ii) Clean their hands and wear gloves even while doing minor surgeries.

(iii) Get immunisation done against all the infectious diseases.

(iv) Take balanced diet (rich in proteins especially) to strengthen their immune system.

(v) Dispose off blood samples, urine or stool, sputum, etc., carefully.

Question 3. Conduct a survey in your neighbourhood to find out what the three most common diseases are. Suggest three steps that could be taken by your local authorities to bring down the incidence of these diseases.

Answer I conducted a survey in my neighbourhood and found following three most common diseases.

Diseases	Symptoms	Steps could be Taken by Local Authorities to Bring Down the Incidence
Typhoid	Headache and fever which remains high in the second week and then declines	• Proper hygiene in surrounding areas of living. • Safe disposal of excreta and other wastes. • Providing TAB and typhoid oral vaccine.
Cholera	Painless watery diarrhoea, effortless vomiting	• Good sanitary condition in community. • Provision of clean, purified drinking water. • Providing standard cholera vaccination in the locality.
Dengue fever	High fever with headache, weakness and joint pains	• Maintenance of hygienic conditions in community . • Preventing the mosquito breeding sites. • Public awarness programme against musquito borne diseases.

Question 4. A baby is not able to tell her/his caretakers that she/he is sick. What would help us to find out

(a) that the baby is sick?

(b) What is the sickness?

Answer
  (a) Symptoms to help in finding out that the baby is sick are:
    (i) continuous crying
    (ii) drooping of eyes
    (iii) redness of eyes
    (iv) high temperature of body.
  (b) Signs which help to indicate the sickness in baby
    (i) loose motions, stomach pain indicate diarrhoea.
    (ii) high fever, headache, muscular pain, feeling of shivering and cold indicate malaria.
    (iii) redness and persistent rubbing of eyes indicate eye flu.
    (iv) pale skin, yellow urine, yellowing of eyes indicate jaundice.
    (v) doctors suggest for laboratory tests, if there is fever with no other symptoms to find out the kind of sickness.

Question 5. Under which of the following conditions is a person most likely to fall sick?
  (a) When she is recovering from malaria.
  (b) When she has recovered from malaria and is taking care of someone suffering from chicken pox.
  (c) When she is on a four-day fast after recovering from malaria and is taking care of someone suffering from chicken pox. Why?

Answer In condition (c), a person is most likely to fall sick. The reasons are:
  (a) Due to malaria, the body becomes weak and loss of body fluids occur. In this condition, it she takes four days fast, her recovery from malaria related weakness will not occur and she will become more weak.
  (b) Her immune system is already weak due to malaria and if she takes care of someone suffering from chicken pox, there is high probability that she may also suffer this diseases.

Question 6. Under which of the following conditions are you most likely to fall sick?
  (a) When you are taking examinations.
  (b) When you have travelled by bus and train for two days.
  (c) When your friend is suffering from measles. Why?

Answers In condition (c), Charles of falling sick are maximum. Measles is an infectious viral disease of young children which spreads through nasal or throat discharge.In contact of a friend suffering from measles can cause you sick.

Selected NCERT Exemplar Problems

Multiple Choice Questions

Question 1. Which one of the following is not a viral disease?

(a) Dengue   (b) AIDS

(c) Typhoid   (d) Influenza

Answer (c) Typhoid is a bacterial disease caused by *Salmonella typhi*.

Question 2. Which one of the following is not a bacterial disease?

(a) Cholera   (b) Tuberculosis (c) Anthrax   (d) Influenza

Answer (d) Influenza is a viral disease.

Question 3. Which one of the following disease is not transmitted by mosquito?

(a) Brain fever   (b) Malaria   (c) Typhoid   (d) Dengue

Answer (c) Typhoid is caused by bacteria.

Question 4. Which one of the following disease is not caused by bacteria?

(a) Typhoid   (b) Anthrax   (c) Tuberculosis   (d) Malaria

Answer (d) Malaria is caused by a Protozoa *Plasmodium* which is spread by the mosquito bites in humans.

Question 5. Which one of the following disease is caused by protozoans?

(a) Malaria   (b) Influenza   (c) AIDS   (d) Cholera

Answer (a) Malaria is caused by a protozoan *Plasmodium*.

Question 6. Which one of the following has a long term effect on the health of an individual?

(a) Common cold   (b) Chicken pox

(c) Chewing tobacco   (d) Stress

Answer (c) Chewing tobacco may have chronic effects on health in long term. For example, it may cause oral or throat cancer.

Question 7. Which of the following can make you ill if you come in contact with an infected person?

(a) High blood pressure   (b) Genetic abnormalities

(c) Sneezing   (d) Blood cancer

Answer (c) Sneezing releases water droplets in the air. If they contain germs, these may infect a healthy person in the surroundings.

Question 8. AIDS cannot be transmitted by
    (a) sexual contact   (b) hugs
    (c) breast feeding   (d) blood transfusion

Answer (b) Hugging of an AIDS person cannot spread because there will be no contact with blood or body fluids.

Question 9. Making anti-viral drugs is more difficult than making anti-bacterial medicines because
    (a) viruses make use of host machinery
    (b) viruses are on the border line of living and non-living
    (c) viruses have very few biochemical mechanisms of their own
    (d) viruses have a protein coat

Answer (c) Viruses enter our cells and use our machinery for their life processes that is why making anti-viral drugs is difficult than making bacterial medicines.

Question 10. Which one of the following causes kala-azar?
    (a) *Ascaris*   (b) *Trypanosoma*
    (c) *Leishmania*   (d) Bacteria

Answer (c) *Leishmania* is a protozoan parasite transmitted by sandfly. It causes leishmaniasis.

Question 11. If you live in a over crowded and poorly ventilated house, it is possible that you may suffer from which of the following diseases?
    (a) Cancer   (b) AIDS
    (c) Air borne diseases   (d) Cholera

Answer (c) In over crowded and poorly ventilated house, chances of air borne diseases to happen are more because the disease causing germs released by a patient (if any) will remains in the air. The air inhaled by other persons will make them also ill.

Question 12. Which disease is not transmitted by mosquitoes?
    (a) Dengue   (b) Malaria
    (c) Brain fever or encephalitis   (d) Pneumonia

Answer (d) Pneumonia is a bacterial disease. It infect lungs.

Question 13. Which one of the following is not important for individual health?
    (a) Living in clean space
    (b) Good economic conditions
    (c) Social equality and harmony
    (d) Living in a large and well furnished house

Answer (d) It is not necessary to live in a large and well furnished house to stay healthy. For good health, clean space, good economic conditions, social equality and harmony are essential.

Question 14. Choose the wrong statement.

(a) High blood pressure is caused by excessive weight and lack of exercise
(b) Cancers can be caused by genetic abnormalities
(c) Peptic ulcers are caused by eating acidic food
(d) Acne in not caused by staphylococci

Answer (c) Peptic ulcer is caused by a bacterium called *Helicobactor pylori*. Acidity, pain and bleeding of the stomach are its symptoms.

Question 15. We should not allow mosquitoes to breed in our surroundings because they

(a) multiply very fast and cause pollution
(b) are vectors for many diseases
(c) bite and cause skin diseases
(d) are not important insects

Answer (b) Mosquitoes are the vectors of diseases like malaria, dengue, brain fever, etc.

Question 16. You are aware of Polio Eradication Programme in your city. Children are vaccinated because

(a) vaccination kills the polio causing microorganisms
(b) prevents the entry of polio causing organism in the body
(c) it creates immunity in the body
(d) All of the above

Answer (c) Polio vaccination is an immunization process to get immunity against polio virus.

Question 17. Viruses, which cause hepatitis are transmitted through

(a) air   (b) water
(c) food   (d) personal contact

Answer (b) Hepatitis is a water borne disease caused by a virus.

Question 18. Vectors can be defined as

(a) animals carry the infecting agents from sick person to another healthy person
(b) microorganisms which cause many diseases
(c) infected person
(d) diseased plants

Answer (a) Vectors are the carriers of diseases from sick persons to another healthy person. For example, mosquitoes spread malaria.

Short Answer Type Questions

Question 19. Which bacterium causes peptic ulcers? Who discovered the above pathogen for the first time?

Answer
(a) *Helicobactor pylori*   (b) Marshall and Warren

Question 20. What is an antibiotic? Given two examples.

Answer Antibiotic is a chemical substance that kills bacteria, secreted by the microorganisms. Examples are penicillin and streptomycin.

Question 21. Name the target organs for the following diseases
  (i) Hepatitis targets.........
  (ii) Fit or unconsciousness targets......
  (iii) Pneumonia targets......
  (iv) Fungal disease targets......

Answer   (i) liver   (ii) brain   (iii) lungs   (iv) skin

Question 22. Name any two groups of microorganisms from which antibiotics could be extracted?

Answer Bacteria and fungi.

Question 23. Explain giving reasons.
  (i) Balanced diet is necessary for maintaining healthy body.
  (ii) Health of an organism depends upon the surrounding environmental conditions.
  (iii) Our surrounding area should be free of stagnant water.
  (iv) Social harmony and good economic conditions are necessary for good health.

Answer
  (i) Balanced diet provides nutrients and energy in appropriate amount required for the substances like protein, carbohydrates, fats, minerals, etc. These are essential for proper growth and functioning of healthy body.
  (ii) Health depends on surrounding environmental conditions. If surrounding area is unhygenic, chances of getting infections are more.
  (iii) Stagnant water conditions lead to many water borne diseases. So, there should not be stagnant water.
  (iv) For better living, money is necessary, we need good food for a healthy body, for the treatment of diseases, all these need good economic conditions.

Long Answer Type Questions

Question 24. What precaution will you take to justify prevention is better than cure?

Answer Precautions to be taken for the prevention of disease are
(i) maintenance of hygienic conditions.
(ii) awarness about the disease and causal organism.
(iii) balanced diet.
(iv) regular medical check up.

Question 25. Why are antibiotics not effective for viral disease?

Answer Antibiotics generally block the biosynthetic pathways and they block these pathways of the microbes/bacteria. However, viruses have very few biochemical machanisms of their own and hence are unaffected by the antibiotics.

Question 26. Becoming exposed to or infected with an infectious microbe does not necessarily mean developing noticeable disease. Explain.

Answer The strong immune system of a healthy person normally fights off microbes. The body has specialised cells to kill the pathogenic microbes. These cells are active when infecting microbes enter the body and if they are successful in removing the pathogen, we ramain disease-free. So, even exposure to infectious microbes may not cause disease to a person having strong immune system.

Question 27. Why is AIDS considered to be a syndrome and not a disease?

Answer AIDS virus called HIV enters the body a sexual contact, blood transfusion, from pregnant mother to bady. The virus damages the immune system of the body and due to this, the body cannot fight off many minor infections. Instant minor cold can become pneumonia or minor stomach infections can become severe diarrhoea with blood loss. The effect of disease becomes very severe and complex, at times killing the person suffering from AIDS. Hence, there is no specific disease symptoms for AIDS but it results in complex disease and symptoms. Therefore, it is known as a syndrome.

14

Natural Resources

Important Concepts

1. Life exists on the Earth because of the resources available and the energy from the sun meets the basic requirements of all living things.

2. Life-supporting zone of the Earth, where the atmosphere, the hydrosphere and the lithosphere interact and make life possible is called **biosphere**.

3. Air contains many gases like oxygen, nitrogen, carbon dioxide and water vapour. This particular composition of these gases in the air makes life possible on the Earth.

4. All kind of cells, *i.e.,* eukaryotic and prokaryotic need oxygen to breakdown glucose molecules and get energy for their activities. This releases carbon dioxide.

5. The other sources of CO_2 in the air are:
   (i) Combustion of fuels
   (ii) Forest fires
   (iii) Burning of fossil fuels.

6. Despite of these sources, the percentage of carbon dioxide in air is a mere fraction of a per cent because CO_2 is fixed in two ways:
   (i) Green plants convert CO_2 into glucose in the presence of sunlight.
   (ii) Many marine animals use carbonates dissolved in sea water to make their shells.

7. Atmosphere acts as a blanket around the Earth. It keeps the average temperature of the Earth fairly steady during the day and even during the course of whole year.

8. Water vapour is formed due to the heating of water bodies and the activities of living organisms. The atmosphere can be heated from below by the radiation that is reflected back or re-radiated by the land or water bodies. On being heated, convection currents are set up in the air.

9. In coastal areas, during the day, the air above the land gets heated faster and starts rising. As the air rises, a region of low pressure is created and air over, the sea moves into this area of low pressure. The movement of air from one region to the other creates winds.

   The direction of wind would be from sea to the land during the day. At night, both land and sea start to cool. Since, water cools down slower than the land, the air above water would be warmer than the air above land.

10. Rainfall occurs by the following events in the atmosphere:

    (i) Water bodies are heated during the day and large amount of water evaporates that goes into the air.

    (ii) This air also gets heated and carry the water vapour with it.

    (iii) As the air rises, it expands and cools. This cooling causes the water vapour in the air to condense in the form of tiny droplets.

    (iv) This condensation of water is facilitated, if some particles could act as the 'nucleus' for these drops to form around. Normally dust and other suspended particles in the air perform this function.

    (v) Once the water droplets are formed, they grow bigger by the 'condensation' of these water droplets. When the drops have grown big and heavy, they fall down in the form of rain.

    (vi) Sometimes, when the temperature is low enough, percipitation may occur in the form of snow, sleet or hail.

11. In large parts of our country, rains are mostly brought by the South-West or North-West monsoons.

12. An increase in the content of harmful substances in the air is called **air pollution**. The causes of air pollution are

    (i) Burning of fossil fuels produces different oxides of nitrogen and sulphur. These oxides dissolve in rain to cause acid rain.

(ii) Combustion of fossil fuels also increases, the amount of suspended particles in the air. These suspended particles are unburnt carbon particles called **hydrocarbons**.

13. Effects of air pollution
    (i) Visibility becomes lower.
    (ii) Allergies can occur.
    (iii) Diseases like cancer and heart problems may occur.

14. Water is a natural resource. The various source of water are
    (i) Rain water
    (ii) Surface water (lakes, ponds, rivers, etc.)
    (iii) Ground water.

15. Water occupies a large area of the Earth's surface and also found underground. Some amount of it exists in the form of water vapour in the atmosphere. Most of the water on Earth's surface is found in seas and oceans and is saline. Freshwater is found frozen in the ice caps at the two poles and snow-covered mountains. The underground water and the water in rivers, lakes, ponds is also fresh.

16. Importance of water for living things
    (i) It is required as a medium for all the cellular processes to take place.
    (ii) It is necessary for the transportation of substances from one part of the body to the other in a dissolved form.
    (iii) It is required to maintain balance of salts within the body.

17. The availability of water decides not only the number of individuals of each species that are able to survive in a particular area, but it also decides the diversity of life there.

18. Rainfall patterns are decided by the prevailing wind patterns. In many areas of our country, rains are mostly brought by the South-West or North-East monsoons.

19. Causes of water pollution
    (i) Water dissolve the fertilizers and pesticides and take them to nearby water bodies, where it causes harmful effects on aquatic life.
    (ii) Dumping of sewage and other wastes into water bodies.
    (iii) Industries use water for cooling various machines and later release this water into water bodies. This causes sudden change in temperature of water that affects the breeding of aquatic organisms. The eggs and larvae of many animals are susceptible to temperature changes.

(iv) The temperature also occurs when water is released from dams. The water inside the deep reservoir would be colder than the water at the surface which gets heated by the sun.

20. Soil is the outermost layer of our Earth called crust and the minerals present in it supply a variety of nutrients to life forms. These minerals are formed by the breaking of huge rocks.

21. The factors responsible for the formation of soil are sunlight, water, wind and living organisms.

   (i) The sun heats up rocks during the day so that they expand. At night, the rocks cool down and contract. This results in the formation of cracks and ultimately the huge rocks break up into smaller pieces.

   (ii) Water enters into the cracks in the rocks formed due to uneven heating by the sun. If this water later freezes, it would cause the cracks to widen. One other way is that flowing water wears away even hard rock over long period of time. These rocks rub against other rocks and the resultant abrasion causes rocks to wear down into smaller and smaller particles.

   (iii) Wind acts similarly as water. Strong winds also erode rocks down.

   (iv) Living organisms like lichens grow on the surface of rocks. While growing, they release certain substances that cause the rock surface to powder down and form a thin layer of soil. Other small plants like mosses and big trees also cause the rocks to break further.

22. Soil is a mixture of small particles of rocks, bits of decayed dead organisms (humus). It also contains various forms of microscopic organisms.

23. The main components of soil are minerals, air, water, organic matter and living organisms.

24. The type of soil is decided by the average size of particles found in it. The quality of soil is decided by the amount of humus and microorganisms present in it.

25. Humus plays an important role in deciding soil structure. It causes soil to become more porous and allows water and air to penetrate deep underground.

26. The nutrient content of a soil, the amount of humus present in it and depth of the soil are some of the factors that decide which plant will thrive on that soil.

27. Top soil is the top most layer of the soil that contains humus and living organisms in addition to soil particles. The quality

of top soil is an important factor that decides biodiversity in that area.

28. Soil loses its fertility by the frequent use of fertilizers and pesticides over long periods of time. It destroys the soil structure by killing the soil microorganisms that recycle nutrients in the soil. It also kills the earthworm which are instrumental in making the rich humus. Fertile soil can quickly be turned barren, if sustainable practices are not followed.

29. **Soil pollution** is the removal of useful components from the soil and the addition of other substances into it. This adversely affects the fertility of the soil and kills, the diversity of organisms that live in it.

30. **Biogeochemical cycle** is the cyclic flow of nutrients between non-living environment (soil, rocks, air and water) and living organisms. The four main nutrients present in nature are carbon, hydrogen, oxygen and nitrogen which constitute about 95% mass of the living organisms. These are cycled again and again between the living and non-living components of the ecosystem.

31. The whole process in which water evaporates and falls on the land as rain and later flows back into the sea *via* rivers is called **water cycle**.

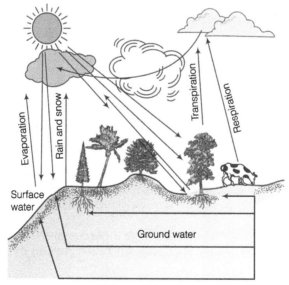

Water cycle in nature

32. The cyclic process in which nitrogen passes from its elemental form in the atmosphere into simple molecules in the soil and water which get converted to more complex molecules in living beings and back again to the simple nitrogen molecule in the atmosphere is called nitrogen cycle.

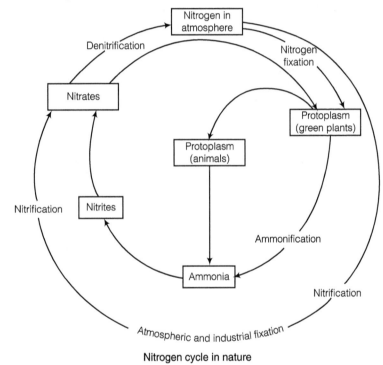

Nitrogen cycle in nature

33. Some gases prevent the escape of heat from the Earth. An increase in the percentage of such gases in the atmosphere would cause the average temperature to increase world wide. This is called **greenhouse effect**.

34. Carbon dioxide is one of the greenhouse gas. An increase in the carbon dioxide content in the atmosphere would cause more heat to be retained by the atmosphere. This leads to **global warming**.

35. The cyclic flow of carbon through different forms by the various physical and biological activities is called **carbon cycle**.

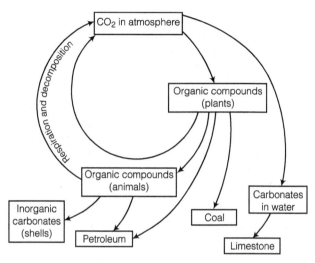

Carbon cycle in nature

36. The whole process in nature which maintains the levels of oxygen in the atmosphere is called **oxygen cycle**. Oxygen is returned to the atmosphere mainly through photosynthesis and used by three processes, *i.e.*, combustion, respiration and in the formation of oxides of nitrogen.

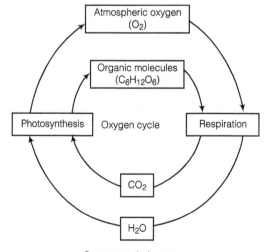

Oxygen cycle in nature

37. **Ozone layer** is present in the stratosphere region of atmosphere. Ozone is a triatomic molecule.

(i) **Importance of Ozone** Ozone layer forms a thick layer in the upper regions of atmosphere and absorbs harmful radiations from reaching the surface of the Earth. Thus, it helps in protecting life forms by its damaging effects.

(ii) **Threat to Ozone Layer** Various man made compounds like CFCs (carbon compounds having both fluorine and chlorine which are very stable and not degraded by any biological process) reach the ozone layer. They react with ozone molecule, resulting in a reduction of ozone layer. It results in a hole in the ozone layer above the Antarctica.

(iii) **Effects of Ozone Layer Depletion** The depletion of ozone layer causes the entry of harmful ultraviolet radiations of the sun on the surface of Earth thus, damaging all the living organisms. The disease like cancer and cataract can occur in human beings due to UV rays.

Intext Questions

On Page 193

Question 1. How is our atmosphere different from the atmospheres on Venus and Mars?

Answer The atmosphere of Earth contains a mixture of many gases like nitrogen (78.08%), oxygen (20.95%), carbon dioxide (0.03%) and water vapour (in varying proportion). On the other hand, the atmosphere on Venus and Mars mainly contains carbon dioxide, *i.e.,* about 95-97%. It may be the reason that due to this, no life is known to exist in both Venus and Mars.

Question 2. How does the atmosphere act as a blanket?

Answer The atmosphere mainly contains air which is a bad conductor of heat. Due to this, the atmosphere keeps the average temperature of the Earth fairly balanced during the day and even throughout the year. The atmosphere prevents the sudden increase in temperature during the daylight hours and during the night, it slows down the escape of heat into the outer space. In this way, atmosphere acts as a blanket.

Question 3. What causes winds?

Answer Winds occur due to unequal heating of atmospheric air. The heat causes rising up of air along with water vapour. As the air rises, it expands and cools. This cooling causes the water vapour in the air to condense. The condensation of water occurs if some particles (like dust particles) act as the 'nucleus' for these drops to stick around. These tiny droplets grow bigger by more and more condensation of other water droplets and finally form the clouds.

Question 4. How are clouds formed?

Answer Water evaporates from water bodies and goes into the atmosphere. Air also becomes hot due to sunlight and starts rising up taking along with water vapour. As the air rises up, it expands and cools. This cooling of air causes water vapour in the air to condense. The process of condensation of water occurs, if some particles (like dust) act as the 'nucleus' for these drops to form around. None these small droplets grow and become big by more and more condensation of other droplets of water. These steps form the clouds.

Question 5. List any three human activities that you think would lead to air pollution.

Answer The following activities lead to air pollution:
  (i) Excessive burning of fossil fuels, *i.e.,* coal and petroleum produces high amount of oxides of nitrogen and sulphur. These oxides mix with air and cause acid rain leading to many harmful effects.
 (ii) Many industries release high amount of poisonous gases into the atmosphere causing air pollution.
(iii) Forest fires, excessive use of chlorofluorocarbons (CFCs) used in refrigerators, excessive mining and ore refining release harmful gases into the air leading to pollution.

On Page 194
Question 1. Why do organisms need water?

Answer Organisms need water because:
  (i) Cellular processes need water for their functioning.
 (ii) Substances dissolve in water for reactions to take place within the cells.
(iii) Transportation of substances within the body need water.
(iv) Water helps in digestion of food and its absorption in the blood.
 (v) It helps to maintain body temperature.

Question 2. What is the major source of freshwater in the city/town/village where you live?

Answer In city/town/village, the major source of water is underground water. It is drawn with the help of hand pumps and tube-wells. The other nearby sources are rivers, lakes and ponds.

Question 3. Do you know of any activity which may be polluting this water source?

Answer The activities which may be polluting the water bodies are:
  (i) Disposal of garbage or sewage from cities/towns and from factories.
 (ii) Hot water may be released from the industries which may disturb the temperature of water body leading to death of many aquatic organisms.

On Page 196

Question 1. How is soil formed?

Answer The formation of soil takes place in the following ways:
  (i) Rocks near the surface of Earth are broken down by various physical, chemical and some biological processes. This process takes millions of years.
  (ii) This weathering leads to the formation of fine particles called soil.
  (iii) Some other factors also lead to the formation of soil. These are:
    (a) Sun causes heating of rocks that causes cracking and breaks down them into small particles.
    (b) Water dissolve rocks by freezing and fast flowing.
    (c) Wind causes erosion of rocks by fast blowing.
    (d) Liches and mosses grow on rock surfaces and break them into powder down and form a thin layer of soil. The big trees sometimes enter into cracks in the rocks and force them to break further during their growth.

Question 2. What is soil erosion?

Answer Soil erosion is the process of removal of top soil. It is rich in humus and nutrients. The agents of soil erosion are mainly flowing water or wind. If soil erosion is continued for a long time, the land becomes infertile and barren due to the loss of its valuable nutrients.

Question 3. What are the methods of preventing or reducing soil erosion?

Answer Preventive methods of soil erosion
  (i) **Afforestation** Planting more trees reduces soil erosion.
  (ii) **Contour Ploughing** Ploughing land in furrows across the natural slope of the land helps trap water and prevent the washing away of top soil along with it.
  (iii) **Step (terrace) Farming** Farmers form a series of steps by making horizontal strips supported by walls to catch the descending water. It gives the water sufficients time to percolate into the soil and nourish the crop.
  (iv) **Soil Cover** After harvesting a crop, soil is covered with dried vegetation to prevent its erosion.
  (v) **Overgrazing** Grasses tend to bind soil particles to prevent their erosion. If overgrazing is allowed, the grasses are uprooted and soil gets eroded.

On Page 201

Question 1. What are the different states in which water is found during the water cycle?

Answer Water can be seen in water cycle in its all three different states. These are:

(i) **Gaseous State** It occurs in the form of water vapour. It evaporates from the surface of water bodies and mixes with air.

(ii) **Liquid State** Water vapour condense high up in the atmosphere. It falls on the Earth in the form of rain.

(iii) **Solid State** It is formed by the freezing of liquid droplets in the upper layer of atmosphere. These droplets fall on the Earth in the form of snow, hail or sleet.

Question 2. Name two biologically important compounds that contain both oxygen and nitrogen.

Answer The biologically important compounds that contain both oxygen and nitrogen are nitrates (NO_2^-) and nitrates (NO_3^-). These are important forms of nitrogen to be utilized by the plants to synthesize biomolecules like proteins.

Question 3. List any three human activities which would lead to an increase in the carbon dioxide content of air.

Answer The human activities which would lead to an increase in CO_2 content of air are:

(i) **Respiration** is the natural way to release of CO_2 by both plants and animals. It is balanced by the release of oxygen by plants. So, it is not harmful for the environment.

(ii) **Deforestation** increases the level of CO_2 in the environment. Trees carry out photosynthesis and convert CO_2 into organic compounds such as glucose, starch, etc. In their absence, CO_2 cannot be utilized.

(iii) **Combustion of fuels** leads to increase in CO_2 level in the atmosphere. Fuels are burnt to carryout activities like cooking, transportation and in industrial processes.

Question 4. What is the greenhouse effect?

Answer Some gases called greenhouse gases, e.g., CO_2 prevent the escape of heat from the Earth. When the amount of such gases increases more than their normal levels, the average temperature of the Earth increases. This is called greenhouse effect.

Question 5. What are the two forms of oxygen found in the atmosphere?

Answer The two forms of oxygen found in the atmosphere are:

(i) Elemental oxygen is normally found in the form of diatomic molecule (O_2) in the lower part of atmosphere. It is about 21% in the air and non-poisonous.

(ii) Ozone is found in the stratophere part of atmosphere. It contains three atoms of oxygen (O_3). It is the poisonous form of oxygen.

(iii) Some other forms of oxygen are also found in the combined state. In Earth's crust, it is found as the oxides of most metals and silicon and also as carbonate, sulphate, nitrate and other minerals. In other forms, it is the part of biological molecules like carbohydrates, proteins, fats and nucleic acids, etc.

Exercises

Question 1. Why is the atmosphere essential for life?

Answer Atmosphere is important for life due to following reasons:

(i) It keeps the average temperature of the Earth steady during the day and even throughout the year.

(ii) It prevents the sudden increases in temperature during the daylight hours.

(iii) The gases it contains are required for sustaining life on Earth. These gases are:
   (a) Oxygen which is required for respiration by all living organisms.
   (b) Carbon dioxide is used in photosynthesis by plants to synthesize food.
   (c) Nitrogen provides intert atmosphere and an important components of proteins.

(iv) A thick layer of ozone (in stratosphere) of atmosphere, filters the harmful UV radiations reaching the Earth. The UV rays produce harmful effects on all living organisms.

Question 2. Why is water essential for life?

Answer Water is essential for life because of these reasons:

(i) It provides medium to carryout all the cellular processes.

(ii) All the reactions that occur in our body and within cells occur between substances that are dissolved in water.

(iii) It is required for the transportation of materials from one part of the body to the other.

(iv) It helps to maintain body temperature.

(v) Water makes up about 70% of body weight of all the living organisms.

Question 3. How are living organisms dependent on the soil? Are organisms that live in water totally independent of soil as a resource?

Answer Living organisms depend on soil in the following ways:

(i) It provides natural habitat for various living organisms, *e.g.,* bacteria, fungi, algae, earthworms, etc. These help to maintain the fertility of soil.

(ii) Earthwrom performs all its activities in the soil. It maintains the fertility of soil by releasing nitrogen rich excreta.

(iii) Many animals like rats, rabbits, etc., make their home in the soil.

(iv) Soil helps to bind the roots of plants to provide them anchorage. The nutrients in soil are absorbed by the plants for their growth and development.

All organisms that live in water are totally dependent on soil because the mineral nutrients are present in water in the dissolved form. But, their recycling depends on the decomposers which are present in soil beds. For this, all water bodies have soil beds which contain decomposers for the recycling of nutrients.

Question 4. You have seen weather reports on television and in newspapers. How, do you think we are able to predict the weather?

Answer Meterologists collect information regarding the pattern of temperature, speed of wind, air pressure and all other features which influence weather. All these information are collected by remote sensing and weather forecast satellites. This information is then compiled in meterological departments which prepare a weather report that is displayed on the maps. This information is further transmitted through radio, television and newspaper.

Question 5. We know that many human activities lead to increasing levels of pollution of the air, water-bodies and soil. Do you think that isolating these activities to specific and limited areas would help in reducing pollution?

Answer Isolating human activities to specific and limited areas would definitely help in reducing pollution to some extent. For example,

(i) If sewage and garbage generated by homes and industries is treated properly before discharging into water sources, it will reduce water pollution and cause less harm to the aquatic life.

(ii) If hot water generated by the industries is collected at common place, allowed to cool and then discharged in water bodies, will not affect the breeding capacity of aquatic organisms.

(iii) If commercial areas, factories and industries are shifted to the isolated are a far away from residential areas, it can reduce the effect of air pollution on people.

Question 6. Write a note on how forests influence the quality of our air, soil and water resources.

Answer Forests influence the quality of air, soil and water resources in following ways:

(i) Influence of forests on air occurs in these ways:

(a) Forests help to maintain oxygen and carbon dioxide balance in the air. They reduce the level of CO_2 in the air and to prevent greenhouse effect.

(b) These maintain temperature of the environment.

(c) Forests increase the rate of photosynthesis in surrounding region.

(ii) Influence of forests in quality of soil:

(a) Trees spread their roots deep inside the Earth and bind the soil particles firmly. This reduces soil erosion.

(b) Forests help to maintain nutrient cycles (biogeochemical cycles) in the atmosphere.

(iii) Influence of forests in quality of water:

(a) Trees help to maintain water cycle.

(b) Forests conserve water and make them available on the surface of Earth as water sources.

Selected NCERT Exemplar Questions

Multiple Choice Questions

Question 1. The atmosphere of the Earth heated by radiations which are mainly

(a) radiated by the sun

(b) re-radiated by land

(c) re-radiated by water

(d) re-radiated by land and water

Answer (d) The atmosphere can be heated from below by the radiation that is reflected back or re-radiated by the land or water bodies. On being heated, convection currents are set up in the air.

Question 2. If there were no atmosphere around the Earth, the temperature of the Early will

(a) increase

(b) go on decreasing

(c) increase during day and decrease during night

(d) be unaffected

Answer (c) The atmosphere prevents the sudden increases in temperature during the day and during the night, it slows down escape of heat into outer space.

Question 3. What would happen, if all the oxygen present in the environment is converted to ozone?

(a) We will be protected more

(b) It will become poisonous and kill living forms

(c) Ozone is not stable, hence it will be toxic

(d) It will help harmful sun radiations to reach Earth and damage many life forms

Answer   (b) Ozone is a poisonous form of oxygen gas, so it is toxic for the life forms.

Question 4. One of the following factors does not lead to soil formation in nature

    (a) the sun   (b) water

    (c) wind   (d) polythene bags

Answer   (a) Polythene bags are non-biodegradable materials. These cannot be broken down into smaller particles.

Question 5. The two forms of oxygen found in the atmosphere are

    (a) water and ozone   (b) water and oxygen

    (c) ozone and oxygen   (d) water and carbon-dioxide

Answer   (c) Oxygen is a diatomic form (O_2) and ozone is a triatomic form (O_3) of oxygen gas. Both of these exist in atmosphere. Ozone is found in the stratosphere layer of the atmosphere and oxygen is present in lower atmosphere.

Question 6. The process of nitrogen-fixation by bacteria does not take place in the presence of

    (a) molecular form of hydrogen   (b) elemental form of oxygen

    (c) water   (d) elemental form of nitrogen

Answer   (b) In nitrogen-fixation, bacteria do not take any from of oxygen. They use only elemental form of nitrogen for nitrogen fixation. Bacteria are poisoned by the elemental form of oxygen.

Question 7. Rainfall patterns depend on

    (a) the underground water table

    (b) the number of water bodies in an area

    (c) the density pattern of human population in an area

    (d) the prevailing season in an area

Answer   (b) The rainfall occurs due to watercycle in nature water cycle depends in evaporation from water bodies.

Question 8. Among the given options, which one is not correct for the use of large amount of fertilizers and pesticides?

    (a) They are eco-friendly

    (b) They turn the fields barren after sometime

    (c) They adversally affect the useful components from the soil

    (d) They destroy the soil fertility

Answer   (a) Use of fertilizers and pesticides is not environment friendly, because they are not biodegradable.

Question 9. The nitrogen molecules presence in air can be converted into nitrates and nitrites by
  (a) a biological process of nitrogen fixing bacteria present in soil
  (b) a biological process of carbon fixing factor present in soil
  (c) any of the industries manufacturing nitrogenous compounds
  (d) the plants used as cereal crops in field

Answer (a) *Rhizobium* bacteria convert nitrogen molecules into nitrates and nitrites.

Question 10. One of the following processes is not a step involved in the water-cycle operating in nature
  (a) evaporation   (b) transpiration
  (c) precipitation   (d) photosynthesis

Answer (d) Photosynthesis is the process of food synthesis by green plants.

Question 11. The term 'water-pollution' can be defined in several ways. Which of the following statements does not give the correct definition?
  (a) The addition of undesirable substances to water-bodies
  (b) The removal of desirable substances from water bodies
  (c) A change in pressure of the water bodies
  (d) A change in temperature of the water bodies

Answer (c) Water pollution does not occur by the change in water bodies.

Question 12. Which of the following is not a greenhouse gas?
  (a) Methane   (b) Carbon dioxide
  (c) Carbon monoxide   (d) Ammonia

Answer (a) Ammonia is not a greenhouse gas. It is released by the metabolism of nitrogens compounds.

Question 13. Which step is not involved in the carbon-cycle?
  (a) Photosynthesis   (b) Transpiration
  (c) Respiration   (d) Burning of fossil fuels

Answer (b) Transpiration is loss of water from the plant body.

Question 14. 'Ozone-hole' means
  (a) a large sized hole in the ozone layer
  (b) thinning of the ozone layer
  (c) small holes scattered in the ozone layer
  (d) thickening of ozone in the ozone layer

Answer (b) Thinning of ozone layer allows UV rays to enter the atmosphere. This creates hole in it.

Question 15. Ozone-layer is getting depleted because of
  (a) excessive use of automobiles
  (b) excessive formation of industrial units
  (c) excessive use of man made compounds containing both fluorine and chlorine
  (d) excessive deforestation

Answer (c) CFCs containing fluorine and chlorine) are stable compounds caused by air pollution which lead to thinning of ozone layer.

Question 16. Which of the following is a recently originated problem of environment?
  (a) Ozone layer depletion   (b) Greenhouse effect
  (c) Global warming   (d) All of these

Answer (d) All these problems are caused by air pollution.

Question 17. When we breathe in air, nitrogen also goes inside along with oxygen. What is the fate of the nitrogen?
  (a) It moves along with oxygen into the cells
  (b) It comes out with the CO_2 during exhalation
  (c) It is absorbed only by the nasal cells
  (d) Nitrogen concentration is already more in the cells so, it is not at all absorbed

Answer (b) Nitrogen can be used by living things in its elemental form, so it come out during exhataton.

Question 18. Top-soil contains the following
  (a) humus and living organisms only
  (b) humus and soil particles only
  (c) humus, living organisms and plants
  (d) humus, living organisms and soil particles

Answer (d) Top soil is a fertile layer of soil which contains all these components.

Question 19. Choose the correct sequences.
  (a) CO_2 in atmosphere → decomposers → organic carbon in animals → organic carbon in plants.
  (b) CO_2 in atmosphere → organic carbon in plants → organic carbon in animals → inorganic carbon in soil.

   (c) Inorganic carbonates in water → organic carbon in plants → organic carbon in animals → scavengers.

   (d) Organic carbon in animals → decomposers → CO_2 in atmosphere → organic carbon in plants.

Answer (b) This is the correct sequence for carbon cycle in nature.

Question 20. Major source of mineral in soil is the

   (a) parent rock from which soil is formed

   (b) plants

   (c) animals

   (d) bacteria

Answer (a) Rocks are rich source of minerals.

Question 21. Total Earth's surface covered by water is

   (a) 75%   (b) 60%   (c) 85%   (d) 50%

Answer (a) About 75% of Earth's surface is covered by water

Question 22. Biotic component of biosphere is not constituted by

   (a) producers   (b) consumers   (c) decomposer   (d) air

Answer (a) Air is an abiotic component of the atmosphere.

Question 23. An increase in carbon dioxide content in the atmoshere would not cause

   (a) more heat to be retained by the environment

   (b) increase in photosynthesis in plants

   (c) global warming

   (d) abundance of desert plants

Answer (d) Desert plants do not need carbon dioxide to grow.

Question 24. Oxygen is returned to the atmosphere mainly by

   (a) burning of fossil fuel   (b) respiration

   (c) photosynthesis   (d) fungi

Answer (c) Photosynthesis is the only process by which oygen is released into the atmosphere.

Question 25. Low visibility during cold weather is due to

   (a) formation of fossil fuel

   (b) unburnt carbon particles of hydrocarbons suspended in air

   (c) lack of adequate power supply

   (d) None of the above

Answer (b) Low visibility occurs especially in cold weather when unburnt carbon particles mix with water that is condense in the air. This creates smog.

Question 26. Growth of lichens on barren rocks is followed by the growth of

(a) moss   (b) ferns   (c) gymnosperms   (d) algae

Answer (b) Lichens powder down the rock surface and form a thin layer of soil. On to this, the other small plants like moss are able to grow in it.

Question 27. Marked temperature changes in aquatic environment can affect

(a) breeding of animals   (b) more growth of aquatic plants
(c) process of digestion in animals (d) availability of nutrients

Answer (a) Because the eggs and larvae of various animals are particularly susceptible to temperature changes.

Question 28. Soil erosion can be prevented by

(a) raising forests   (b) deforestation
(c) excessive use of fertilizer   (d) overgrazing by animals

Answer (a) The roots of trees bind soil particles firmly and prevent their erosion by wind, water, etc.

Question 29. What happens when rain falls on soil without vegetation cover?

(a) Rain water percolates in soil efficiently
(b) Rain water causes loss of surface soil
(c) Rain water leads to fertility of the soil
(d) Rain water does not cause any change in soil

Answer (b) The land without vegetation cover will be eroded easily and the top soil will be last.

Question 30. Oxygen is harmful for

(a) ferns   (b) nitrogen fixing bacteria
(c) *Chara*   (d) mango tree

Answer (b) Bacteria are poisoned by the elemental oxygen, infact, the process of nitrogen fixing by bacteria does not take place in presence of oxygen.

Short Answer Type Questions

Question 31. Rivers from land, add minerals to sea water. Discuss how?

Answer Water is capable of dissolving a large number of substances. As water flows over the rocks containing soluble minerals, some of them get dissolved in the water. Thus, river water carries many nutrients from land to the sea.

Question 32. In coastal areas, wind current moves from the sea towards the land during day, but during night it moves from land to the sea. Discuss the reason.

Answer Air above the land gets heated quickly during day and start rising. This creates a region of low pressure. As a result, air above sea rushes into this area of low pressure. This movement of air from one regions to the other creates winds. During night as the water cools down slowly, the air above water is warmer than the air on land. So, air moves from land to sea creating winds.

Question 33. Why does the percentage of gases like oxygen, nitrogen and carbon dioxdie remain almost the same in the atmosphere?

Answer In the environment, the percentage of these gases is maintained by their cyclic flow. The oxygen cycle, nitrogen cycle and carbon cycle continuously operate in nature by the constant interaction between the biotic and abiotic components of the biosphere. These interactions consist of a transfer of matter and energy between the different components of the biosphere.

Question 34. Why does Moon have very old and very hot temperature variations, *e.g.*, from – 190° C to 110° C even though it is at the same distance from the Sun as the Earth is?

Answer The Moon is at the same distance from the Sun as the Earth is, but there is very cold and hot temperature variations, *e.g.*, from 190°C to 110°C. This is because, Moon has no atmosphere. The atmosphere plays very important role in the temperature control.

Question 35. Why do people love to fly kites near the seashore?

Answer In sea shore or coastal regions, during the day, the air above the land gets heated faster and starts rising. As this air rises, a region of low pressure is created and air over the sea moves into this area of low pressure. This movement of air from one region to the other creates winds. During the day, the direction of wind would be from the sea to the land. So, flying kite near seashore is easy.

Question 36. Why do not lichens occur in Delhi, whereas they commonly grow in Manali or Darjeeling?

Answer Lichens are bioindicators of air pollution. They are sensitive to SO_2 pollution in air from automobiles. Delhi has maximum air pollution due to a large number of vehicles compared to Manali and Darjeeling. Therefore, the growth of lichens cannot occur in Delhi or any place where air pollution is high.

Question 37. 'Soil is formed by water'. If you agree to this statement then give reasons.

Answer Yes, water plays an important role in soil formation in the following ways :
  (i) It causes wear off of rocks over a long period of time.
  (ii) Water also causes rocks to rub against other rocks creating small particles which are taken away downstream and deposited as soil.
  (iii) Water expands on freezing in crevices of rocks and cracks rocks into smaller pieces.

Question 38. Fertile soil has lots of humus. Why?

Answer Fertile soils are rich in organisms that decompose dead organic matter forming humus. Humus gives minerals, absorbs water and makes soil porous.

Long Answer Type Questions

Question 39. A motor car, with its glass totally closed, is parked directly under the sun. The inside temperature of the car rises very high. Explain why?

Answer Sunlight emits infra-red radiations which pass through the glass and heat the car. The radiation emitted by other inner parts of the car cannot pass out of the glass, so the heat trapped inside raises the temperature of the interior. This is because glass is transparent to infrared radiations released from the sun, havings smaller wavelength than that emitted by the interior of the car which have longer wavelength to which glass is opaque.

Question 40. Justify 'Dust is a pollutant'.

Answer Dust remains present in air as suspended particles can cause allergy and other respiratory diseases. It also affects plant growth, by covering the stomata on leaf surface. It acts as the carrier of toxic compounds like heavy metals.

15

Improvement in Food Resources

Important Concepts

1. Living organisms need food which supplies nutrients like carbohydrates, proteins, fats, vitamins and minerals. These are required for body development, growth and health.
2. The food is obtained from agriculture and animal husbandry.
3. Different crops require different climatic conditions, temperature and photoperiod for their growth and completion of their life cycle. Photoperiod is related to the duration of sunlight. Growth of plants and flowering are dependent on sunlight.
4. The successful crop production depends on following factors:
   (i) Understanding how crops grow and develop.
   (ii) Effect of various nutrients, climate, water on the growth of the plant.
   (iii) Modification and management of each factor for increasing the crop yield.
5. The crops which are grown in rainy season are called **Kharif** season (June-October) crops. The Kharif crops are paddy, soyabean, pigeon pea, maize, cotton, green gram, black gram, etc.
6. The crops which are grown in winter season (November-April) are called Rabi crops. Examples, of Rabi crop are wheat, peas, mustard and linseed, etc.

7. The major activities which are involved in crop improvement can be classified as:
   (i) Crop variety improvement
   (ii) Crop production improvement
   (iii) Crop protection management

8. Crop variety improvement depends on finding a crop variety that can give a good yield. It can be done by following methods:
   (i) Crop improvement by hybridisation.
   (ii) Crop improvement by introducing a gene.

9. Hybridisation refers to crossing between genetically dissimilar pants. This crossing may be intervarietal (between different varieties), interspecific (between two different species of the same genus) or intergeneric (between different genera).

10. Introduction of gene provides the desired characteristics and results in genetically modified crops.

11. Cultivation practices and crop yield are related to weather, soil quality and availability of water. Since, weather conditions such as drought and flood situations are unpredictable, varieties that can be grown in diverse climatic conditions are useful.

12. Some of the factors for which variety improvement is done are:
   (i) **Higher yield** To increase the productivity of the crop per acre.
   (ii) **Improved quality** Quality considerations of crop products vary from crop to crop. For example, baking quality in wheat, protein quality in pulses, oil quality in oil seeds, etc.
   (iii) **Biotic and abiotic resistance** The biotic factors are diseases, insects and nematodes while abiotic factors are the drought, salinity, water logging, heat, cold and frost. Varieties resistant to these stresses can improve crop production.
   (iv) **Change in maturity duration** The shorter the duration of maturity of crop, the more economical is the variety. Uniform maturity makes the harvesting process easy and reduces losses during harvesting.
   (v) **Wider adaptibility** This feature helps in stabilising crop production under different environmental conditions.
   (vi) **Desirable agronomic characteristics** It helps in developing desired agronomic characters for higher productivity.

For example, tallness and profuse branching is required for fodder crops. Dwarfness is required in cereals, so that less nutrients are consumed by these crops.

13. Nutrients are supplied to plants by air, water and soil. There are sixteen different nutrients which are essential for plants. Air supplies carbon and oxygen, hydrogen comes from water and soil supplies the other thirteen nutrients to plants. Among these thirteen nutrients, six are required in large quantities and are called **macronutrients**. The other seven nutrients are used by plants in small quantities and are called **micronutrinets**.

Nutrients Supplied by Air, Water and Soil

Source	Nutrients
Air	Carbon and oxygen
Water	Hydrogen and oxygen
Soil	(i) **Macronutrients** Nitrogen, phosphorus, potassium, calcium magnesium and sulphur.
	(ii) **Micronutrients** Iron, Manganese, boron, zinc, copper, molybdenum and chlorine.

14. Manure contains large quantities of organic matter and also supplies small quantities of nutrients to the soil. It is prepared by the decomposition of animal excreta and plant waste. Manure enriches the soil with nutrients and organic and increase the soil fertility.

15. Type of manure is based on the kind of biological material used as given below:

   (i) Compost contains farm waste material such as livestock excreta (cow dung etc.), vegetable waste, sewage waste, straw, eradicated weeds, etc. These waste materials are decomposed in pits and this process of decomposition is called composting. The compost is rich in organic matter and nutrients.

   (ii) Vermicompost is made by the decomposition of plant and animal refuse with the help of earthworms.

   (iii) Green manure helps in enriching the soil in nitrogen and phosphorus. Prior to sowing of the crop seeds, some plants like sunnhemp or guar are grown and then mulched by ploughing them into the soil. These green plants thus turn into green manure.

16. Fertilisers are commercially produced plant nutrients. These supply nitrogen, phosphorus and potassium. They ensure good

vegetative growth (leaves, branches and flowers), giving rise to healthy plants. Fertilisers are important factors in the higher yields of high-cost farming.

17. Fertilisers should be applied carefully in terms of proper dose, time and observing pre and post application precautions for their complete utilisation.

18. The continuous use of fertilisers in an area can destroy soil fertility because the organic matter in the soil is not replenished and microbes in the soil are harmed by the fertilisers used.

19. Organic farming is a farming system with minimal or no use of chemicals as fertilisers, herbicides, pesticides, etc., and with a maximum input of organic manures, recycled farm wastes (straw and livestock excreta), use of bioagents such as culture of blue-green algae in preparation of biofertilisers, neem leaves or turmeric specifically in grain storage as biopesticides, with healthy cropping syems, *i.e.,* mixed cropping, inter-cropping and crop rotation. These cropping systems are beneficial in insect, pest and wheat control besides providing the nutrients.

20. Irrigation is very important for the success of crops. Various irrigation system include wells, canals, rivers and tanks.

    (i) Wells are of two types, *i.e.,* dug wells and tube wells. In a dug well, water is collected from water bearing strata. Tube wells can tap water from the deeper strata. Water is lifted from these wells for irrigation.

    (ii) Canals are an elaborater and extensive irrigation system. The canals receive water from one or more reservoirs or from rivers. These are further branched into distributaries to irrigate fields.

    (iii) River lift systems are useful in areas where canal flow is insufficient or irregular due to inadequate reservoir release. Water is directly drawn from rivers for irrigation in areas close to rivers.

    (iv) Tanks are small storage reservoirs which intercept and store the run-off of smaller catchment areas.

21. Cropping patterns are different ways of growing crops to get maximum production. The different cropping patterns are mixed-cropping, inter-cropping and crop rotation.

22. Mixed cropping is growing two or more crops simultaneously on the same piece of land. For example, wheat, gram or wheat, mustard or groundnut and sunflower. This reduces risk and gives some insurance against failure of one of the crops.

23. Inter-cropping involves growing two or more crops simultaneously on a same field in a definite pattern. A few rows of one crop alternate with a few rows of anotehr crop. For example, soyabean, maize or finger millet (bajara) and cowpea (lobia). The crops are selected in a way that their requirements are different. This is to ensure maximum utilisation of nutrients and to prevent pests and diseases from spreading to all the plants belonging to one crop in a field. This way, both crops can give better returns.

24. Crop rotation is a growing of different crops on a piece of land in a pre-planned succession. Depending upon the duration, crop rotation is done for different crop combinations. The availability of moisture and irrigation facilities decide the choice of the crop to be cultivated after one harvest. If crop rotation is done properly then two or three crops can be grown in a year with good harvests.

25. Weeds are unwanted plants in the cultivated field. Some weeds are *Xanthium* (gokhroo), *Parthenium* (gajar ghas), *Cyperinus rotundus* (motha). These weeds compete for food, space and light. The weeds take up nutrients and reduce the growth of the crop. So, the removal of weeds from the field during the early stages of crop growth is necessary for good production. Weed control can be done by mechanical removal (most effective method). Some other preventive methods are proper seed bed preparation, timely sowing of crops, inter-cropping and crop rotation.

26. Insert pests generally attack the plants in three ways:
    (i) They cut the root, stem and leaves.
    (ii) They suck the cell sap from various parts of the plant.
    (iii) They bore into stem and fruits.

27. Control of pests can be done by
    (i) The use of disease resistant varieties.
    (ii) Growing two or more crops simultaneously on the same field, *i.e.*, inter-cropping.
    (iii) Summer ploughing, the fields are ploughed deep in summers to destroy both pests as well as weeds.

28. Storage losses in agriculture produce can be very high. The factors responsible for such losses are biotic (insects, rodents, fungi, mites and bacteria) and abiotic (inappropriate moisture and temperatures) in the place of storage. These factors cause degradation in quality, loss in weight poor germinability, discolouration of produce, all leading to poor market sale.

29. Control measures to prevent storage losses area:
    (i) Cleaning of produce before storage.
    (ii) Proper drying of produce first in sunlight and then in shade.
    (iii) Fumigation (using chemicals that kill pests).
    (iv) Proper treatment of the storage structures and systematic management of ware houses.
30. Animal husbandry is the scientific management of animal livestock. It includes feeding, breeding and disease control of the livestock.

    Animal based farming includes cattle, goat, sheep, poultry and fish farming.
31. Cattle husbandry is done for two purposes milk and draught labour for agricultural work such as tilling, irrigation and carting.
32. Milk-producing females are called **milk animals** and the animals used for farm labour are called **draught animals**.
33. Dairy animals require food for two purposes:
    (i) Maintenance requirement, which is the food required to support the animal to live a healthy life.
    (ii) Milk-producing requirement, which is the type of food required during the lactation period.
34. Animal feed includes
    (i) Roughage, which is largely fibre
    (ii) Concentrates, which are low in fibre and contain relatively high levels of proteins and other nutrients.
35. Cattle suffer from a number of diseases. Vaccinations are given to farm animals against many major viral and bacterial diseases.
36. Poultry farming is related to raise domestic fowls for egg production and chicken meat. The cross-breeding programmes between Indian and foreign breeds of fowls for the variety improvement to get following desirable traits:
    (i) Number and quality of chicks.
    (ii) Dwarf broiler parent for commercial chick production.
    (iii) Summer adaptation capacity/tolerance to high temperature.
    (iv) Low maintenance requirements.
    (v) Reduction in the size of the egg-laying bird with the ability to utilise more fibrous cheaper diets formulated using agricultural byproducts.

37. For good production of poultry birds, good management practices are important. The housing, nutritional and environmental requirements of broilers are somewhat different from those of egg layers. The ration for broilers is protein rich with adequate fat. The level of vitamin-A and K is kept high in the poultry feeds.

38. Fish is a cheap source of animal protein for our food. Fish production includes the finned true fish as well as shell fish such as prawns and molluscs.

39. Popular marine fish varieties include pomfret, mackerel, tuna, sardines and bombay duck. Some marine fish are of high economic value, *e.g.,* finned fishes like mullets, bhetki and pearl spots, shell fish such as, prawns, mussels and oysters as well as seaweed.

40. As marie fish stock further get depleted, the demand more fisheries can only be met by culture fisheries, a practice called **mariculture**.

41. Inland fisheries include fish capture from resources like canals, ponds, reservoirs, rivers and brackish water resources, such as estuaries and lagoons.

42. Intensive fish farming can be done in composite fish culture systems in which both local and imported fish species are used in such systems.

43. **Composite fish culture** system include a combination of five or six fish species in a single fishpond. These species are selected so that they do not compete for food among them having different types of food habits. Due to this, food available in all the parts of the pond is used. For example, catalas are surface feeders, rohus feed in the middle zone at pond, mrigals and common carps are bottom feeders and grass carps feed on the weeds. These fishes together can use all the food in pond without competing with each other.

44. Fish farming depends on the availability of good quality seeds. To solve this problem, fish are breed in ponds using hormonal stimulation.

45. **Apiculture** is the rearing and breeding of honey bees for the production of honey and wax. The local varieties of bees used for commercial honey production are *Apis cerana indica* (Indian bee), *A. dorsata* (rock bee) and *A. florae* (little bee). An Italian bee variety, *A. mellifera* has also been introduced to increase the yield of honey.

46. The Italian bees have high honey collection capacity. They sting somewhat less. They stay in a given beehive for long periods and breed very well. Apiaries are established for commercial production of honey.

47. The quality and taste of honey depends upon the pasturage or the flowers available to the bees for nectar and pollen collection.

Intext Questions

On Page 204

Question 1. What do we get from cereals, pulses, fruits and vegetables?

Answer Cereals (wheat, rice, maize, etc.) are the sources of carbohydrates which provide energy. Pulses (pea, gram and soyabean, etc.) are the source of proteins. Vegetables and fruits provide us vitamins, minerals, carbohydrates, proteins and fats.

On Page 205

Question 1. How do biotic and abiotic factors affect crop production?

Answer Factors which affect crop production are:
  (i) Biotic factors which cause loss of grains are rodents, pests, insects, etc.
 (ii) Abiotic factors, such as temperature, humidity, moisture, etc.
      Both biotic and abiotic factors affect crop production in following ways:
 (a) Poor germination ability
 (b) Infestation of insects
 (c) Weight loss
 (d) Discolouration

Question 2. What are the desirable agronomic characteristics for crop improvement?

Answer Desirable agronomic characteristics are:
  (i) Tallness and profuse branching are desirable characters for fodder crops.
 (ii) Dwarfness is desired in cereals, so that less nutrients are consumed by these crops.

On Page 206

Question 1. What are the macro-nutrients and why are they called macronutrients?

Answer Macronutrients are essential elements which are required by plants in major quantities. Some of the main macronutrients are:

(i) N, P, S which are present in proteins.

(ii) Ca is present in cell wall.

(iii) Mg is a part of chlorophyll.

Question 2. How do plants get nutrients?

Answer Plants get nutrients from the soil. Nutrients are dissolved in soil and absorbed by the roots of plants. This water absorbed by the roots is transported by the xylem tissue throughout the plant body.

On Page 207

Question 1. Compare the use of manure and fertilisers in maintaining soil fertility.

Answer **Effect of the use of manure in maintaining soil quality**

(i) Manures provide a lot of organic matter (humus) to the soil. Humus helps to restore water retention capacity of sandy soil and drainage in clayey soil.

(ii) These are the sources of soil organisms like soil friendly bacteria.

Effect of fertilisers on soil quality

(i) Use of excess fertilisers leads to dryness of soil and the rate of soil erosion increases.

(ii) Due to continuous use of fertilisers, the organic matter decreases which reduces porosity of the soil and the plant roots do not get sufficient oxygen.

On Page 208

Question 1. Which of the following conditions will give the most benefits? Why?

(i) Farmers use high-quality seeds, do not adopt irrigation or use fertilisers.

(ii) Farmers use ordinary seeds, adopt irrigation, use fertilisers and use crop protection measures.

(iii) Farmers use quality seeds, adopt irrigation use fertiliser and use crop protection measures.

Answer (iii) Will provide conditions to get most benefits. For this, farmers use quality seeds, adopt irrigation, use fertilizers and use crop protection measures. This is because the use of only quality seeds is not sufficient until they are properly irrigated, enriched with fertilizers and protected from biotic factors.

On Page 209

Question 1. Why should preventive measures and biological control methods be preferred for protecting crops?

Answer Pathogens are causative agents of diseases in plants. To remove pathogens, some preventive measure and biological control methods are used which are

(i) simple   (ii) economic

(iii) minimise pollution without affecting the soil quality.

Question 2. What factors may be responsible for the losses of grains during storage?

Answer The following factors are responsible for loss of grains during storage:

(i) Abiotic factors like humidity and temperature.

(ii) Biotic factors like insects, rodents, birds, mites and bacteria.

On Page 210

Question 1. Which method is commonly used for improving cattle breeds and why?

Answer Cross breeding is a method commonly used for improving cattle breeds. It is a process in which indigenous varieties of cattle are crossed by exotic breeds to get a cross breed which is high-yielding. During cross breeding, the desired characters taken into considerations are the offsprings should be high yielding, should have early maturity and should be resistant to diseases and climatic conditions.

On Page 211

Question 1. Discuss the implications of the following statement :

It is interesting to note that poultry is India's most efficient converter of low fibre food stuff (which is unfit for human consumption) into highly nutritious animal protein food.

Answer The poultry birds are efficient converters of agricultural by products, particularly cheaper fibrous wastes into high quality meat and in providing egg, feathers and nutrient rich manure. So, the given statement is correctly said for the poultry birds.

Question 2. What management practices are common in dairy and poultry farming?

Answer (i) Poultry birds require well designed and hygenic shelter.

(ii) Proper food is required to get good yield of egg and meat.

(iii) Birds must be protected from diseases causing agents like virus, bacteria or fungi.

Question 3. What are the differences between broilers and layers and in their management?

Answer The poultry bird giving meat are called broilers and the egg laying birds are called layers. The ration required for broilers should be rich in protein with sufficient fat. The food should also have high vitamin-A and K. Layers require enough space and lighting.

On Page 213

Question 1. How are fish obtained?

Answer Fish are obtained by two ways:
- (i) Capture fisheries from natural resources
- (ii) Fish farming by culture for commercial purposes.

Question 2. What are the advantages of composite fish culture?

Answer Composite fish culture is done by a combination of five or six fish species in a single fish pond. The species are selected on the basis of food habits so that they do not compete for food among themselves. As a result, the food available in all parts of the pond is utilized without competing with each other. This increases the fish yield from the pond.

Question 3. What are the desirable characters of bee varieties suitable for honey production?

Answer Desirable characters in varieties for honey production are:
- (i) They should be able to collect a large amount of honey.
- (ii) They should stay in beehive for a longer time.
- (iii) They should have good breeding capacity.

Question 4. What is pasturage and how is it related to honey production?

Answer Pasturage for bees is the flowers available for nectar and pollen collection. The quality and taste of honey depends on adequate quantity of pasturage and flowers available.

Exercises

Question 1. Explain any one method of crop production which ensures high yield.

Answer A high yielding, crop production method is inter cropping. In this method, two or more crops are grown simultaneously on the same field in definite pattern. A few rows of one crop alternate with a few rows of second crop. For example, soyabean, maize or finger millet (bajara) and cow pea (lobia). The crops are selected such that their nutrient requirements are different. This ensures maximum utilisation of the nutrients supplied. It also prevents pests and diseases from spreading to all the plants belonging to one crop in a field. This method yields better crop yield.

Question 2. Why are manure and fertilizers used in fields?

Answer Manures and fertilizers supply essential nutrients to the soil. Therefore, they help in good vegetative growth, giving rise to healthy plants that rise in high crop production.

Question 3. What are the advantages of inter-cropping and crop rotation?

Answer Advantages of inter-cropping
   (i) Maintain soil fertility.
   (ii) Increases productivity per unit area.
   (iii) Save time and labour.
   (iv) Both crops can be easily harvested and threshed separately.

Advantages of crop rotation
   (i) Improves soil fertilitiy.
   (ii) Reduces pest infestation and diseases.
   (iii) Helps in weed control.
   (iv) Avoids depletion of a particular nutrient from soil.

Question 4. What is genetic manipulation? How is it useful in agricultural practices?

Answer Genetic manipulation can be defined as the process of transferring desirable genes from one plant to another plant for the production of varieties with desirable characters like profuse branching in fodder crops, high yielding varieties in maize wheat, etc.

Uses in agricultural practices:
   (i) Helps in increasing yield and quality.
   (ii) Maturation period is shorter.
   (iii) Better adaptability to adverse environmental conditions.
   (iv) Contain desirable features.

Question 5. How do storage grain losses occur?

Answer The losses of storage grain occur due to abiotic and biotic factors. The abiotic factors responsible for losses are moisture and temperature and the biotic factors are insects, rodents, birds, mites and bacteria, etc.

Question 6. How do good animal husbandry practices benefit farmers?

Answer　Benefits of good farming practices:
   (i) Improved breeds of domestic animals.
   (ii) Increased production of productis like milk, egg and meat.
   (iii) Proper shelter, feeding, care and protection against disesase help the farmers to improve their economic conditions.

Question 7. What are the benefits of cattle farming?

Answer　Benefits of cattle farming
   (i) Milk production is increased.
   (ii) Good quality meat, fibre and skin is obtained.
   (iii) Good breed of draught animals can be obtained.

Question 8. For increasing production, what is common in poultry, fisheries and bee keeping?

Answer　Cross breeding is a common practice between poultry fisheries and bee keeping for increasing production.

Question 9. How do you differentiate between capture fishing, mariculture and aquaculture?

Answer　Differences between capture fishing, mariculture and aquaculture

S.No.	Capture Fishing	Mariculture	Aquaculture
1.	Fish are obtained from natural resources, like ponds, canals, rivers, etc.	A method of marine fish culture in the open sea.	Production of fish from freshwater and brackish water resources.
2.	Locating fish is easy and can be captured by using fishing nets.	Fish can be located with the help of satellites and echosounders. These can be caught by many kinds of fishing nets using fishing boats.	Can be located easily and caught using fishing nets.

Selected NCERT Exemplar Problems

Multiple Choice Questions

Question 1. Which one is an oil yielding plant among the following?
   (a) Lentil
   (b) Sunflower
   (c) Cauliflower
   (d) *Hibiscus*

Answer　(b) Sunflower seeds produce oil.

Question 2. Which one is not a source of carbohydrate?

(a) Rice   (b) Millets   (c) Sorghum   (d) Gram

Answer   (d) Gram is pulse which is rich in proteins.

Question 3. Find out the wrong statement from the following.

(a) White revolution is meant for increase in milk production.
(b) Blue revolution is meant for increase in fish production.
(c) Increasing food production without compromising with environmental quality is called as sustainable agriculture.
(d) None of the above

Answer   (d) White revolution states high milk production, blue revolution is for increased fish production and sustainable agriculture in increasing food production without harming the environment.

Question 4. To solve the food problem of the country, which among the following is necessary?

(a) Increased production and storage of food grains
(b) Easy access of people to the food grain
(c) People should have money to purchase the grains
(d) All of the above

Answer   (d) All these conditions are essential to solve the food problem in our country.

Question 5. Find out the correct sentence.

I. Hybridization means crossing between genetically dissimilar plants.
II. Cross between two varieties is called as inter specific hybridization
III. Introducing genes of desired character into a plant gives genetically modified crop.
IV. Cross between plants of two species is called as inter varietal hybridization

(a) I and III   (b) II and IV
(c) II and III   (d) III and IV

Answer   (a) Both hybridization and introducing genes methods are used in crop improvement programmes.

Question 6. Weeds affect the crop plants by

(a) Killing of plants in field before they grow
(b) Dominating the plants to grow
(c) Competing for various resources of crops (plants) causing low availability of nutrients
(d) All of the above

Answer (c) Weeds compete with crop plants for the nutrients and other resources causing their low availability for crops.

Question 7. Which one of the following species of honey bee is an Italian species?

    (a) *Apis dorsata*   (b) *Apis florae*
    (c) *Apis cerana indica*   (d) *Apis mellifera*

Answer (d) *Apis mellifera* is an Italian species of honey bee introduced for the increased production of honey.

Question 8. Find out the correct sentence about manure.

    I. Manure contains large quantities of organic matter and small quantities of nutrients.
    II. It increases the water holding capacity of sandy soil.
    III. It helps in draining out of excess of water from clayey soil.
    IV. Its excessive use pollutes environment because it is made of animal excretory waste.

    (a) I and III   (b) I and II
    (c) II and III   (d) III and IV

Answer (b) Both I and II statements related to manure are correct.

Question 9. Cattle husbandry is done for the following purposes:

    I. Milk production   II. Agricultural work
    III. Meat production   IV. Egg production
    (a) I, II and III   (b) II, III and IV
    (c) III and IV   (d) I and IV

Answer (a) Egg production is done by poultry farming.

Question 10. Which of the following are Indian cattle?

    I. *Bos indicus*   II. *Bos domestica*
    III. *Bos bubalis*   IV. *Bos vulgaris*
    (a) I and III   (b) I and II
    (c) II and III   (d) III and IV

Answer (a) *Bos indicus* is an Indian cow and *Bos bubalis* is an Indian buffalo.

Question 11. Which of the following are exotic breeds?

    I. Brawn   II. Jersey
    III. Brown Swiss   IV. Jersey Swiss
    (a) I and III   (b) II and III
    (c) I and IV   (d) (II) and (iv)

Answer (b) Jersey and Brown Swiss are exotic (foreign) breeds of cows.

Improvement in Food Resources

Question 12. Poultry farming is undertaken to raise following

I. Egg production
II. Feather production
III. Chicken meat
IV. Milk production

(a) I and III
(b) I and II
(c) II and III
(d) III and IV

Answer (a) Poultry farming is done mainly to raise egg production and meat.

Question 13. Poultry fowl are susceptible to the following pathogens

(a) Viruses
(b) Bacteria
(c) Fungi
(d) All of these

Answer (d) All these microbes are disease causing pathogens for poultry fowl.

Question 14. Which one of the following fishes is a surface feeder?

(a) Rohus
(b) Mrigals
(c) Common carps
(d) Catlas

Answer (d) Catlas are surface feeders. These are suitable for composite fish culture.

Question 15. Animal husbandry is the scientific management of

I. animal breeding
II. culture of animals
III. animal livestock
IV. rearing of animals

(a) I, II and III
(b) II, III and IV
(c) I, II and IV
(d) I, III and IV

Answer (d) Animal husbandry is the scientific management of breeding, rearing and care of animal livestock.

Question 16. Which one of the following nutrients is not available in fertilizers?

(a) Nitrogen
(b) Phosphorus
(c) Iron
(d) Potassium

Answer (c) Fertilizers supply mainly nitrogen, phosphorus and potassium to the plant. These are macronutrients. Iron is a micronutrients and required in large quantities.

Question 17. Preventive and control measures adopted for the storage of grains include

(a) Strict cleaning
(b) Proper disjoining
(c) Fumigation
(d) All of these

Answer (d) To prevent grains from storage losses, all these steps are essential.

Short Answer Type Questions

Question 1. What are GM crops? Name any one such crop which is grown in India.

Answer Crop which has been developed by introducing a new gene from any other source, to obtain the desired character is called Genetically Modified (GM) crop. *Bt* cotton is an example of GM crop which is made insect-resistant by introducing a new gene from a bacteria.

Question 2. Why is organic matter important for crop production?

Answer Organic matter is important for crop production because :
- (i) It helps in improving soil structure.
- (ii) It helps in increasing water holding capacity of sandy soil.
- (iii) In clayey soil, large quantity of organic matter helps in drainage and in avoiding water logging.

Question 3. If there is low rainfall in a village throughout the year, what measures will you suggest to the farmers for better cropping?

Answer Suggestion for farmers:
- (i) Practice farming with drought resistant and early maturing varieties of crops.
- (ii) To enrich soil with more humus content as it increases the water-holding capacity and retains water for longer duration.

Question 4. Cultivation practices and crop yield are related to environment condition. Explain.

Answer Different crops and cultivation practices require different climatic conditions, temperature, photoperiod for their growth and completion of life cycle. These are some crops which are grown in rainy season (Kharif crops) while some others are grown during winter season (Rabi crops).

Question 5. An Italian bee variety *A. mellifera* has been introduced in India for honey production. Write about its merits over other varieties.

Answer Merits of Italian bee variety *A. mellifera* are:
- (i) It stings less.
- (ii) It has high honey collection facility.
- (iii) It stays in given beehive for long periods and breeds very well.

Question 6. In agricultural practices, higher inputs give higher yield. Discuss how?

Answer In agricultural practices, higher inputs give higher yield. This means higher money inputs to raise the yield. Financial conditions of the farmers allow them to take up different farming practices and technologies. The farmer's purchasing capacity for input decides cropping system and production practices.

Long Answer Type Questions

Question 7. The following figure shows the two crop fields [Plots A and B] have been treated by manures and chemical fertilisers respectively. Keeping others environmental factors same. Observe the graph and answer the following questions.

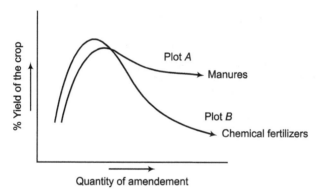

(i) Why does plot B show sudden increase and then gradual decrease in yield?

(ii) Why is the highest peak in plot A graph slightly delayed?

(iii) What is the reason for the different pattern of the two graphs?

Answer

(i) Plot B refers to chemical fertilizers which give short-term benefits because they are nutrient specific. The continuous use of fertilizers in an area destroy soil fertility so there is gradual decrease in yield after sometime.

(ii) Manures help in enriching soil with nutrients and organic matter and increase the soil fertility. They also improve the soil structure. The plot A demonstrates the trend that the addition of manures into the soil have long term benefits in terms of high yield.

(iii) Manures are natural ways of enriching the soil whereas fertilizers are commercially produced plant nutrients. They do not have organic matter like in manure to replenish the soil with useful microbes. Therefore, in plot *A* manures give high yield while plot *B* gives high yield for a short time and then it decreases.

Question 8. Define
  (i) Vermicompost
  (ii) Green manure
  (iii) Biofertilizer

Answer

  (i) **Vermicompost** The compost prepared by using earthworms to hasten the process of decomposition of plants and animal refuse is called vermicompost.

  (ii) **Green manure** The manure which is prepared by decomposing green plants in field itself is called green manure.

    For example, sunnhemp is grown in fields, mulched by ploughing and allowed to decompose in field for the preparation of green manure.

  (iii) **Biofertilizers** Living organism which are used as fertilizer to supply, the nutrients to plants, are called biofertilizers. For example, blue-green algae which fix nitrogen in soil, rice fields are called as biofertilizers.

Ingram Content Group UK Ltd.
Milton Keynes UK
UKHW020909090423
419869UK00013B/237